Active Galaxies

S381
The
Energetic
Universe

4

Carole Haswell

S381 COURSE TEAM

Course Team Chair	Dr Andrew Norton
Authors	Dr Carole Haswell, Dr Ulrich Kolb, Dr Sean Ryan
Reader	Dr Mark Jones
Course Manager	Gillian Knight
Editor	Dr Rebecca Graham
Course Secretaries	Valerie Cliff, Tracey Moore
Software Designer	Dr Will Rawes, Callum Lester
Multimedia Producer	Dr Kate Bradshaw
Graphic Designer	Debbie Crouch
Graphic Artist	Pam Owen
Picture Researcher	Deana Plummer
Consultants	Dr Katherine Blundell, Oxford University Dr Atsunori Yonehara, Tsukuba University Dr Martin Hardcastle, Bristol University
Block Readers	Dr Christopher Tout, Cambridge University Professor Andrew King, Leicester University Dr Christine Done, Durham University
Course Assessor	Professor Michael Merrifield, Nottingham University

This publication forms part of an Open University course S381 *The Energetic Universe*. The complete list of texts which make up this course can be found on the back cover. Details of this and other Open University courses can be obtained from the Course Information and Advice Centre, PO Box 724, The Open University, Milton Keynes MK7 6ZS, United Kingdom: tel. +44 (0)1908 653231, e-mail ces-gen@open.ac.uk

Alternatively, you may visit the Open University website at http://www.open.ac.uk where you can learn more about the wide range of courses and packs offered at all levels by the Open University.

To purchase this publication or other components of Open University courses, contact Open University Worldwide Ltd, Walton Hall, Milton Keynes MK7 6AA, United Kingdom: tel. +44 (0)1908 858785; fax +44 (0)1908 858787; e-mail ouwenq@open.ac.uk; website http://www.ouw.co.uk

The Open University
Walton Hall, Milton Keynes
MK7 6AA

First published 2002

Edited, designed and typeset by The Open University.

Printed and bound in the United Kingdom by Bath Press, Bath

ISBN 0 7492 9766 2

1.1

CONTENTS

AIM

The aim of Block 4 is to explore the physical processes which occur within active galaxies, to explain various emission mechanisms which operate in different physical regions of these systems, and to present the evidence for unification schemes of their various subclasses.

LEARNING OUTCOMES

This block provides opportunities for students to develop and demonstrate the following learning outcomes:

1   A familiarity with the terminology which is used to describe the properties and behaviour of active galactic nuclei (AGN).

2   The ability to organize and clearly present relevant information in response to defined tasks, including the expression of mathematical and scientific concepts using clear, concise and correct scientific prose.

3   The ability to learn from a variety of sources and media including books and journal articles which are not specifically written for an undergraduate audience.

4   The ability to search for and download relevant information from the World Wide Web.

5   The ability to evaluate and synthesize information from a variety of sources and media.

6   The ability to manipulate numbers, algebraic symbols and mathematical functions in equations.

7   An appreciation of the techniques of differentiation and integration and the ability to manipulate differential equations which are of relevance to astrophysics.

8   The ability to derive and manipulate quantitative theoretical models of physical processes and to derive physical estimates.

9   The ability to use spreadsheets to model physical processes and present the results graphically.

10   An appreciation of the interplay between theoretical modelling and observation or experiment.

11   Knowledge of the methods used, and the inherent uncertainties, in extragalactic astronomy.

12   An understanding of the arguments which lead to the conclusion that AGN are powered by accretion onto supermassive black holes.

13   Knowledge of the various components of electromagnetic radiation that are emitted by AGN and an understanding of how their locations and emission mechanisms can be explained in terms of a 'unified model' of the various classes of AGN.

INTRODUCTION

In this block we will study the most luminous and distant detected objects in our Universe. While this will draw upon many of the ideas you will have encountered in Blocks 2 and 3, here we move into the realm of **extragalactic astrophysics**, the study of objects outside our own Galaxy. The enormous distances between us and the objects we will consider mean that we must necessarily content ourselves with less clear-cut observational information than is available for studies of stars in our own Galaxy.

Because in this block you will study a young subject, there are fundamental issues which are still being vigorously debated by the experts and are subject to current research activity. Consequently, it is not possible to give clear definitive explanations of all aspects of the subject. The textbook we have chosen for you to work from primarily in this block, *An Introduction to Active Galactic Nuclei* by Bradley M. Peterson, aims to provide the background needed by those intending to begin research in active galaxies. We hope you will enjoy sharing this knowledge. You have probably become accustomed to reading unfamiliar words and phrases as you studied Blocks 2 and 3. In this block you will not only encounter new and specialized vocabulary, you will meet ideas which are currently being shaped and tested. Do not be dismayed if you fail to immediately grasp the underlying principles behind some of the material you will read: it is possible no-one has yet elucidated them!

Explanations of some of the words and phrases used in Peterson are included within the activity text in this Study Guide. When this occurs the **word or phase** in question is indicated as in this sentence. As you are reading Peterson you might want to glance over the activity text to search for this help whenever you come across something which seems difficult to understand. If you don't find the help you need within the activity text, then consult Collins, the S381 *Glossary*, the previous blocks, the S381 website and if all else fails, your tutor or the FirstClass conference.

The questions interspersed throughout the text are an integral part of the course. Please attempt them as you proceed. Many of them are designed to help you assess whether you have understood and retained information from the activities. We have endeavoured to provide detailed answers to all the questions, and consequently you may find that often more detail is provided than you personally require. In this case, please skim-read the answer rather than skipping it completely — sometimes hints on how to check your working have been included, which might be useful to you, especially in an exam. This is a specific example of an information management technique; these are vital for all researchers. No researcher can thoroughly read all of the new research papers which appear every day (a quick look at the astro-ph journal archive, a link is provided via the S381 website, will give you a taste of the volume of work produced). Instead researchers skim over the titles, then skim the abstracts of any papers which look like they might be relevant, and often researchers build on work reported in specific sections of published papers, without reading the whole paper. In order to make the best use of your time and prior knowledge, you need to make analogous informed judgements about what to study. Some of the activities in this block will require you to make such judgements in an open-ended context.

This Study Guide will supplement your preparation in physics and extragalactic astronomy, but it is vital that you are familiar with Blocks 1, 2 and 3 before you proceed to study Block 4. We have opted to organize this block into sections determined by the natural grouping of related material. Consequently the sections in this Study Guide do not neatly correspond to weeks of study time in all cases. In particular, Sections 1 and 5 are rather longer than normal, whilst Sections 2, 4, 6 and 7 are a little shorter and each should not occupy you for a whole week. A suggested division of time for this block is presented in Table 1, although you may find some other breakdown suits you better.

Table 1 Suggested division of study time for Block 4.

Section	No. of study weeks
1	2
2	1/2
3	1
4	1/2
5	2
6	1/2
7	1/2
8	1
9	1

1 OVERVIEW OF ACTIVE GALAXIES

We begin Section 1 by studying evidence leading to our basic hypothesis that active galactic nuclei (AGN) are accreting, supermassive black holes, in Section 1.7 we cover some physics of radiation which you will need to be able to interpret the observed emission of AGN, and in Section 1.8 we begin our detailed examination of AGN.

1.1 Meet your first active galactic nuclei

Figure 1 compares two nearby spiral galaxies of similar distance and type. NGC 5548, on the left, has a brighter nucleus than that of NGC 3277, on the right. This extra emission from the central regions of NGC 5548 is not generated by stars. Instead this light is thought to be ultimately powered by material falling in the gravitational field of a supermassive black hole at the centre of NGC 5548. Similar non-stellar emission is also seen at the centre of many other galaxies. These bright central regions are generally known as **active galactic nuclei** or **AGN**. In this block you will learn about these enormously energetic objects, examining the observations astronomers have made of them, and studying the ways in which the observations have been used to generate understanding of the underlying physical processes.

As you learned in Block 1, Activity 4, the first AGN was discovered in 1908 when E. A. Fath took a spectrum of M77, also known as NGC 1068. This nearby spiral galaxy is shown in Figure 2 (overleaf). Carl Seyfert was the first to realize that there were other similar galaxies, when he discovered that NGC 1275, NGC 3516, NGC 4015, NGC 4151 and NGC 7469 all had spectra similar to that of NGC 1068. Consequently these objects, and others like them, are called **Seyfert galaxies**.

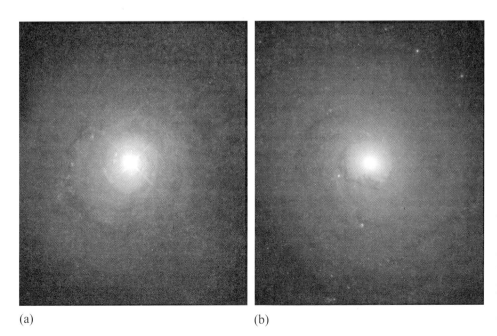

(a)   (b)

Figure 1 Optical images of the nearby spiral galaxies (a) NGC 5548, (b) NGC 3277. Note that the nucleus in NGC 5548 appears brighter than that in NGC 3277. It is the very concentrated bright central source in NGC 5548 which causes the diffraction pattern apparent as the diagonal spikes emanating from the centre of image (a).

Figure 2 An optical image of Messier 77, also known as NGC 1068. This image was produced by combining exposures made with several different filters to give the colour, and has been processed to reduce the contrast between the brightest and faintest regions, so that more of the detailed structure is visible.

1.2 Black holes: a reminder

In Block 2, Activity 46 you read a little about the formation of a black hole at the end of the life of a massive star. Block 3 mentioned accreting black holes, which were formed in this way and are members of close binary star systems.

A **black hole** is formed when self-gravity causes material to collapse to such high densities that the escape speed (see Collins entry for **escape velocity**) reaches the speed of light. Using Newtonian dynamics we can calculate the magnitude of the escape velocity from planet Earth (mass M_E, radius R_E) by saying that the kinetic energy of a mass m travelling vertically upwards with speed v_{esc} must equal the change in gravitational potential energy required to completely escape from the Earth's gravitational field, i.e.

$$\frac{1}{2} m v_{esc}^2 = \frac{GM_E m}{R_E} - \frac{GM_E m}{\infty}$$

Cancelling the common factor m and recognizing that the second term on the right-hand side is zero, this becomes:

$$\frac{1}{2} v_{esc}^2 = \frac{GM_E}{R_E}$$

which means

$$v_{esc} = \sqrt{\frac{2GM_E}{R_E}} \tag{1}$$

To self-consistently calculate the magnitude of the escape velocity from an object with a density so high that the escape velocity reaches the speed of light requires the use of general relativity, which is beyond the scope of this course. By a lucky coincidence, however, the correct general relativistic result is exactly what we obtain by setting $v_{esc} = c$ in Equation 1. That is to say, a black hole is formed when a mass M collapses to within a sphere of radius R_S, where

$$R_S = \frac{2GM}{c^2} \tag{2}$$

R_S is the **Schwarzschild radius**, which is the radius of the sphere surrounding the collapsed mass at which the escape speed equals the speed of light. Within this sphere is a region of spacetime which is cut off from the rest of the Universe, since neither light nor any other form of information can escape from it. The sphere itself is known as the **event horizon**. Immediately outside the event horizon is a region of spacetime in which there is an extremely strong gravitational field.

A black hole forms at the end of the life of a massive star because there is no pressure source sufficient to oppose the self-gravitational contraction of the remnant star core. Similarly, if a much larger mass collapsed under self-gravity, a black hole would ultimately form, and indeed it is now thought that black holes of mass $M \geq 10^6 M_\odot$ are present at the cores of most (or possibly all) galaxies.

1.3 AGN reside at the centres of galaxies

It is clear that the objects studied by Fath and Seyfert, such as those shown in Figure 1 and Figure 2, are bright nuclei at the centres of apparently otherwise normal galaxies. For many AGN this fact is not immediately obvious. One of the two bright objects in Figure 3 is an AGN, the other is a foreground star in our own Galaxy. It is impossible to tell from the image which is which. Like many AGN, this one appears as a point source of light, just as stars do. Hence their discoverers called these objects **quasi-stellar objects** or **QSOs**, which have been contracted to **quasars**. Seyferts and quasars are among the subclasses of AGN.

Initially only AGN which were detected as radio sources were called quasars as opposed to QSOs. Now most astronomers use the terms interchangeably.

Figure 3 This image, taken by the Hubble Space Telescope, shows two very bright objects which appear to be point sources of light. Both these bright objects show diagonal spikes which are caused by diffraction of light within the telescope. The bright object at the centre of the image is an AGN, the other bright object (to the right of the AGN) is a foreground star in our own Galaxy. Also apparent is a faint elliptical galaxy just above the AGN, a distorted spiral galaxy towards the top of the image, and a scattering of other galaxies.

It only became apparent that these quasi-stellar objects were not stars when their spectra were examined. At first astronomers could not interpret their spectra because the spectral lines did not appear at appropriate wavelengths for atoms of any known chemical element. The spectrum shown in Figure 4 provided the breakthrough: Maarten Schmidt identified the three indicated lines as common emission lines of hydrogen, but redshifted by a factor

$$z = \frac{\Delta\lambda}{\lambda_0} = 0.158$$

where the redshift, z, wavelength shift, $\Delta\lambda$, and rest wavelength λ_0, are quantities explained in Block 1, Section 2.14.

If this redshift is interpreted as cosmological (i.e. due to the overall expansion of the Universe described by Hubble's law, see Block 1 for details) then the distances to these QSOs are huge, and their luminosities prodigious. For example, Schmidt's redshift measurement would imply that the point optical source 3C 273 is 100 times as luminous as the entire Milky Way Galaxy! Naturally there was some reluctance to adopt this interpretation, and a few sceptics vigorously persisted into the 1980s in advocating the view that the QSOs were much closer than Hubble's law would imply.

■   How would these sceptics have explained the measured redshifts of QSOs?

❑   They asserted that the QSOs had large motions through space, rather than receding as part of the overall cosmological expansion of space. One suggestion was that QSOs were ejected from nearby galaxies at relativistic velocities. ■

Just as in democratic politics, the scientists who argue a minority viewpoint perform an invaluable function by ensuring that the accepted view indeed stands up to all possible rational criticism. Any scientist who has never been proved wrong has probably had a very dull career. Towards the end of this block you will come across contemporary examples of disagreement among expert scientists.

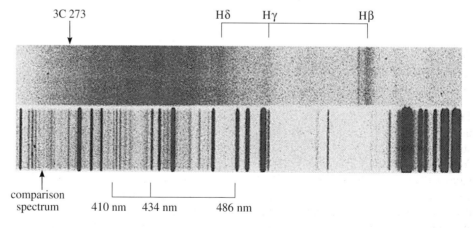

Figure 4 An historic QSO optical spectrum, which was taken using a photographic plate. The darker areas are regions where the intensity of light is higher. The top rectangle is the spectrum of the radio galaxy 3C 273, while the lower rectangle is the spectrum of a comparison emission line source. In both spectra three common lines of hydrogen have been indicated. The lines in the spectrum of 3C 273 appear at a redshift $z = 0.158$.

The issue of whether QSO redshifts are of cosmological origin was unambiguously settled by the work illustrated in Figure 5 (particularly the two leftmost panels). When sensitive enough observations are made, the galaxies in which the quasars reside can be detected. The relatively faint emission from the surrounding stars, gas and dust is called **quasar fuzz**. Since quasar fuzz is clearly emission from distant galaxies, each with the same redshift as the quasar they contain, the redshifts of quasars must be cosmological.

Once we accept that the redshifts of quasars are cosmological, there is no way to avoid the conclusion that they have huge luminosities. The emission from the quasar PG 0052+251, shown in the top-left panel of Figure 5, is clearly brighter than that of the entire surrounding host galaxy, even though in this image the quasar itself is overexposed.

The observation that the active nuclei of even the closest Seyfert galaxies appear as unresolved point sources of the light immediately suggests that the luminosity of an AGN is generated within a volume which is small compared to the size of a galaxy. More stringent limits on the size of the emitting region in AGN arise from

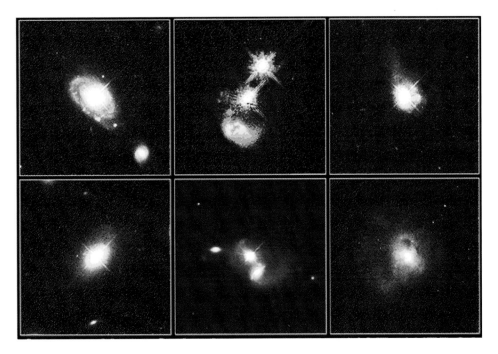

Figure 5 Images taken with the Hubble Space Telescope of six quasars. In each case the quasar itself was overexposed, so that very faint emission surrounding the central point source could be detected. In each case shown here faint nearby emission was discovered from stars in a galaxy. (*Top left*) PG 0052+251 lies at the centre of a normal spiral galaxy. (*Top centre*) IRAS 04505-2958 (the central source) has apparently recently collided with the spiral galaxy whose remains lie towards the bottom of the image. The distance between the quasar and the galaxy is one-seventh the diameter of our Milky Way. (*Top right*) The plumes of emission are from dust and gas which PG 1012+008 has apparently captured in a collision with a nearby galaxy. (*Bottom left*) PHL 909 is at the centre of a normal elliptical galaxy. (*Bottom centre*) The quasar PG 1012+008, at the centre of the image, is merging with the galaxy whose core is the bright object just below it. Wisps of dust and gas show material which is being pulled away from the galaxy by the quasar's gravity. (*Bottom right*) IRAS 13218+0552 appears to be at the centre of two galaxies which have merged.

considering their variability (i.e. how the luminosity changes with time). In some sources the luminosity changes significantly over a few days. This means that the time, Δt, for light to travel across the entire source must be only a few days, because otherwise the changes in luminosity would be smoothed out by the delayed arrival times of the photons from the more distant regions of the source. This can be expressed mathematically by the general requirement that

$$l \lesssim \Delta t \times c \tag{3}$$

where l is the size of the emitting source and Δt is the timescale for observed variability. Using this to work out the size limit corresponding to a **light travel time** (called **light time** in Collins) of a few days we have:

$$l \leq 10 \times 24 \times 60 \times 60 \times 3 \times 10^{10}\,\text{cm}$$

where we have adopted $\Delta t = 10$ days, converted this into seconds, and used an approximate value for the speed of light: $c \approx 3 \times 10^{10}\,\text{cm s}^{-1}$. Evaluating, and retaining only 1 significant figure, we have

$$l \lesssim 3 \times 10^{16}\,\text{cm}$$

which can be converted into length units more convenient for astronomical objects:

$$l \lesssim \frac{3 \times 10^{16}\,\text{cm}}{1.5 \times 10^{13}\,\text{cm AU}^{-1}}, \quad \text{i.e. } l < 2 \times 10^3\,\text{AU}$$

Thus the observations require that a luminosity of around 100 times that of the entire Milky Way Galaxy be generated within a region with a diameter only about 1000 times that of the Earth's orbit! (A truly amazing statement.)

The most obvious mechanism for generating such enormous luminosity within such a tiny region of space is the accretion process you studied in Block 3, but this time instead of compact stars with masses $\sim M_\odot$, the accreting object is required to be a black hole with mass $M \sim 10^8 M_\odot$. As you learned in Block 3, Section 1.2, the accretion luminosity, L_{acc}, generated by an object of mass M and radius R_* is

$$L_{\text{acc}} = \frac{GM\dot{M}}{R_*} \tag{4}$$

where $\dot{M}$ $(= \text{d}M/\text{d}T)$ is the accretion rate.

■ Why are astronomers forced to infer the existence of supermassive black holes rather than attributing the luminosity of quasars to a very high accretion rate onto a mass $M \sim M_\odot$?

❑ Because the accretion luminosity cannot exceed the Eddington Limit, which is proportional to M. ■

Sir Arthur Eddington (Figure 6) was responsible for many of the underpinnings of modern astrophysics, including the concept of the limiting Eddington luminosity. Beyond this limit, radiation pressure will cause outflow.

Figure 6 Portrait of Sir Arthur Eddington.

Context: AGN, a developing research field

Read the first paragraph in Chapter 7 of FKR, which sets the contents of the current block in the context of accretion in binary stars (the subject of Block 3 of this course).

Apparently stellar in this context means a point source of light, rather than an extended object such as a galaxy.

In describing the observational characteristics of AGN, FKR use the term **non-thermal spectrum**. This concise term means that the electromagnetic radiation emitted does not have the **blackbody spectrum** (Block 1, Section 4.9.3). The blackbody spectrum is physically very simple: its shape is determined by a single parameter, the temperature, T, of the emitting source. However not all sources of light emit blackbody radiation. For example, the electromagnetic radiation emitted by an accelerated electron does not have a blackbody spectrum. We discuss this in Section 1.7 below.

Keywords: **central engine** ▪

Our core textbook

Now read the Preface of Peterson, omitting the last paragraph.

Phenomenology is a term you may not have encountered before. It is an endeavour which lies somewhere between observation and theory. The observations are described and characterized, and underlying causes are sought, but there isn't a rigorous theory.

Keywords: none ▪

Question 1

What is thought to be the energy source which powers active galaxies? See if you can answer this using the astrophysics terms you have learned, and then try to write another answer using only mainstream physics vocabulary. ▪

Example 1

(a) A gravitationally bound uniform density sphere, of radius r, is composed of a large number of subelements, with total mass M. Use the virial theorem (Phillips 1.11),

$$2E_{KE} + E_{GR} = 0 \qquad (5)$$

to show that the typical velocity, v, of a subelement is related to M according to:

$$\langle v^2 \rangle \approx \frac{GM}{r} \qquad (6)$$

(b) Astronomers observing a Seyfert galaxy obtain some spectra and high-quality images, in which the light from a point source was spread over only a fraction of an arc second. Despite the excellent spatial resolution of the images, the nucleus of the galaxy is unresolved, and hence its size is known to be $r < 50\,\mathrm{pc}$. The emission lines have full width at zero intensity of $6000\,\mathrm{km\,s^{-1}}$. Estimate the mass of the central black hole.

Solution

(a) From Block 2, Example 1 we know that the gravitational energy is given by

$$E_{\text{GR}} = -\frac{3}{5}\frac{GM^2}{r}$$

where G is Newton's constant of gravitation, and that the kinetic energy is

$$E_{\text{KE}} = \frac{1}{2}M\langle v^2 \rangle$$

Here we have used the angle brackets $\langle \, \rangle$ to indicate a mean, typical, or expected value of the quantity enclosed. The right-hand side of the expression for E_{KE} comes from summing up all the individual $\frac{1}{2}mv^2$ contributions, giving the total mass multiplied by the typical value of v^2. The v in the equation indicates the **velocity dispersion**, i.e. how fast the subelements of the gravitationally bound system are moving with respect to the centre of gravity. Substituting the above expressions into Equation 5 we obtain:

$$2 \times \left(\frac{1}{2}M\langle v^2 \rangle\right) + \left(-\frac{3}{5}\frac{GM^2}{r}\right) = 0$$

Making $\langle v^2 \rangle$ the subject of the equation, therefore

$$\langle v^2 \rangle = -\frac{1}{M}\left(-\frac{3}{5}\frac{GM^2}{r}\right)$$

Since measurements of $\langle v^2 \rangle$ in extragalactic astrophysics are often somewhat imprecise, we can ignore the difference between 3/5 and 1, and hence we obtain

$$\langle v^2 \rangle \approx \frac{GM}{r}$$

as required. This result is stated as Peterson Equation 1.1, which you read in Block 1, Activity 4. You may wish to consult your notes from this activity and attempt part (b) of this example before reading on. If you didn't make any notes, or perhaps even if you did, you may wish to reread this part of Peterson before reading on.

(b) We can apply this approximate version of the virial theorem to the observations of the Seyfert galaxy. From the information given, we need to substitute values of r and v to make the estimate. We are told r is the 'size' of the nucleus, which you could think of as its diameter, however in estimates of this type astronomers are often vague about distinctions between quantities such as radius and diameter. Such distinctions are unnecessary whenever the calculation includes unavoidable uncertainties much greater than a factor of 2.

Clearly we can use the upper limit on r straight from the information supplied, but we should work in consistent units. Since Peterson adopts the cgs system, we will generally adopt it in this Study Guide, and will use this example to illustrate how (just as in SI) systematic use of the cgs system will give you answers in the appropriate cgs unit. The full width of the emission lines gives us an indication of the velocity dispersion, and the value of the full width is $6000\,\text{km s}^{-1}$. This presumably means that some material is moving away from us at $3000\,\text{km s}^{-1}$, while other material is moving towards us at this speed. Therefore a value of $v = 3000\,\text{km s}^{-1}$ seems an appropriate estimate. (*Note*: Since v is going to be squared to give our mass estimate, we keep the factor of 2 here.)

We now have values for both the unknowns, but we must convert them into cgs units. Recalling that 'cgs' stands for 'centimetre-grams-seconds', the cgs unit of length is clearly the centimetre (cm); similarly, the cgs unit of velocity is centimetres per second (cm s^{-1}). Therefore we need to convert from parsecs (pc) to centimetres (cm).

1 pc = 3.086×10^{16} m, and 100 cm = 1 m, therefore 1 pc = 3.086×10^{18} cm. Since none of the measurements we are given have more than 1 significant figure, and we are asked only for an estimate, it is probably safe *in this instance* to use 1 pc = 3×10^{18} cm. In other calculations you may need to use higher precision.

Using this conversion factor, $r < 50$ pc becomes $r < 50 \times 3 \times 10^{18}$ cm, i.e. $r < 1.5 \times 10^{20}$ cm. Similarly we should express v in cgs units by converting km s^{-1} into cm s^{-1}. Since 1 km = 1×10^3 m, and 100 cm = 1 m, 1 km = 1×10^5 cm, $v = 3000$ km s^{-1} becomes $v = 3000 \times 10^5$ cm s^{-1}, i.e. $v = 3 \times 10^8$ cm s^{-1}.

We also need the value of G in cgs units. You can convert G by noting that its SI unit is m^3 kg^{-1} s^{-2} and applying the factor of 10^2 to convert from m to cm, and the factor of 10^3 to convert from kg to g. Whenever you do this sort of conversion make sure you go in the right direction: a centimetre is much smaller than a metre, so a length given in cm will be a number 100 times greater than the same length given in units of metres. In the case of G, the conversion is from m^3, so the conversion needs to be from metres *cubed* to centimetres *cubed*. Similarly the *inverse* kilograms need to be converted into *inverse* grams. From the list of constants at the back of Phillips, $G = 6.673 \times 10^{-11}$ m^3 kg^{-1}s^{-2}, which is equivalent to $G = 6.673 \times 10^{-11} \times (100 \text{ cm})^3 \times (1000 \text{ g})^{-1} \times (\text{s})^{-2}$. Collecting all the numerical factors, $G = 6.673 \times 10^{-8}$ cm^3 g^{-1} s^{-2}. Of course, we could simply have looked up the value of G in cgs units rather than SI units; the table in Appendix A2 at the back of this Study Guide give the values of constants in both systems of units.

Substituting in these values, therefore,

$$M \approx \frac{v^2 r}{G} \lesssim \frac{(3 \times 10^8)^2 \times 1.5 \times 10^{20}}{6.673 \times 10^{-8}} \times \frac{(\text{cm s}^{-1})^2 \times \text{cm}}{\text{cm}^{-3}\,\text{g}^{-1}\,\text{s}^{-2}}$$

The symbol '$\lesssim$' is used to indicate 'less than approximately'. The 'less than' is because $r < 1.5 \times 10^{20}$ cm, and the 'approximately' because we have used estimates. Cancelling units and multiplying out numbers we arrive at the estimate: $M \lesssim 2 \times 10^{44}$ g.

This has provided the mass estimate we wanted, but this is not exactly the answer Peterson would have given. The example above uses pure cgs units, but in fact if you return to Peterson, you will see that velocities are generally measured in km s^{-1}, and masses in M$_\odot$. These units are generally used by astronomers, irrespective of whether they are working in the SI or cgs system, because they are the most convenient (and easily visualized) choice. Hence we will convert the mass above from grams into solar masses. Noting that $1 \text{M}_\odot \approx 2 \times 10^{30}$ kg $\approx 2 \times 10^{33}$ g, we obtain

$$M \lesssim \frac{2 \times 10^{44}\,\text{g}}{2 \times 10^{33}\,\text{g M}_\odot^{-1}}$$

which reduces to

$$M \lesssim 1 \times 10^{11} \text{M}_\odot$$

Therefore we conclude that the mass of the central black hole is less than but comparable to the mass of 10 billion stars like the Sun. Hence the label **supermassive** seems to be justified. ■

What assumption is implied in the use of the virial argument in Example 1? Do you think the assumption is justified?

(*Hint*: You studied the virial theorem in Block 2 of this course.) ∎

1.4 Black holes at the centres of ordinary galaxies

Figure 1 showed two spiral galaxies: NGC 5548, which has an active nucleus, and NGC 3277 which does not. If we accept that AGN are the result of accretion on to supermassive black holes at the centres of the galaxies which harbour them, it is natural to ask the question whether galaxies like NGC 3277, which do not have active nuclei, are without central supermassive black holes, or simply without significant amounts of accretion on to their central black holes. Recent observations have made it clear that in some cases at least, apparently ordinary non-AGN galaxies seem to harbour supermassive black holes at their centres.

Perhaps most dramatic is the evidence for a supermassive black hole at the centre of our own Milky Way Galaxy. It is impossible to study the centre of our Galaxy in optical light because there is lots of gas and dust in the plane of the Galaxy which obscures our view of the central regions. At other wavelengths, however, the optical depth is less, and it has long been known that the centre of our Galaxy harbours a compact radio source which is called Sgr A* (pronounced 'sadj ay-star'), and is shown in Figure 7. Apart from Sgr A*, the radio emission from the centre of our Galaxy is diffuse and filamentary. The stars near the centre of the Galaxy are not visible because they are not strong radio sources. The infrared (IR) view shown in Figure 8 is very different. The IR image shown in Figure 8 is **diffraction-limited**, and gives a resolution of 0.15 arcsec. The blobs are individual stars within 0.02 pc of the Sgr A* radio source, whose position is marked with the small cross at the centre of Figure 8.

■   How do the scales of the images in Figure 7 and Figure 8 compare?

❑   The bar in Figure 7 represents 8 arcsec, while the image in Figure 8 is only about 3 arcsec across: the scale on the axis extends from about −1.5 arcsec to about +1.5 arcsec, and is centred on Sgr A*. ∎

Figure 8 is one frame of the short animation you will see in Activity 3. The animation shows a series of high spatial resolution infrared images of the centre of our Galaxy, which were taken during the 1990s. The motions of individual stars are clearly apparent. By measuring these motions, the strength of the gravitational field experienced by the stars can be deduced. This is analogous to the determination of the Sun's gravitational field (and hence the Sun's mass) by studying the orbits of the planets in the Solar System. As you will see in the animation, however, the stars at the centre of the galaxy are not neatly aligned in a plane analogous to the ecliptic in the Solar System. Instead, the stars follow randomly oriented orbits, and the virial theorem rather than Kepler's third law is used to deduce the gravitational field. The motions you will see in Activity 3 require the presence of a dark body with mass $2.45 \pm 0.4 \times 10^6 M_\odot$ at the centre of our Galaxy. This dark central body is almost certainly a black hole.

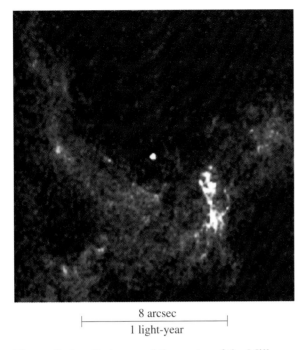

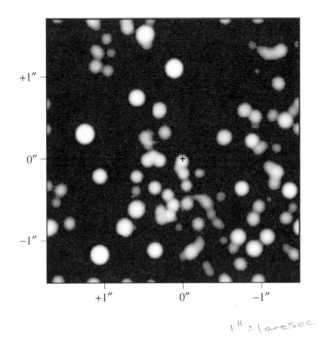

8 arcsec
1 light-year

$1'' \simeq 1$ arcsec

Figure 7 A radio image of the centre of the Milky Way Galaxy. White areas indicate intense radio emission and the red and black areas are progressively less intense. This image was taken with the Very Large Array (VLA) by Jun-Hui Zhao and W. M. Goss. The white dot at the centre of the image is the Sgr A* compact radio source.

Figure 8 A high spatial-resolution K-band image of the central regions of our own Galaxy. The bright blobs are individual stars. The small cross at the centre of the image shows the position of the compact radio source Sgr A*.

Activity 3

Stars orbiting our local supermassive black hole

From *The Energetic Universe* MM guide, view the animation entitled 'Stellar proper motions in the central 0.1 pc of the Galaxy' which shows the proper motions of stars in the central regions of our own Galaxy.

Keywords: **speckle imaging**, **enclosed mass** ▪

1.5 Distances in extragalactic astronomy

Block 1, Equation 67 introduced you to **Hubble's law**:

$$z = \frac{H_0 d}{c} \tag{7}$$

This relationship between **redshift**, z, of a distant galaxy which is given by

$$z = \frac{\Delta \lambda}{\lambda_0} \tag{8}$$

and its distance, d, from us arises because space is expanding. When the large redshifts of quasars were first discovered, there was naturally some reluctance to straightforwardly apply Hubble's law to them because the distances, and consequently the inferred luminosities were enormous. In fact, quasars are the most intrinsically luminous persistently bright objects we have discovered, and the most distant quasars are the most distant individual objects we know about. Consequently, active galaxies are of fundamental importance to **cosmology**, the study of the Universe as a whole. Cosmology is a huge subject and here in S381 we will focus on the active galaxies themselves, using only those cosmological ideas necessary to understand them.

The astronomical research required to determine the value of the Hubble constant, H_0, and thereby calibrate the extragalactic distance scale has filled entire textbooks, and we will not discuss it in this course, focusing instead on astrophysics. (If you are interested in learning more about the cosmic distance scale, look for links on the S381 website.) In this course we will generally adopt the same approach as Peterson, and use h_0 to represent the value of the Hubble constant in units of $100 \, \mathrm{km \, s^{-1} \, Mpc^{-1}}$, i.e.

$$H_0 = h_0 \times 100 \, \mathrm{km \, s^{-1} \, Mpc^{-1}} \tag{9}$$

Astronomers favour a value of around $H_0 = 60 \, \mathrm{km \, s^{-1} \, Mpc^{-1}}$, i.e. $h_0 = 0.6$, but this is continuously being debated and refined as new observations are made. Wherever a result is strongly dependent on the value of the Hubble constant, h_0 will appear explicitly.

The **Hubble time** is the inverse of H_0. If the Universe has always expanded at a constant rate, this is the time required for the Universe to expand from the Big Bang to its current size. The Hubble 'constant' has probably actually changed over time since the Big Bang, with the **deceleration parameter**, q_0, describing the change in the expansion rate. We will consider what AGN might be able to reveal about the expansion history of the Universe in Section 8.

Question 3

What is meant by the 'cosmological redshift'? ∎

1.6 The key questions

Some of the most important issues which astronomers working in this field are currently trying to resolve are:

- How and when did the supermassive black holes at the centres of galaxies form?
- What role did the central black holes play in the formation of galaxies?
- To what extent are the observed differences between AGN attributable to the orientation at which we view them?
- What governs the evolution of individual AGN, and of the Universe's population of AGN?
- Is there a link between AGN and star formation?

The third of these points is considered extensively in Section 7 of this block, where **unified models** are examined. If you have studied any astrophysics before S381 you may already have a qualitative overall picture of simple unified models for AGN. One of the goals of this block is to give you a thorough and detailed knowledge of the evidence astronomers have gathered about AGN, the extent to which it can be understood within the simplifying conceptual framework of unified models, and the issues which remain puzzling in this context. Consequently, in the first six sections of this block we will systematically cover the observations of AGN, along with the relevant theory. This will give you the appropriate background to be able to appreciate how the unified models are derived, and where their limitations lie. In Section 8 we will undertake a case study of contemporary research on the evolution of radio galaxies. This will give you a flavour of the research in the evolution of AGN, but an exhaustive discussion is beyond the scope of this course. The first two points in the list above are questions about the cosmological era which pre-dates AGN activity, and are being addressed with the latest instrument technology at cutting-edge observatories and with numerical simulations of the formation of structure in the Universe. Astrophysicists anticipate exciting future discoveries in these areas, which will build on the knowledge presented in this block.

1.7 Continuum emission processes

Interpretation of the light astronomers collect from AGN depends on understanding the physical processes leading to the emission of that light. Because the conditions in the emitting regions of AGN are very different from those on the surface of the Earth, some of these processes may be entirely unfamiliar to you. This subsection begins with a discussion of blackbody radiation, which should be familiar, and covers material which you will need to appreciate Peterson's discussion of AGN.

1.7.1 Blackbody radiation

In Block 1 you read about blackbody radiation, which is in thermal equilibrium with matter at a fixed temperature. Often the emission from astronomical objects is a close approximation to this **thermal radiation**. Many thermal sources of radiation, for instance stars, have spectra which resemble the blackbody spectrum, which is mathematically described by the Planck function, as introduced in Block 1. In Block 3 the spectrum of an accretion disc was modelled as the sum of blackbody spectra of varying temperature, and this work can be applied to accretion discs in AGN as well as those in binary star systems.

The blackbody spectra shown in Figure 9 illustrate the way that the spectra peak at wavelengths which depend on temperature. Away from the peak, the shape of the

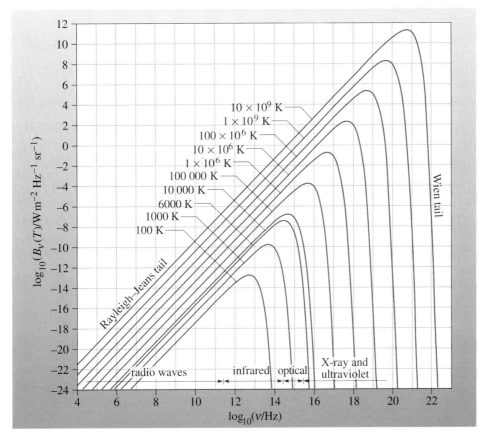

Figure 9 The blackbody spectrum for various temperatures. The peak emission occurs at a wavelength described by the Wien displacement law. The shape at substantially longer wavelengths is known the Rayleigh–Jeans tail, at substantially shorter wavelengths it is the Wien tail.

Planck function at substantially shorter wavelengths (high energies) is known as the **Wien tail**, which is mathematically described by

$$B_\nu(T) = (2h\nu^3/c^2)\exp(-h\nu/kT) \tag{10}$$

The shape of the Planck function at substantially longer wavelengths than the peak (low energies) is known as the **Rayleigh–Jeans tail**, which is mathematically described by

$$B_\nu(T) = 2kT\nu^2/c^2 \tag{11}$$

These 'tails' at both extremes of wavelength are sometimes referred to as the long-wavelength (or low-energy) cutoff and the short-wavelength (or high-energy) cutoff.

1.7.2 Free-free radiation

The blackbody spectrum is emitted when thermally emitting matter is optically thick. Optically thin matter can also emit thermal radiation. Whenever a charged particle is accelerated it emits electromagnetic radiation. When the acceleration is due to the electric field of another charged particle the emitted radiation is called **free-free** emission or **bremsstrahlung**. The radiation emitted by an optically thin, thermal equilibrium distribution of electrons is called **thermal bremsstrahlung**, which is a bit of a mouthful, so astronomers sometimes colloquially refer to it as 'thermal brems'.

Bremsstrahlung is a German word meaning 'braking radiation'.

The 'free-free' label makes an analogy with the formation of atomic spectral lines as discussed in Block 1, Section 4.9. When an electron in an atom makes a transition to another atomic energy level this is a **bound-bound** transition, because the electron is bound to the atom in both the initial and final states. Photoionization of an atom is a **bound-free** transition, because the electron is removed from the atom into a 'free' state. Conversely recombination of an ion and an electron, which liberates **recombination radiation** is a **free-bound** transition. The energy levels in an atom are discrete, so a bound-bound transition results in a spectral line at the precisely defined wavelength corresponding to the transition in question. There are 'free' quantum states at essentially all energies above the ionization energy, hence free-free emission, produced by free electrons in the Coulomb fields of ions, is a continuum spectrum.

POLARIZATION OF ELECTROMAGNETIC RADIATION

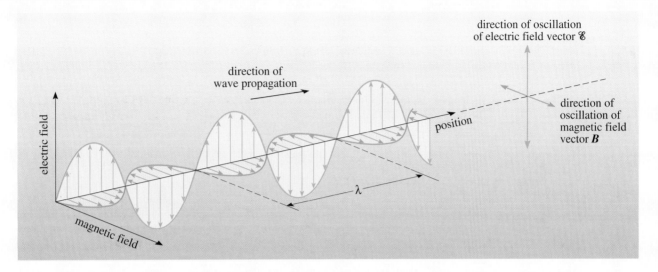

So far we have described electromagnetic radiation in terms of its wavelength, frequency and speed. It has another, sometimes important, property: **polarization**, which was briefly mentioned in Block 3, Section 7.2. Figure 10 shows the electric and magnetic field in a **plane-polarized** electromagnetic wave. In any electromagnetic radiation, the electric and magnetic fields are *always* perpendicular to each other, as well as perpendicular to the direction of propagation of the wave. In plane-polarized radiation the electric field vector always lies in a single plane, the vertical plane in the example shown in Figure 10.

Figure 10 Diagram illustrating the relative orientations of the electric and magnetic field vectors in plane-polarized light.

In general, sources of electromagnetic radiation are not polarized. In such **unpolarized** light, each photon has its own, randomly oriented, electric field direction. Only if all the photons in the radiation are oriented somehow, will net polarization occur. There are several ways this can happen. The most familiar everyday example is the plane polarization which occurs because of reflection. When a light ray is reflected the electric field vector of the incident ray will, in general, have two non-zero components as shown in Figure 11 (overleaf): one perpendicular to the reflecting surface, i.e. parallel to the page (represented with arrows in Figure 11), and one parallel to the reflecting surface, i.e. perpendicular to the page (dots in Figure 11 represent the arrow tips of this component). These two components are reflected with different efficiencies, so reflected light is consequently partially or totally plane-polarized. This is why Polaroid sunglasses are so effective at cutting down the glare from sunlight reflected by water or glass. In astrophysics, light is often scattered by dust, and this scattered light becomes polarized in the same way. Synchrotron radiation, the subject of the next section, is **intrinsically polarized**: it is emitted as a result of electrons interacting with a magnetic field, and the orientation of the polarization of synchrotron radiation is governed by the orientation of the magnetic field.

The flux of energy associated with an electromagnetic wave is given by the

Poynting vector, $S = \dfrac{c}{4\pi} \mathscr{E} \times B$, where here $\mathscr{E}$ and B are the fields comprising the electromagnetic wave. Referring to Figure 10, and applying the rule for forming a vector product (Block 1, Section 1.12.6) you can see that the Poynting vector is clearly along the direction of propagation of the wave.

Note: you may have previously studied electromagnetism in SI units. In this case you may have seen the Poynting vector expressed as $S = \mathscr{E} \times H$, which is equivalent to the cgs version given here.

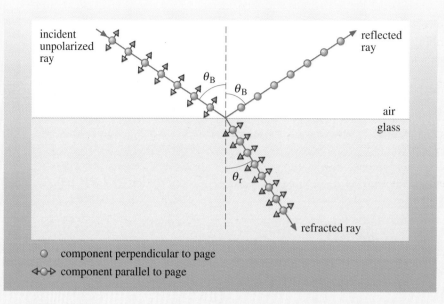

Figure 11 Reflection of light at a surface. The arrows indicate the component of the electric field vector which is in the plane of the page, the dots represent the electric field component which is parallel to the reflecting surface. If the angle of incidence is equal to the Brewster angle, θ_B, the reflected ray is 100% polarized, as shown. For other angles of incidence the reflected ray is only partially polarized.

FARADAY DEPOLARIZATION

Radiation of wavelength λ which starts off linearly polarized in a particular direction and travels through a plasma has its direction of polarization rotated by an angle

$$\Delta\phi \propto \lambda^2 \int n_e B_{\parallel}(x)\,\mathrm{d}x$$

where n_e is the electron density, $B_{\parallel}$ is the component of the magnetic field which is parallel to the direction in which the wave is travelling, and x is the distance along the line of propagation. This is known as **Faraday rotation**, or the **Faraday effect**. The integral is known as the **rotation measure**.

Radiation from an extended synchrotron source travelling through an ionized medium will have a rotation measure which depends on the electron density and magnetic field along the propagation path. The rotation measure will, therefore, vary for radiation emitted from different locations within an extended source. Consequently, even if the radiation were initially very highly linearly polarized, the different values of rotation measure for various emission locations, will reduce the observed polarization fraction. This effect is known as **Faraday depolarization**.

1.7.3 Emission from spiralling electrons: synchrotron radiation

In the very first reading (Activity 1) we encountered the term 'non-thermal' describing the spectrum of light emitted from AGN. In this subsection we will learn more about the most important type of non-thermal radiation: synchrotron emission.

When a charged particle moves in the presence of a magnetic field it experiences a **Lorentz force** (see Block 1, Equation 139) which produces an acceleration whose direction is perpendicular to both the magnetic field line and the velocity of the particle, v. Consequently the path followed by the electron is a helix, as shown in Figure 12. The radius of the circle described in the plane perpendicular to the magnetic field line is known as the cyclotron radius (see Block 1) and is also sometimes referred to as the **Larmor radius**, r_L or the **gyroradius**. It is given by

$$r_L \equiv \frac{m v_\perp}{|q| B} \qquad (12)$$

where $|q|$ is the magnitude of the charge of the particle, m is its mass, B is the magnetic field strength, and $v_\perp$ is the component of the particle's velocity which is perpendicular to the field.

Any accelerated charged particle produces electromagnetic radiation, and the radiation produced in the case of electrons accelerated by a magnetic field is known as **cyclotron radiation**; you read about this in Block 3, Section 7. When the electrons in question are high-energy relativistic electrons (i.e. when the electrons have speeds approaching c), the cyclotron radiation is known as **synchrotron radiation**. In most cases of astrophysical importance, synchrotron radiation is the most plentiful type of non-thermal radiation.

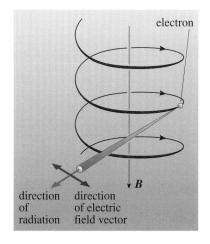

Figure 12 Synchrotron emission: an electron moving in a uniform magnetic field follows a helical path. Because it is constantly being accelerated, it emits electromagnetic radiation.

◼   What two ingredients are required for synchrotron emission to occur?

❑   Magnetic fields and relativistically moving electrons. ◼

Synchrotron radiation can, of course, be produced in a laboratory by arranging for electrons to be deflected by a magnetic field. Figure 13 shows a beam of synchrotron radiation produced at the European Synchrotron Radiation Facility (Figure 14).

Figure 13 A beam of synchrotron emission created in a particle accelerator.

Figure 14 An aerial view of the European Synchrotron Radiation Facility where the beam of synchrotron radiation shown in Figure 13 was created.

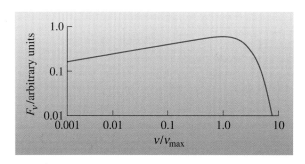

Figure 15 The spectrum of synchrotron emission from a single electron: the peak of the spectrum occurs at frequency v_{max}.

The spectrum of synchrotron emission produced by a single electron has the shape shown in Figure 15: a broad spectrum with a maximum at frequency

$$v_{max} \propto B_\perp \gamma^2 \tag{13}$$

where $B_\perp$ is the magnetic field strength perpendicular to the velocity of the electron, and γ is the **Lorentz factor**, given by

$$\gamma = \frac{1}{\sqrt{1 - \dfrac{v^2}{c^2}}} \tag{14}$$

The Lorentz factor, which is one of the fundamental ingredients of special relativity, is proportional to the total energy E_{TOT} (i.e. the kinetic energy plus the rest mass energy) of the electron: $E_{TOT} = \gamma m_e c^2$, where m_e is the electron rest mass. Hence we could alternatively write

$$v_{max} \propto B_\perp E_{TOT}^2 \tag{15}$$

The power, P, emitted in synchrotron radiation from a single electron depends on the energy of the electron. If we assume that the electron is highly relativistic (i.e. $v \sim c$) the power emitted is

$$P \propto E^2 \tag{16}$$

We have dropped the subscript 'TOT', but are still referring to the total energy of the electron.

In astronomy we detect the radiation from large numbers of electrons, rather than being able to distinguish the contributions of individual electrons. The electrons will have a range of velocities and of orientations with respect to the magnetic field, so the synchrotron spectrum we observe will be the sum of lots of individual spectra with varying values of v_{max}. The resulting observed synchroton spectrum is illustrated in Figure 16.

How much radiation is emitted at frequency v depends predominantly on how many electrons have $v_{max} \approx v$. That is to say the shape of the summed spectrum in Figure 16 depends on the distribution of electron energies. Mathematically, this distribution can be described by saying $N(E)dE$ is the number density (i.e. number per unit volume) of electrons with energies between E and $E + dE$. For many sources of

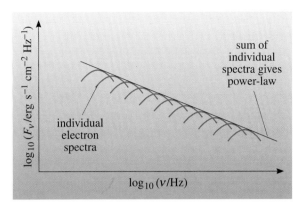

Figure 16 The observed synchrotron emission from a cloud of electrons is the sum of the emission from many individual electrons, each with a different energy and each with velocity at a different orientation to the magnetic field. Hence each individual electron produces a contribution peaking at its own value of v_{max}. At each frequency, v, the emission comes predominantly from the electrons which have $v_{max} \approx v$. Consequently, if the distribution of electron energies follows a power law then the observed synchrotron spectrum will also be a power law.

non-thermal emission, a **power-law distribution** of electron energies seems to hold, i.e.

$$N(E)\, \mathrm{d}E = N_0 E^{-s}\, \mathrm{d}E \qquad (17)$$

where N_0 is a constant of normalization, and s is a constant known as the **particle exponent**. When astrophysical sources of synchrotron emission are studied, it is found that typically s lies between 2 and 3.

■   If the number of electrons per unit volume is n_e, write down a mathematical expression relating n_e and $N(E)$.

❏   The total number of electrons is equal to the sum over all possible energies, E, of the number of electrons with energy E, so $n_e = \int_0^\infty N(E)\, \mathrm{d}E$. ■

Notice that the relationship between the electron energy, E, and the frequency, v, at which it produces most synchrotron radiation is described by Equation 15, and if we want to use the distribution of electron energies to deduce the distribution of radiation with frequency (i.e. the spectrum), we must remember to include the relationship between an energy interval $\mathrm{d}E$ and a frequency interval $\mathrm{d}v$ which is implicit in Equation 15. That is to say, differentiating Equation 15, treating $B_\perp$ as constant, we obtain

$$\frac{\mathrm{d}v}{\mathrm{d}E} \propto 2E \qquad (18)$$

Example 2

Show that the synchrotron spectrum produced by a power-law distribution of electron energies $N(E)\, \mathrm{d}E = N_0 E^{-s}\, \mathrm{d}E$, is described by

$$F_v \propto v^{-(s-1)/2} \qquad (19)$$

You may use the approximation that all the power radiated by the electron has frequency $v = v_{max}$, where v_{max} is given by Equation 15.

Solution

The flux emitted at a particular frequency, v, is determined by the number of electrons emitting at that frequency, $N(v)$, and the power, P, emitted by each of these. Expressing this mathematically:

$$F_v \propto PN(v) \tag{20}$$

The power P is given by Equation 16, and the number of electrons is determined by Equation 17, but we must transform this distribution from the number of electrons with a particular energy, E, into the number of electrons emitting at a particular value of v. This is accomplished by noting that the electrons and their properties are unchanged irrespective of how we decide to label them, so that

$$N(E)\,\mathrm{d}E = N(v)\,\mathrm{d}v$$

i.e. $$N(v) = N(E)\frac{\mathrm{d}E}{\mathrm{d}v} \propto N(E) \times \frac{1}{E}$$

where we have used Equation 18 in the final step.

Collecting these expressions for P and N in terms of E and substituting into Equation 20 we obtain

$$F_v \propto E^2 N(E)\frac{1}{E} \propto E \times E^{-s} \propto E^{-(s-1)}$$

where we have substituted for $N(E)$, and collected powers of E to arrive at the final result. The only remaining work is to express the result in terms of v rather than E, and this can be accomplished using Equation 15, which tells us that

$$v \propto E^2$$

which can be recast as

$$E \propto v^{1/2}$$

Substituting for E, therefore, we obtain

$$F_v \propto (v^{1/2})^{-(s-1)} \propto v^{-(s-1)/2}$$

as required. ∎

The observed power-law spectrum described by Equation 19 is often more concisely written as

$$F_v = v^{-\alpha} \tag{21}$$

where the new constant $\alpha\, (= (s-1)/2))$ is known as the **power-law index**. In Activity 4 we explore the production of power-law synchrotron spectra.

There is a generally useful trick to finding and measuring power-law dependencies. Taking logs of Equation 19 for F_v we obtain

$$\log_{10}(F_v) = \log_{10}(v^{-(s-1)/2}) \tag{22}$$

which can be rewritten using the properties of logs as

$$\log_{10}(F_v) = -\left(\frac{s-1}{2}\right)\log_{10} v \tag{23}$$

Hence it is clear that the overall synchrotron spectrum shown in Figure 16, which shows $\log_{10}(F_\nu)$ versus $\log_{10}(\nu)$, appears as a straight line with gradient $-(s-1)/2$, or more concisely with gradient $-\alpha$, where $\alpha = (s-1)/2$. The trick of using logarithmic axes makes it easy to recognize when the variables being plotted on the graph are related by a power law. If the variables are related by a power law, the power-law index can be determined by measuring the gradient of the straight line on the 'log–log' graph. This is a widely used technique, and astronomers often plot observed quantities on a log–log graph to check quickly whether there is a power-law relationship between them.

Question 4

Figure 17 shows the spectrum of synchrotron emission from a particular astronomical source. What is the *particle* exponent describing the distribution of electron energies in that source?

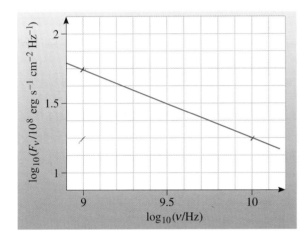

Figure 17 The spectrum of radio emission observed at a particular location in the sky. ■

Question 5

What is the power-law frequency dependence of the Rayleigh–Jeans tail? That is, if we write $B_{\nu,\text{Rayleigh–Jeans}} \propto \nu^p$, what is the value of p? ■

Activity 4   (30 minutes)

Do-it-yourself synchrotron emission

In this activity we will adopt the SI system of units, rather than the cgs system which Peterson favours. The cgs system has two versions of the electromagnetic equations we will use here. In the SI system there is no such confusion. For convenience we will also use eV for the electron energies. We will divide an energy in eV by another energy in eV, so *in this case* it doesn't matter that we adopted a non-SI unit for part of the calculation.

In this activity you will use a spreadsheet to produce a synchrotron spectrum, given an input spectrum of electron energies. In particular you will use the spreadsheet's 'slope' function to measure the gradient of a logarithmic graph. You will consequently rederive the result expressed by Equation 19. The power of the spreadsheet method is that the synchrotron spectrum could be calculated even if it was not possible to describe the electron energy distribution with a simple equation. Begin by starting up the StarOffice software and open a blank spreadsheet.

Note that we will be using σ_e for the Thomson cross-section in this block to align with the notation used in Peterson. This is exactly the same quantity that you have already encountered in Block 3 and FKR where it was given the symbol σ_T.

1   First, enter the values of the physical constants you will need into cells near the top of the spreadsheet. Enter the electron mass m_e in kg, the speed of light c in m s^{-1}, the electron charge e in coulombs, and the mass energy of an electron $m_e c^2$ in electronvolts (remember to convert from joules to electronvolts by dividing by e). Finally enter the value of the Thomson cross-section σ_e in units of m^2.

2   Next enter parameters for the synchrotron radiation you will produce. Enter the electron power-law index s with a value of 2.4, the electron normalization N_0 with a value of 1×10^{24} and the magnetic field B with a value of 1×10^{-9} tesla.

3   Now, in column A of the spreadsheet enter values of the electron energies you will use. Start with an initial energy of 1×10^7 eV (i.e. 10 MeV) in cell A20, and in steps of 1×10^7 eV, fill 1000 cells with values up to 1000×10^7 eV (i.e. 10 GeV) in cell A1019.

4   In column B enter the corresponding values of γ for these electron energies. Since $E = \gamma m_e c^2$, the gamma factor is a pure number obtained when you divide an energy in eV by a mass energy in eV.

5   Now, in column C calculate the number of electrons with each value of energy according to $N(E) = N_0 E^{-s}$. (Remember to use the dollar notation ($) to 'freeze' the values of those cells which you do not want to vary from one row to the next.)

6   In column D calculate the frequency, ν_{max}, of the radiation produced by a single electron with the energy corresponding to each gamma factor. Use the relationship

$$v_{max} = \frac{\gamma^2 eB}{2\pi m_e} \tag{24}$$

7   For convenience later, fill column E with the logarithm to the base ten of the values in column D (i.e. `E20 = log10(D20)` etc.).

8   In column F we need the power radiated by each electron with a particular energy. An appropriate formula to use is

$$P = \gamma^2 c\sigma_e B^2 / 4\pi$$

9   Now, we need to calculate the total power emitted by all electrons with a given energy and plot this against the frequency at which that radiation appears. So, in column G calculate $N(E) \times P/E$ for each value of electron energy. This is effectively the flux density.

$N(E)$ is the number of electrons with energy between E and $E + dE$ and $N(E) \times P$ is the power emitted by these electrons. The frequency interval $d\nu$ over which this power is radiated is determined by Equation 18, which shows that the frequency interval is larger when E is larger. Hence when we observe the spectrum, the power contributed by the higher energy electrons is spread over a larger range in frequency than is the power contributed by the lower energy electrons. The relationship between dE and $d\nu$ described by Equation 18 means we must divide $N(E) \times P$ by E to calculate the power emitted per unit frequency interval, $d\nu$, i.e. the flux density.

10   Finally in column H calculate the log to the base 10 of the flux density values in column G. We now have all the values we need to plot the synchrotron spectrum!

11   Now to plot a graph. Select the values in columns E and H (i.e. those containing the logarithms of the frequency, ν_{max}, and the flux density). Using the insert chart option, plot a graph of log(flux density) on the y-axis against log(frequency) on the x-axis. Ensure that the axes are labelled in a sensible manner.

12   As a final step, measure the slope of the graph you have plotted. To do this, move to a blank cell (for instance one underneath your graph) and click on Insert then Function. Choose the Slope function from the list presented, and when prompted on the next screen, enter the 'data_Y' values as H20:H1019 and the 'data_X' values as E20:E1019. The value of the slope of the graph will then be returned in the cell you have selected.

If you wish, try varying the value of the input power-law slope s and see how the slope of the synchrotron spectrum varies. Try varying the input magnetic field too and see what effect this has. Just changing these single numbers should propagate changes throughout your spreadsheet and graph. Consult the comments on this activity if you wish, then answer the following questions. ▪

Question 6

(a) With a magnetic field strength of 10^{-9} tesla, what values of electron energies are required in order to produce synchrotron radiation at radio frequencies of a few GHz? (b) What values of electron energies are required for radio frequency production if the magnetic field is 10^{-10} tesla? ▪

Question 7

Using the graph you produced in Activity 4, what is the slope of the synchrotron spectrum for an input electron power-law index of 2.7? ▪

So far we have seen that the synchrotron emission from a power-law distribution of relativistic electrons is a power-law spectrum with increasing flux at decreasing frequencies. Like all good things, this must come to an end: absorption of photons by the synchrotron-emitting electrons can also occur. This process is known as **synchrotron self-absorption (SSA)**, and is particularly important for photons with low frequency, v. For these low-frequency photons, SSA can mean that the probability of a photon escaping from the synchrotron emitting region is small, i.e. at low frequencies the synchrotron emitting region becomes optically thick. This modifies the spectrum of the escaping radiation at low frequencies from $F_v \propto v^{-\alpha}$ to $F_v \propto v^{5/2}$, as Figure 18 shows. This downturn in the spectrum at low frequencies is known as a **low-frequency cutoff**. The frequency at which self-absorption becomes important depends on the magnetic field strength, the density of electrons and the particle exponent. The details of these dependencies are beyond the scope of this course, but an obvious consequence of them is that the low-frequency cutoff can occur at a range of different frequencies, depending on the particular parameters of the emitting region. If an astronomical source has a spatially varying magnetic field, density, or electron energy distribution, then the overall emitted spectrum could be a sum of individual spectra like that shown in Figure 18, but shifted in frequency relative to each other. This is how so-called **flat-spectrum radio sources** are thought to arise. You will read about these in Activity 6.

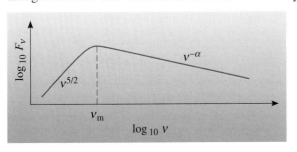

Figure 18 The full synchrotron spectrum from a power-law distribution of electron energies. At high photon energies the emission is optically thin, and the power-law dependence on the particle exponent holds. At low photon energies the emission is optically thick, and self-absorption causes a $F_v \propto v^{5/2}$ spectral shape.

1.7.4 Compton scattering

Electromagnetic radiation interacts strongly with electrons. If a photon encounters an electron, there is a high probability that a **scattering** interaction will occur. In the low-energy non-relativistic regime, i.e. where $hv \ll m_e c^2$ the interaction is called **Thomson scattering**, and its likelihood is described by the classical **Thomson scattering cross-section**, σ_e. In general, interactions between a photon and an electron include quantum mechanical and relativistic effects which modify the classical Thomson scattering process. The process in the regime where quantum and relativistic effects are included is known as **Compton scattering**, and a full discussion requires quantum electrodynamics, which is beyond the scope of this course. One of the immediate effects of the quantum nature of light is that the scattering of a photon by an electron is, in general, an **incoherent** process, i.e. in general energy will be exchanged between the electron and the photon, so the incoming and outgoing photons differ in frequency. Whenever the electron has sufficient kinetic energy compared to the photon, energy can be transferred from the electron to the photon. This is the so-called **inverse Compton process**, and is important in astrophysics.

■   What frame of reference would you choose to assess whether 'the electron has sufficient kinetic energy compared to the photon'?

❑   The rest frame of the observer is the obvious choice, since this is the frame in which the initial and final energies of the photon are to be measured. In the case of inverse Compton scattering occurring in an AGN, the rest frame of the AGN itself is a sensible alternative choice, since both the initial and final photon energies will be affected by the cosmological redshift. ■

For a population of relativistic electrons threaded by a magnetic field, loss of energy from the electrons due to synchrotron emission (see Section 1.7.3), P_{synch}, and the loss of energy from the electrons due to the inverse Compton process, P_{compt}, are related by the ratio of the magnetic field energy density, U_{mag}, and the photon energy density, U_{rad}:

$$\frac{P_{synch}}{P_{compt}} = \frac{U_{mag}}{U_{rad}} \qquad (25)$$

The physical reason behind this simple relationship is that from a quantum viewpoint the synchrotron and inverse Compton processes are analogous. Synchrotron radiation involves scattering of electrons by the quanta associated with the magnetic field, while in inverse Compton scattering the electrons are scattered by real photons: quanta of electromagnetic radiation.

Radiation which has been boosted to higher energies by the inverse Compton process is often referred to as having been **Compton upscattered**. In the case of AGN, photons emitted by the synchrotron process can themselves be inverse Compton scattered by the population of relativistic electrons emitting them, thus emerging from the source with higher energies than they initially had. This is the so-called **synchrotron self-Compton (SSC)** process, which you will encounter in Activity 27.

1.8 Basic properties and historical perspective

1.8.1 Continuum spectra

General properties of quasars and power-law emission

Read Section 1.3 of Peterson, up to and including the first two paragraphs of Section 1.3.1 (pages 8–10).

Morphology is a technical way of referring to shape. Thus the 'radio morphology' referred to in the opening section of Peterson 1.3.1 is simply the shape(s) of the spatially resolved radio emission. In Activity 47 we will come across another technical definition of morphology, but it is generally clear from context which meaning is intended.

Keywords: **spectral energy distribution (SED)**, **power law**, **power-law index, α** ▨

Question 8

Give six common general properties of quasars. ∎

- A quasar has a power-law spectrum obeying $F_\lambda \propto \lambda$, how would this spectrum be described in terms of F_ν and ν?

- $F_\nu \propto \nu^{-3}$. This comes from the relationship arising from $F_\lambda \, d\lambda = F_\nu \, d\nu$ (see Block 1) on Peterson page 8: $F_\lambda \propto \lambda^{\alpha-2}$, so $\alpha - 2 = 1$, therefore $\alpha = 1 + 2 = 3$. ∎

Example 3

Figure 19 shows a schematic spectral energy distribution. In which part of the electromagnetic spectrum is most energy emitted per unit interval on the logarithmic frequency axis? Fully justify your answer, including an explanation of why $\log_{10} \nu$ is the most convenient choice of variable on the horizontal axis of a graph for this purpose.

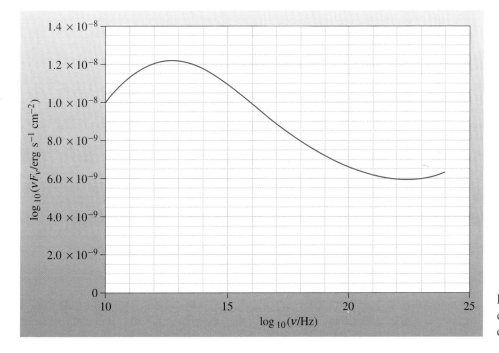

Figure 19 A schematic energy distribution of a hypothetical quasar.

Solution

The graph in Figure 19 shows $\log_{10}(\nu F_\nu)$ versus $\log_{10}\nu$. The flux emitted between any two frequencies ν_1 and ν_2 is given by

$$F_{12} = \int_{\nu_1}^{\nu_2} F_\nu\,d\nu = \int_{\nu_1}^{\nu_2} \nu F_\nu\,\frac{d\nu}{\nu} = \int_{\log_{10}\nu_1}^{\log_{10}\nu_2} \nu F_\nu\,d(\log_{10}\nu) \tag{26}$$

Looking at this final expression for F_{12}, we see it is of the form $F_{12} = \int_{lower}^{upper} y\,dx$, where $x = \log_{10}\nu$, i.e. F_{12} is the area under the curve of νF_ν between the two specified values on the horizontal (or $\log_{10}\nu$) axis. Generally νF_ν will have values varying by many orders of magnitude over the full electromagnetic spectrum, so usually the logarithm of νF_ν is a more useful quantity to plot on the graph than νF_ν itself. The part of the electromagnetic spectrum where the most energy is emitted per unit interval on the logarithmic frequency axis will be where νF_ν reaches a maximum: this occurs at $\log_{10}\nu \sim 12.5$, i.e. at wavelength

$$\lambda = \frac{c}{\nu} \approx \frac{3\times10^{10}\,\text{cm s}^{-1}}{10^{12.5}\,\text{s}^{-1}} \approx 1\times10^{-3}\,\text{cm} \approx 100\,\mu\text{m}$$

i.e. in the far infrared. It is for this reason that spectral energy distributions are generally plotted using this particular choice of axes: the eye easily picks out the location of the dominant contribution to the area under the curve. These axes allow immediate identification of the part of the spectrum which radiates most energy. As Figure 20 shows, different choices of axes can make it much more difficult to do accomplish this. If the horizontal axis was ν rather than $\log_{10}\nu$, the entire low-energy part of the spectrum would be compressed into a tiny space on the extreme left-hand edge of the graph. ■

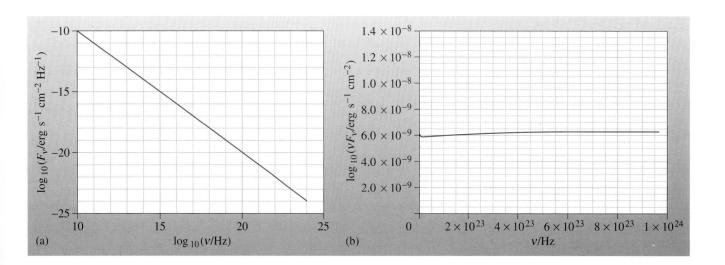

Figure 20 The same spectral energy distribution as in Figure 19, but with two different choices of axes. (a) The vertical axis shows $\log F_\nu$. (b) The horizontal axis shows ν.

1.8.2 Extended radio sources

In Section 1.7.3 we studied the spectrum of the synchrotron emission, i.e. how the flux density of radiation depends on the frequency or wavelength of the radio emission. Using radio telescopes such as the VLA (Figure 21) radio astronomers can also **spatially resolve** the celestial radio emission, that is to say they can study how the flux density of radiation at one particular frequency depends on position in the sky. Hence pictures can be made with radio emission, just as we make pictures showing how optical emission depends on position in the sky (e.g. Figure 1). Figure 22 shows two examples of radio pictures. *Note*: Do not worry about the information in the caption until you undertake Activity 6. Radio emission pictures are often shown graphically as contour maps. You probably noticed Peterson's Figure 1.4 as you completed the previous reading activity: this figure is an example of a radio intensity map. The interpretation of these figures is analogous to reading altitude contours on an everyday map: each contour line represents a particular value, so the highest value in the picture will be inside the largest number of contour lines.

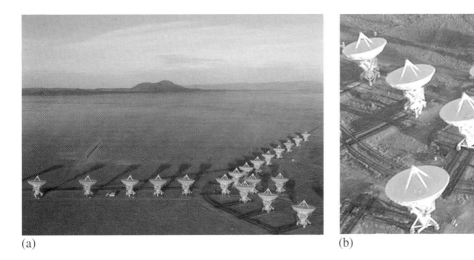

(a)   (b)

Figure 21 (a) and (b) The 'Very Large Array' (VLA) is used to make radio images of the sky. It consists of many individual radio dishes, the signals from which are combined. These individual dishes can be moved, and the spatial resolution of the radio images depends on their separation.

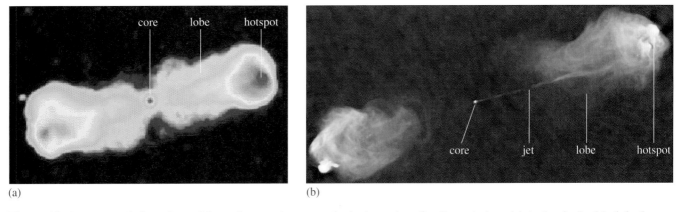

(a)   (b)

Figure 22 Images made by using a false-colour scale to encode the intensity of radio emission. (a) A classic double-lobed radio source (3C 35), showing the core, extended lobes, and hotspots. (b) Cygnus A showing the radio jet.

Activity 6

Pictures via radio: extended radio sources

Read the remainder of Section 1.3.1 of Peterson, beginning at 'Extended radio structures …' on page 11.

Surface brightness refers to the amount of radiation per unit solid angle. An extended source may have a large total brightness, without having a particularly high surface brightness. In contrast, the small nucleus of a Seyfert galaxy emits about the same amount of radiation as the total emitted from the entire host galaxy. The nucleus has high surface brightness, the surrounding galaxy has low surface brightness.

We will examine the physics behind **Doppler beaming** in Section 3.4.

Keywords: **Fanaroff–Riley (FR) classes I and II**, **core**, **lobe**, **jet** ◼

Question 9

Figure 23 shows the radio intensity maps of the active galaxies 3C 465 and 3C 105. (a) Is 3C 465 an FR I or an FR II type radio galaxy? (b) Is 3C 105 an FR I or an FR II type radio galaxy? ◼

The '3C' in the designations of the two active galaxies shown in Figure 23 stands for the 'third Cambridge' catalogue, which you read about in Block 1, Activity 4; see Peterson Section 1.2. This was an early survey, made when the instruments were of poor resolution and relatively insensitive, consequently these are among the strongest radio sources in the sky.

◼ What frequency radio emission was observed to produce the map in Figure 23a?

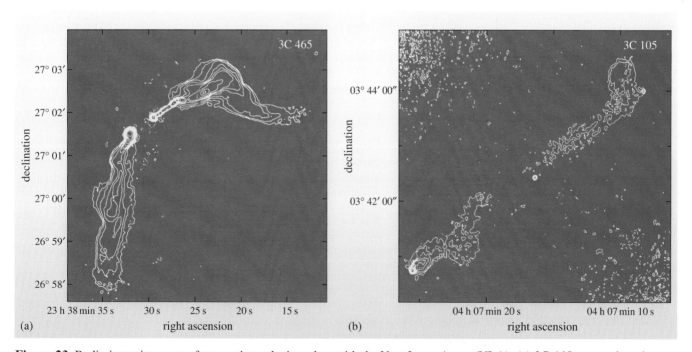

Figure 23 Radio intensity maps of two active galaxies taken with the Very Large Array (VLA). (a) 3C 465 at wavelength 6 cm. (b) 3C 105 at 3.6 cm.

❑   The observation was made at a wavelength of 6 cm. We can work out the corresponding frequency using the equation relating speed, frequency, and wavelength for electromagnetic radiation, $v = c/\lambda$. Inserting values (using cgs units), we find,

$$v = \frac{2.998 \times 10^{10} \text{ cm s}^{-1}}{6 \text{ cm}} \quad \text{i.e. } v = 5 \times 10^9 \text{ Hz or } 5 \text{ GHz} \ \blacksquare$$

1.8.3 Line spectra

For obvious reasons optical astronomy developed earlier than radio and X-ray astronomy, and astronomers are able to learn many things from analysis of optical emission. Just as in the radio band, optical pictures, i.e. the spatial distribution of emission, can be informative. Even when a source is not spatially resolved, astronomers can still deduce some information about what it might look like close-up. These 'visualizations' of what is happening in a particular source result from analysis of how the amount of light detected depends on time, or on wavelength, i.e. by looking at **temporal** or **spectral** properties of the emission. (See the box on 'Ions and spectral lines'.)

IONS AND SPECTRAL LINES

In Block 1 you encountered the idea of atomic energy levels, and in Block 1 Activity 7 and Block 1 Figure 84 the **spectral lines** arising from the energy levels in the hydrogen atom were introduced. Since hydrogen is the most abundant chemical element in the Universe, its spectral lines are particularly important in astrophysics. The **Balmer series** are the transitions in which the $n = 2$ energy level is the lower level. This series of lines appears in the optical wavelength region, and the **Hα line** (transitions between $n = 2$ and $n = 3$) is often the most prominent line in optical spectra. The highest energy transitions in the hydrogen line spectrum are those to and from the lowest energy level, i.e. transitions to and from $n = 1$. This series of lines is called the **Lyman series**, and the **Lyα line** (transitions between $n = 1$ and $n = 2$) is prominent in ultraviolet spectra. See Collins for further details in the entry for the 'hydrogen spectrum'.

The **Balmer limit**, which occurs at 3646 Å corresponds to transitions between the $n = 2$ level of hydrogen and unbound states, i.e. this is the ionization transition from the $n = 2$ level. Similarly the **Lyman limit** at 912 Å corresponds to ionization from the ground state ($n = 1$). Consequently radiation with $\lambda < 912$ Å is known as **ionizing radiation**. Photons with energies just exceeding the Lyman limit are highly prone to absorption by neutral hydrogen gas: consequently the plane of our own Milky Way Galaxy is essentially opaque at wavelengths just short of the Lyman limit.

Generally astronomers label spectral lines using notation like CIV $\lambda\lambda$1548, 1551, which concisely gives an enormous amount of information. Going through this piece by piece:

'C' indicates the chemical element, carbon in this example,

'IV' indicates the ionization state. 'I' indicates the neutral atom, with successive roman numerals indicating successive positively charged ions, hence 'IV' indicates that three electrons have been removed. The CIV ion is C^{3+}; the roman numeral is always one more than the number of positive charges.

'λ' indicates the following numerals give wavelength. In this case we have '$\lambda\lambda$', which means that the spectral line is a **multiplet**. In the case of a multiplet there are two or more 'fine structure' sublevels to one or both of the energy levels involved in the transition, so that there are multiple components to the spectral line, corresponding to the various possible energy differences between the initial and final states. This is illustrated in Figure 24. In our example, the line is a **doublet**, having two components. **Triplets** and higher multiplets are also possible.

'1548, 1551' gives the wavelength in Å of the two components of the doublet.

Spectral lines arise as a result of atomic transitions which are governed by quantum mechanical selection rules. Most common lines correspond to transitions which are **permitted** by the selection rules. For reasons which we will not explore here, it is also possible (with low probability) for transitions to occur which do not obey all of the selection rules. Such transitions are called **forbidden** or **semiforbidden lines**, depending on which of the selection rules are violated. Semiforbidden lines are also sometimes called **intercombination lines**. The astrophysically important point is that permitted transitions are, in general, much more likely than forbidden or semiforbidden transitions. This means that if an excited atom has a permitted transition that it can make to a lower level, it is not likely to make a non-permitted transition. Consequently the only forbidden and semiforbidden lines which are observed are those where no permitted transition is available. Furthermore, because non-permitted transitions have low probability of occurrence, an excited atom will remain in the excited state for a long time before the transition occurs. During this time, a collision with another atom, ion, or free electron may occur, and **collisional de-excitation** will result. Hence forbidden and semiforbidden lines are only observed from low-density regions, where collisions are relatively infrequent.

The notation used to indicate a forbidden line is a pair of square brackets around the chemical element and ionization state, e.g. [OII]. Similarly, a semiforbidden line is indicated by just the closing bracket, e.g. NIV]

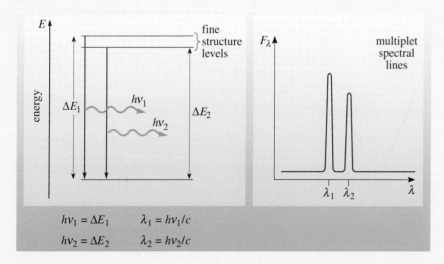

Figure 24 Fine structure sublevels in initial or final energy levels lead to a multiplet spectral line.

$hv_1 = \Delta E_1$ $\lambda_1 = hv_1/c$

$hv_2 = \Delta E_2$ $\lambda_2 = hv_2/c$

Question 10

List the permitted lines, the forbidden lines, and the semiforbidden lines present in optical and UV spectra of the Seyfert 1 galaxy NGC 5548. Refer to Peterson Figs. 1.1 and 1.2. ■

Question 11

The ionization of hydrogen from the ground state requires radiation of wavelength less than 912 Å. Calculate the frequency corresponding to this wavelength, and the equivalent photon energy. Give the energy in joules, in ergs and finally in electronvolts. Which of these three energy units is the most natural choice in this instance? ■

Activity 7

Quasar variability

Read Peterson Section 1.3.2 (pages 13–14).

Coherence arguments are the light travel time arguments we discussed in Section 1.3. The chanting of the crowd at a football match is often incoherent: several versions of the same chant will be heard from different sections of the crowd, with perceptible time delay(s) compared to the leading chant. This occurs not because football crowds are a disorganized rabble, but because the time taken for sound to travel from one end of the stadium to the other causes an appreciable delay. In contrast, members of a choir inside a concert hall sing coherently. They have no difficulty in keeping in time, because the distance between the singers is small, so the sound travel time from one to another is imperceptibly small.

Keywords: **variability**, **timescale** ▪

LINE FLUX AND EQUIVALENT WIDTH

In general, astronomical objects emit both continuous emission and lines superimposed on this continuous emission. The **equivalent width** is a useful way of describing the relative strength of a line compared to the continuous emission at nearby wavelengths. The flux level of the continuous spectrum is called the **continuum** level, and at an emission line the spectrum rises above this level, while at an absorption line the spectrum dips below this level, as Figure 25 shows.

The **line flux** is simply the total amount of energy per unit collecting area per unit time carried by line photons. On a graph of the spectrum this is the area corresponding to the line.

The equivalent width, W_λ, is the width of a rectangle having the height of the continuum and which has the same area as the line; the units of equivalent width are thus the same as the units of wavelength.

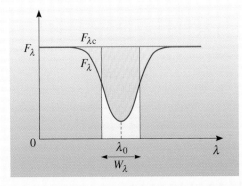

Figure 25 The continuum level, $F_{\lambda c}$, (blue), and an absorption line (red). The equivalent width, W_λ, is the width of a rectangle the same height as the continuum which has the same area as the absorption line.

In Block 2 the Hertzsprung–Russell (H–R) diagram was used to characterize the properties of stars. The colour (e.g. *B*–*V*; see also Block 1, Section 2.8) was used on the horizontal axis of the Hertzsprung–Russell diagram as an empirical indicator of temperature. Magnitude, or another luminosity indicator, was plotted on the vertical axis. Consequently, the H–R diagram is also sometimes referred to as a **colour–magnitude diagram**. The main sequence formed a roughly diagonal locus across the colour–magnitude diagram. *B*–*V* is just one of a number of possible colours, and each spectral type has a definite expected value for any colour. In the next activity you will encounter a **colour–colour diagram**.

■ What advantage does a colour–colour diagram have over a colour–magnitude diagram when comparing objects which have varied and unknown distances?

❑ Colours are unaffected by changes in distance (except if reddening is important), so objects can be compared by simply plotting their measured colours. To make a colour–magnitude diagram the distance is needed to convert from apparent magnitude to absolute magnitude when the objects are not all at the same distance. ■

The following question is to check you remember a term which is used in the next reading.

■ What is the 'Wien tail'?

❑ The Wien tail is the short-wavelength (or equivalently the high-energy) part of the blackbody spectrum. ■

Activity 8 (20 minutes)

Colours and broad lines

Read Peterson Sections 1.3.3 and 1.3.4 (pages 14–16).

Peterson Fig. 1.6 is a colour–colour diagram and the annotated line is the locus of the main sequence in this graph: that is to say, any main-sequence star should fall on (well, nearby!) this line. Any source of light which has intrinsic colours which deviate from this line cannot be a normal main-sequence star. Thus probable quasars can quickly be picked out.

In Section 1.3.3 Peterson refers to the **blackbody distribution**, this is just shorthand for 'blackbody spectral energy distribution', which you know as the 'blackbody spectrum'.

The **Balmer continuum absorption edge** is also known as the **Balmer jump**. This feature corresponds to the threshold ($\lambda = 3646$ Å) at which a photon can cause an ionization from the $n = 2$ level of hydrogen (see the Collins entry for hydrogen spectrum). Less energetic photons can only be absorbed by hydrogen in the $n = 2$ initial state if their wavelength corresponds to one of the Balmer series lines. Photons with energies just above the Balmer continuum absorption edge are very likely to be absorbed by any hydrogen atom in the $n = 2$ state that they encounter, causing a photoionization. Consequently, for stars hot enough for there to be significant numbers of hydrogen atoms in the $n = 2$ excited state, the emitted flux drops appreciably at wavelengths $\lambda < 3646$ Å compared with $\lambda > 3646$ Å.

Keywords: **Balmer jump (= Balmer continuum absorption edge), UV excess, flux-limited sample, equivalent width** ■

■ Why are stars of spectral type O and B most likely to contaminate samples of quasars chosen for U-excess?

❑ Because these are the hottest stars, and therefore will have the largest U-excess (see the vertical axis of Peterson Fig. 1.6). ■

In the preceding reading from Peterson, the first of many possible **selection effects** arose. In Section 1.3.4 Peterson discusses how quasars with $z \approx 2$ appear bright in the U band, because the Lyman α emission line falls within the U band for this redshift (see Figure 26). Selection effects can cause serious misunderstandings: one of the most important checks an astronomer must perform is to ascertain whether any observed trends are simply a by-product of the particular sample of objects chosen for study, rather than being an intrinsic property of the objects in general.

For example, if a sample of quasars was selected by looking for objects which are particularly bright in the U band (i.e. objects showing a U-excess relative to typical stars and galaxies), objects with $z \approx 2$ would be appear to be even more plentiful than they really are. In Activity 10 you will explore the effects of the most important selection effect of all.

■ What is the 'Lyα selection effect'?

❑ This effect occurs for quasars with redshifts such that the Lyman α emission line (which has rest wavelength 1216 Å) appears in the observed U band (i.e. between 3000 Å and 4000 Å). Because Lyman α is such a strong emission line, it causes an appreciable enhancement in the U band apparent brightness. Consequently quasars whose continuum emission would have been too faint to detect without the contribution of the line emission can be detected. As a result it might appear that there are more quasars than otherwise expected at these redshifts. ■

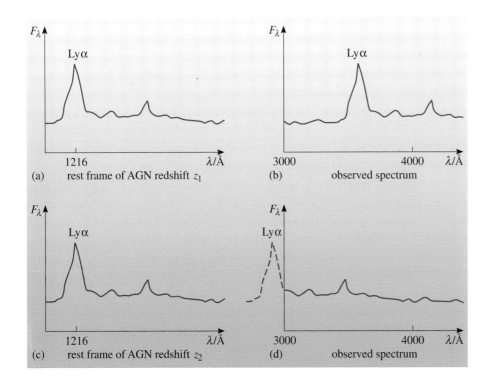

Figure 26 The wavelength at which Lyα is detected depends on the redshift. At redshift z_1 (panels a and b) Lyα appears between 3000 Å and 4000 Å, while at redshift z_2 (panels c and d) it does not.

Quasar redshifts

Read Peterson Section 1.3.5 (pages 16 and 17).

Keywords: **cosmological probes**, **luminosity function**, **quasar absorption lines** ■

■ How can astronomers detect cool intergalactic gas in distant parts of the Universe?

❏ By detecting redshifted absorption lines in the spectra of even more distant quasars. ■

As Peterson stressed in the section you have just read, high-redshift quasars are important for a variety of reasons. Consequently astronomers are currently investing time, energy and many nights of telescope usage on searching for ever more distant quasars. At the time this Study Guide was written, the most distant known quasar was that shown in Figure 27a. The identification of these distant quasars is done photometrically by looking for **Lyman-break** objects, where there is no detected flux in the blue part of the observed optical spectrum because it has been absorbed by high-redshift hydrogen gas, as shown in Figure 27b.

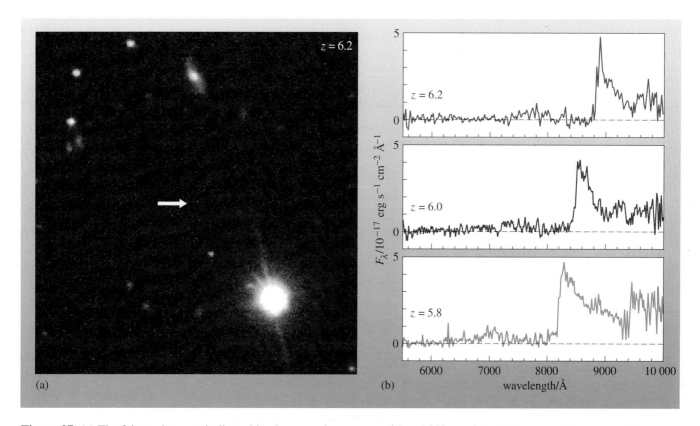

Figure 27 (a) The faint red source indicated by the arrow is a quasar with redshift $z = 6.2$. (b) Spectra of three very distant quasars. In each case the highest observed flux is the Lyα emission line, which has been redshifted into the red part of the optical spectrum. To shorter wavelengths the detected flux is zero because all these photons have undergone Lyman absorption by less redshifted neutral hydrogen gas between us and the quasar.

1.8.4 Luminosity functions

Pick a card, any card: choices are sometimes forced

In this activity you will investigate how samples of galaxies are biased due to the flux limit of the sample that is observed. This is the so called **Malmquist bias**. In particular you will use the spreadsheet's 'sort' facility to select a subset of the input data as an 'observational sample'.

Using StarOffice, open up the initial spreadsheet for this activity which is installed on your hard disk. You should find it by clicking on the Spreadsheet tab on the Block 4 screen of *The Energetic Universe* MM guide. It is called B4_Ac10_initial.sdc

This spreadsheet contains absolute magnitudes and distances for over 300 galaxies. The numbers of galaxies are such that there are more galaxies at fainter absolute magnitudes than there are at brighter absolute magnitudes, as in the galaxy **luminosity function** (see Collins) in the real Universe. All the galaxies in this sample are at distances of less than 25 Mpc and randomly distributed in space.

1   First, calculate the apparent magnitudes of all the galaxies using $m = M - 5 + 5 \log_{10}(d/\text{pc})$ and fill column C with these values.

2   Next, calculate the luminosity of all the galaxies and fill column D with these values. You can use the standard relationship

$$M_1 - M_2 = 2.5 \log_{10}(L_2/L_1)$$

and the result that a galaxy with absolute magnitude $M_1 = -20.5$ has a luminosity of $L_1 = 3 \times 10^{43}\,\text{erg s}^{-1}$. (*Hint*: You will need to rearrange the formula above to obtain an expression for L_2 in terms of L_1, M_1 and M_2 and then calculate L_2 for each of the galaxies in the spreadsheet.)

3   Now, sort the galaxies into order of ascending *apparent* magnitude. Select the four columns of data, then click on Data then Sort to sort the data according to the values in column C. This will list the 300+ galaxies in order of increasing apparent magnitude.

4   Now, have a look at the distribution of luminosity of these galaxies with distance. Select *all* the data in columns A and D and produce a graph (Insert then Chart) showing an XY scatter plot of luminosity against distance. When you have produced the graph make the vertical (luminosity) axis logarithmic. To do this, select the graph then click on Format then Axis then Y-axis and check the Logarithmic scale box. Make sure the axes are labelled in an appropriate manner. You should see that the complete sample of galaxies is indeed distributed randomly with distance.

5   A flux-limited sample, by definition, has a limiting apparent magnitude beyond which no more objects are detected. Let us suppose that our flux limit is apparent magnitude 14. Select (highlight) those data in columns A and D corresponding *only* to those galaxies with $m < 14$ (since they are sorted in order of increasing apparent magnitude, this will be the upper portion of the spreadsheet). Then click on Insert then Chart and produce an XY scatter graph of the luminosity versus distance for this flux-limited sample. Again, make the vertical axis logarithmic.

6   Try choosing a different flux (apparent magnitude) limit (say $m < 12$) and produce a graph of this flux-limited sample.

If you wish, refer to the comments on this activity, then try answering the following question. ▪

What is the difference between the flux-limited samples and the complete sample of galaxies? ■

■   What is meant by an unbiased sample?

❑   An unbiased sample is one which properly represents the population of objects under consideration. Selecting a sample of British adults by interviewing people as they leave a football match would probably give a biased sample. ■

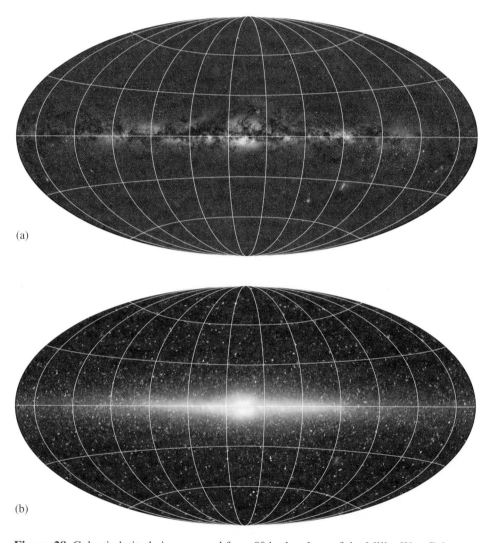

(a)

(b)

Figure 28 Galactic latitude is measured from 0° in the plane of the Milky Way Galaxy. The figure shows lines of constant Galactic latitude and longitude overlaying (a) an optical image of the entire sky (b) an infrared image of the entire sky. In the optical image the dust in the plane of the Milky Way is clearly apparent. The dust is more transparent at infrared wavelengths, so the centre of the Milky Way is seen in image (b).

Radio-quiet quasars

Read Peterson Section 1.4 (pages 18–20).

High Galactic latitude refers to directions which are away from the plane of the Milky Way Galaxy, see Figure 28. The plane of the Milky Way is at Galactic latitude= 0°, in the same way that the Earth's equator is at (terrestrial) latitude = 0°. Directions close to Galactic latitude = 0° go through the most densely populated parts of the disc of the Milky Way where dust obscures distant sources and there are many foreground stars belonging to the Milky Way. Extragalactic astronomers make observations primarily of objects at high Galactic latitude, where the line of sight is out of the disc, so that a higher proportion of the detected objects will be distant galaxies. The Hubble Deep Field (see the cover of Peterson, the Image Archive and Figure 29) is an example of a high Galactic latitude line of sight.

Keywords: **luminosity function, radio-loud, radio-quiet, sample selections**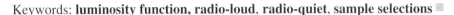

■   Why would astronomers wishing to measure the quasar luminosity function be unlikely to use the 3C catalogue as their sample?

❑   Because there would be several serious selection effects:

•   The 3C catalogue is a radio catalogue, so all the entries are example of radio-loud quasars, which are only about 10% of the total population of quasars.

•   The 3C catalogue only contains objects which appear very bright, so suffers from a strong Malmquist bias.

•   The 3C catalogue was made with low angular resolution observations, and is limited by 'confusion' where sources overlap. This could cause additional selection effects, such as excluding objects in clusters of galaxies. ■

■   The 3C radio survey is biased, can optical surveys be regarded as unbiased?

❑   Not necessarily. Dust in the vicinity of an AGN may absorb optical light, so infrared searches reveal more AGN. ■

Figure 29 The Hubble Deep Field. Most of the objects in this picture are distant galaxies. As well as containing few foreground stars, this line of sight was chosen because it contains no bright nearby extragalactic objects.

1.9 Summary of Section 1

1   Active galactic nuclei (AGN) are powered by accretion onto supermassive black holes. The masses of these central engines of AGN can be estimated by means of the virial theorem, using the size of the nucleus of the galaxy and the velocity dispersion of the material in the vicinity of the nucleus. Estimates of the masses are around $10^{9\pm1}M_\odot$.

2   The Schwarzschild radius of a black hole, i.e. the radius of the sphere from within which light cannot escape, is given by

$$R_S = \frac{2GM}{c^2}$$

where M is the mass of the black hole.

3   An indicator of the distance to an AGN is its cosmological redshift, z. The shift in its spectral lines $\Delta\lambda$ reflects the recession speed of the AGN. According to Hubble's law, the larger the redshift, the more distant is the object.

4   When electrons travel through regions of space containing a magnetic field, they follow helical paths around the magnetic field lines and emit electromagnetic radiation. When the speeds of the electrons are relatively low, the emitted radiation is known as cyclotron radiation, and when the electron speeds are a significant fraction of the speed of light, the emitted radiation is known as synchrotron radiation.

5   The spectrum of synchrotron radiation produced by a single electron travelling with a speed v has a broad shape with a maximum at a frequency v_{max}. This frequency is proportional to $B_\perp \gamma^2$ where $B_\perp$ is the magnetic field component perpendicular to the velocity of the electron and γ is the electron's Lorentz factor, given by

$$\gamma = \frac{1}{\sqrt{1 - \dfrac{v^2}{c^2}}}$$

The Lorentz factor is proportional to the electron's energy, since $E = \gamma m_e c^2$, so v_{max} is also proportional to $B_\perp E^2$.

6   Given an ensemble of electrons whose energies are distributed according to a power law with particle exponent s, the flux density in the spectral energy distribution (SED) of the optically thin synchrotron radiation is given by $F_v \propto v^{-\alpha}$ where $\alpha = (s-1)/2$. At low frequencies synchrotron radiation is optically thick, and $F_v \propto v^{5/2}$. This is known as synchrotron self-absorption (SSA).

7   Free electrons in an ionized gas radiate as they decelerate when they pass by protons or other positively charged ions. The continuous spectrum of electromagnetic radiation which arises is called thermal bremsstrahlung. Since the electrons are unbound throughout the process, the radiation is also known as free-free emission.

8   The Wien tail is the short-wavelength part of the blackbody spectrum (described by $B_\nu(T) = (2h\nu^3/c^2)\exp(-h\nu/kT)$), whilst the Rayleigh–Jeans tail is the long-wavelength part of the blackbody spectrum (described by $B_\nu(T) = 2kT\nu^2/c^2$).

9   Both blackbody radiation and bremsstrahlung are examples of thermal radiation, because the speeds of the electrons that are responsible for them follow a Maxwell speed distribution. Synchrotron radiation is an example of non-thermal radiation.

10 In the process of Compton scattering, high-energy photons scatter off relatively low-energy electrons and lose energy as a result. In the process of inverse Compton scattering, photons gain energy from higher energy electrons. Radiation which has been boosted to higher energies by this process is said to have been Compton upscattered.

11 In the synchrotron self-Compton (SSC) process, synchrotron radiation is upscattered by the same electrons which were responsible for the original emission.

12 The Balmer and Lyman series of hydrogen lines arise from transitions whose lowest energy levels are the $n = 2$ and $n = 1$ levels respectively. Hence the Hα line (in optical spectra) arises from transitions between $n = 3$ and $n = 2$, whilst the Lyα line (in ultraviolet spectra) arises from transitions between $n = 2$ and $n = 1$. The Balmer limit at 3646 Å corresponds to transitions between $n = 2$ and the continuum whilst the Lyman limit at 912 Å corresponds to transitions between $n = 1$ and the continuum.

13 Most common spectral lines are 'permitted' by quantum mechanical selection rules. In low-density regions, so called 'forbidden' lines can also be produced. This is because collisions between atoms are rare if the density is low, so atoms in excited states with no permitted transitions execute low probability forbidden transitions. Forbidden lines are indicated by a square bracket notation, such as [OIII] λ5007 for the forbidden transition in doubly ionized oxygen, leading to emission of radiation of wavelength 5007 Å (5.007×10^{-7} m).

14 When linearly polarized radiation passes through a plasma, its direction of polarization is rotated in a phenomenon known as Faraday rotation. Consequently radiation travelling through an extended synchrotron source will have a rotation measure which depends upon the electron density and magnetic field along the propagation path. The different values of rotation for various emission locations within an extended source will lead to Faraday depolarization.

15 Quasars share some or all of the following properties: they are star-like objects identified with radio sources, they are luminous X-ray sources, they have time variable continuum flux, a large UV flux, broad emission lines and large redshifts. The radio SED of a quasar typically has $F_\nu \propto \nu^{-0.7}$.

16 Radio galaxies and quasars typically show two components: a pair of spatially extended lobes extending for several kpc and a compact (spatially unresolved) core. Extended radio sources can be divided into Fanaroff–Riley class I (FR I) sources whose lobes are brightest in the centre and fainter towards their edges, and Fanaroff–Riley class II (FR II) sources whose lobes are limb-brightened and often show enhanced emission at the edges of the radio structure. FR II sources are more luminous than FR I sources.

17　The compact cores of radio galaxies are smaller than 0.01 pc in size and their spectra are usually flat (i.e. $\alpha < 0.5$) over several orders of magnitude in frequency.

18　Some radio galaxies have extended linear structures known as jets, extending from the core to the lobes. Jets often appear only on one side of the radio galaxy, and in cases where two are seen, one is usually much fainter than the other.

19　Quasars are variable in every waveband in which they have been studied, including both continuum and line emission, on timescales as short as a few days. This indicates that much of the radiation must come from regions of order light-days across.

20　Quasars often have unusually blue colours and an excess at ultraviolet fluxes compared to stars. Their UV–optical spectra have strong, broad emission lines from hydrogen, and other common chemical elements.

21　Since quasars are observed at high redshift, they provide a probe of the Universe when it was only a fraction of its current age. They can serve as luminous background sources against which other, closer structures may be observed.

22　Radio-quiet quasars are around 100 times fainter in radio emission and around 10–20 times more numerous than the radio-loud quasars.

23　Observational samples of galaxies and AGN are subject to the Malmquist bias. It is easier to detect more luminous objects at greater distances than it is to detect low-luminosity objects at these same distances. So, any flux-limited sample will contain a greater representation of high-luminosity objects and will contain relatively few low-luminosity objects at large distances, despite the fact that low-luminosity members of a class of objects are usually the most numerous. The 3C radio catalogue, for example, suffers from a strong Malmquist bias.

2 EXPLORING THE ACCRETION PROCESS

Section 1 covered some of the astronomical evidence leading to the consensus that AGN are powered by accretion. In this section we examine accretion physics from a conceptual viewpoint, building on Block 3. This section begins with a thought-experiment which treats a very simple example of accretion onto a black hole, and moves on to the application of accretion disc physics to AGN. Finally we make a comparison between the predictions of the theoretical disc physics and observations of AGN.

2.1 Accretion onto supermassive black holes

AGN include the most luminous persistently bright objects in the Universe. Astronomers are generally convinced that these systems are powered by accretion onto black holes with masses of order $10^9 M_\odot$. One of the basic reasons why black holes were postulated as the power source for AGN is the need to produce a prodigious luminosity in a small volume. An example of observations requiring this is shown in Figure 30; in particular, in Figure 30b there is variability of about a factor of 2 over a timescale of approximately 2 days.

The words 'persistently bright' which qualify the statement that AGN are the most luminous objects in the Universe are necessary because there are phenomena which release a huge amount of energy in a short amount of time. For example **gamma-ray bursts** (see Collins) are typically more luminous than AGN, but only for their very brief ($\leq 1000\,\text{s}$) duration.

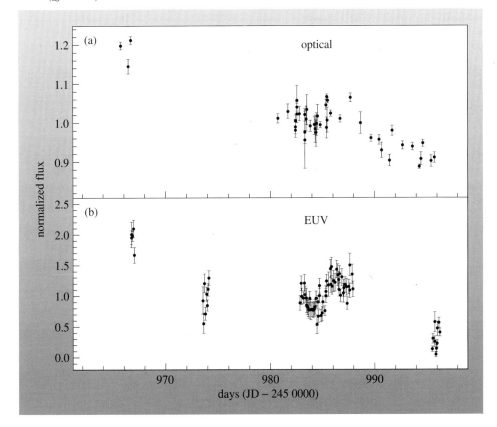

Figure 30 (a) An optical light curve for NGC 5548. (b) An extreme ultraviolet light curve for NGC 5548 covering the same interval.

The horizontal axis of Figure 30 is labelled by 'JD' which stands for **Julian Date**, which is a calendar system allowing time to be specified by a single number rather than year, month and day. For data which spans years or decades, this is obviously an advantage. (See Collins for details.)

Question 13

Estimate the size of the extreme ultraviolet (EUV) emitting region NGC 5548, the object whose EUV light curve is shown in Figure 30b. ■

2.1.1 Accretion of old fridges

In Block 3, accretion-powered emission from interacting binary stars was considered. Here, in Block 4, we have already discussed some of the reasons for astronomers thinking that accretion is the power source of AGN. One important difference between the cataclysmic variables, which have led to most of our detailed knowledge of accretion physics, and AGN is that in the latter the accretor is a black hole. A black hole has an event horizon which can swallow mass and energy. Therefore it is appropriate to ask whether accretion of mass onto a black hole always (or even generally) produces electromagnetic radiation.

Example 4

Figure 31 shows an old fridge of mass m_f at a distance r from a black hole of mass M_{BH}.

(a) Write down an equation giving the gravitational force acting on the fridge (you may assume Newton's law of gravity is sufficient).

(b) Assuming the fridge moves under gravity from rest at an initial distance $r = r_0$, and ignoring relativistic effects, calculate the velocity of the fridge when it reaches the black hole's event horizon, i.e. at distance $r = R_S$ from the centre of the black hole.

(c) How much gravitational potential energy has been liberated by this change in the fridge's position?

(d) How much energy will be liberated as electromagnetic radiation in this process?

Note: In general, when confronted by a problem like this, applying the principle of conservation of energy (which would lead rapidly to the answer) is the most effective approach. In this example we are using an inefficient method (i) to illustrate a point that may have become lost in your work in Block 3, and (ii) to introduce a useful trick.

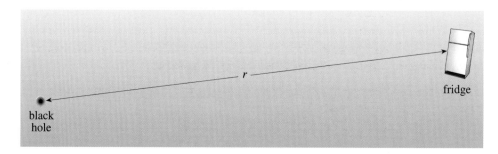

Figure 31 A black hole and a fridge, separated by distance r.

Solution

(a) The fridge will experience a gravitational force F_{GR}. This force is directed towards the black hole. If we choose a coordinate system centred on the black hole this force will be in the direction opposite to the radial coordinate vector, r. It is standard to adopt the symbol $\hat{r}$ to indicate the vector of unit length in the r-direction (similarly $\hat{x}$ is a vector of unit length in the x-direction, and so on). Using Newton's law of gravitation (Block 1, Equation 111), therefore we have

$$F_{GR} = -\frac{GM_{BH}m_f}{r^2}\hat{r}$$

for the force on the fridge, towards the black hole.

(b) Using the assumptions and approximations suggested, the calculation is simple, but requires one trick. Using Newton's laws of motion, the subsequent acceleration of the fridge, d^2r/dt^2, is described by

$$F_{GR} = m_f \frac{d^2r}{dt^2} = m_f \frac{d^2r}{dt^2}\hat{r}$$

Equating the two expressions for F_{GR}, we obtain the differential equation

$$m_f \frac{d^2r}{dt^2} = -\frac{GM_{BH}m_f}{r^2}$$

cancelling m_f, we have

$$\frac{d^2r}{dt^2} = -\frac{GM_{BH}}{r^2} \tag{27}$$

Unfortunately we can't integrate this as written, because the right-hand side is in terms of the variable r while the left-hand side needs integrating with respect to t. Fortunately there is a trick which we can use to recast the left-hand side:

$$\frac{d^2r}{dt^2} = \frac{dv}{dt} = \frac{dv}{dt} \times \frac{dr}{dr} = \frac{dr}{dt} \times \frac{dv}{dr} = v\frac{dv}{dr}$$

Using this to rewrite Equation 27 we have

$$v\frac{dv}{dr} = -\frac{GM_{BH}}{r^2}$$

If we integrate once therefore we have

$$\int v\,dv = \int -\frac{GM_{BH}}{r^2}\,dr$$

and both sides can easily be integrated to give

$$\frac{v^2}{2} = \frac{GM_{BH}}{r} + C \tag{28}$$

where C is a constant of integration. We were asked for the velocity, so all we need to do is to use the initial conditions to determine the constant, C.

At the initial position, $r = r_0$, and the fridge is at rest so $v = 0$, substituting these values into Equation 28, therefore

$$0 = \frac{GM_{BH}}{r_0} + C$$

so $C = -GM_{BH}/r_0$. Substituting this back into Equation 28, therefore we have an equation implicitly giving the velocity of the fridge at any position r:

$$\frac{v^2}{2} = \frac{GM_{BH}}{r} - \frac{GM_{BH}}{r_0} \tag{29}$$

Since the force acting on the fridge is always directed in the minus r-direction, we know we must take the negative square root of the right-hand side of Equation 29. Consequently, the velocity of the fridge when it reaches the event horizon, $r = R_S$, is

$$\boldsymbol{v} = -\sqrt{2GM_{BH}(R_S^{-1} - r_0^{-1})}\,\hat{\boldsymbol{r}}$$

(c) The change in gravitational potential energy is found by applying Block 1, Equation 118

$$E_{GR} = -\frac{GMm}{r}$$

to the initial and final situations, and calculating the difference:

$$\Delta E_{GR} = -GM_{BH}m_f\left(\frac{1}{R_S} - \frac{1}{r_0}\right) \tag{30}$$

(d) We can work out how much energy, ΔE_{RAD}, is available to be liberated by electromagnetic radiation by applying conservation of energy to the process:

$$\Delta E_{RAD} + \Delta E_{GR} + \Delta E_{KE} = 0 \tag{31}$$

where ΔE_{KE} is the change in kinetic energy between the initial and final situation. Using Block 1, Equation 115, we find $\Delta E_{KE} = \frac{1}{2}m_f v^2$, evaluating this by substituting from Equation 29 with $r = R_S$, we find:

$$\Delta E_{KE} = GM_{BH}m_f\left(\frac{1}{R_S} - \frac{1}{r_0}\right) \tag{32}$$

as you might have anticipated. This means the kinetic energy gained by the fridge (Equation 32) is exactly equal to the gravitational potential energy lost (Equation 30). Therefore, using Equation 31, $\Delta E_{RAD} = 0$, meaning that no energy is available to be liberated as radiation. ■

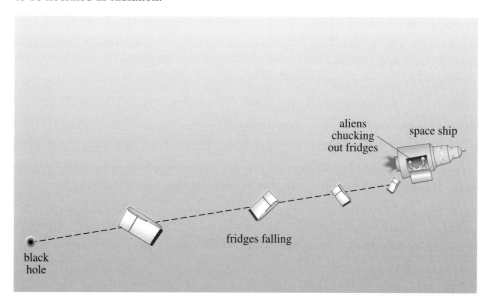

Figure 32 Cartoon showing aliens getting rid of old fridges.

The results obtained above show that in the case of solid objects which start from rest, accretion onto a black hole can occur without any energy being liberated as radiation. Thus, if there was a black hole handy, it would be possible to safely dispose of old fridges by dropping them into it (Figure 32).

■ What is physically different between the situation described above, and the accretion discs discussed extensively in Block 3?

❏ The fridge above started from rest, hence it had no *angular momentum* with respect to the black hole. The material fed through the L_1 point (inner Lagrangian point) in an interacting binary star does have angular momentum, and it is also gaseous, rather than solid. Accretion discs form because in general the accreting material will not start from rest, instead it will be orbiting, and will possess angular momentum. Also, the fridges we have considered were not subject to collisions, so they do not experience anything akin to viscosity. Viscous dissipation in the gaseous material is the mechanism by which some of the gravitational potential energy is made available for conversion into electromagnetic radiation. ■

To actually get rid of the fridges, it would be necessary to feed them to the black hole in such a way that they don't carry any angular momentum with respect to the black hole. Figure 33 shows what would happen if the fridges were simply gently pushed out of an orbiting spacecraft.

In many ways stars behave like the fridges we have discussed. If a star is in orbit around a black hole, it will simply continue in its orbit, just like the fridges in Figure 33. In fact, we have already seen this is the case in Activity 3.

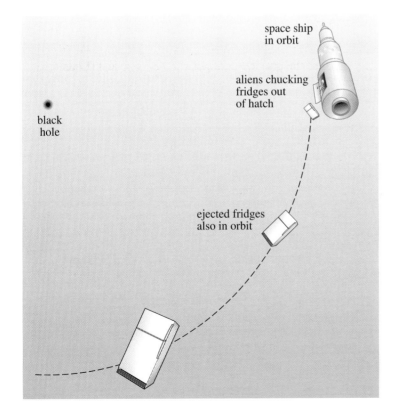

Figure 33 Cartoon showing aliens getting rid of old fridges, which remain in orbit at the same radius as the spaceship.

2.1.2 Accretion of hot gas

Activity 12 (1 hour)

Feeding the black holes in AGN

Read the first part of Chapter 3 of Peterson, up to and including Section 3.2 (pages 32–36).

Note: The definition of the Thomson scattering cross-section, σ_e that Peterson gives at the bottom of page 33 is true only in cgs esu (electrostatic units). The formula is different to that you encountered in Phillips because the definition of e (the charge on the electron) differs in SI units. The numerical value of the cross-section is, of course, the same in the two versions of the formula.

By assuming **isotropy** Peterson is referring to the assumption that the AGN radiates uniformly in all directions, so that the detected energy flux per unit area for an observer is given by $L/4\pi d^2$, where L is the luminosity, and d is the distance between the observer and the source.

Note that we will be using L_E for the Eddington limit in this block to align with the notation used in Peterson. This is exactly the same quantity that you have already encountered in Block 3 and FKR where it was given the symbol L_{edd}.

In the derivation of the **Eddington limit** L_E (Peterson Equation 3.3) given in Peterson Section 3.1, the following argument is implicitly used. The electrostatic force is strong compared to other forces likely to act on protons or electrons, so current flows will be caused in a plasma if ever a large-scale separation of positive and negative charges occurs. The currents will flow until electric charge neutrality is restored. Consequently, though the outward radiation pressure force acts overwhelmingly on the electrons, while the inwards gravitational force acts overwhelmingly on the protons, the electrostatic attraction between the two prevents the electrons from being ejected while the protons fall inwards. The strength of the electrostatic coupling between protons and electrons is high enough that we can treat the plasma as though the radiation pressure and gravitational forces each act on the coupled electron–proton pair.

In considering the Compton process (scattering involving an electron and a photon, see Section 1.7.4), the mathematics is clearest if we use a frame of reference where the total momentum of the electron and the photon is equal to zero: this is known as the **centre of momentum** frame. In this frame, the energy of the photon, $h\nu$, may be either greater than or less than the rest mass energy of the electron, $m_e c^2$. If $h\nu \gtrsim m_e c^2$, a relativistic calculation is needed to predict the interaction, if $h\nu \ll m_e c^2$, a non-relativistic calculation, leading to the Thomson scattering cross-section, σ_e, (as discussed in Block 3) is sufficient. The **Klein–Nishina** limit occurs at the division between these two cases, $h\nu \approx m_e c^2$.

Reverberation-mapping refers to the technique of using reflected light to map out the structures surrounding an emitting source. We will return to this in more detail in Section 5.5.

Don't despair! The familiar **Roche limit** is not something you should remember from Block 3; we will discover the origins of Peterson Equation 3.12 below in Section 2.1.3.

Keywords: **Eddington luminosity, galaxy–galaxy gravitational interactions** ■

■ What is meant by bolometric luminosity?

❑ The bolometric luminosity is the luminosity of an object obtained by summing the radiation emitted over the entire electromagnetic spectrum. ■

■ What is 'spherical accretion' in Peterson Section 3.1? Do you think AGN are likely to be powered by spherical accretion? Briefly explain your reasons.

❑ 'Spherical accretion' would be a spherically symmetrical inflow of material, so that all properties of the accretion flow are determined by the distance r from the central mass, i.e. the material would be falling inwards along the $-\hat{r}$ vector. If the material feeding the accretion flow has any angular momentum, radial infall will not be possible, as it would violate the conservation of angular momentum. As in general there will always be some net angular momentum, AGN are unlikely to be powered by spherical accretion. Instead, as in interacting binary stars, the accretion flow is likely to be in the form of a disc. ■

Question 14

Estimate how many Earth masses are consumed each year by a QSO of luminosity $L_{QSO} = 10^{46}\ \text{erg s}^{-1}$. ■

As you learned in the last reading (Activity 12), gravitational interactions between galaxies can help fuel AGN by removing angular momentum from gas in the galaxy. These galaxy–galaxy collisions can also stimulate **starburst** activity (see Collins entry for **starburst galaxy**), which you will read a bit more about in Activity 15. In the next activity you will see how a collision between two galaxies can lead to dramatic changes in each of them.

Activity 13

Colliding galaxies

From *The Energetic Universe* MM guide, view the animation of the numerical simulation of the colliding galaxies. This animation follows only the stars in these two galaxies. Any gas present in the galaxies before the collision will be affected by gravitational interaction with the mass of the other galaxy, though it is not shown in the animation. This interaction can cause shocks in the gas, triggering starburst activity, and could easily redistribute angular momentum so that some of the gas might fuel a central AGN, as discussed in Peterson Section 3.2.

Keywords: **galaxy–galaxy gravitational interactions** ■

■ Why do you think the simulation in Activity 13 only shows the motion of stars, and not gas motions and starburst activity?

❑ To self-consistently calculate the motion of all the gas in each galaxy would require a lot more computational effort. To determine whether star formation is triggered would require calculation of the thermodynamic properties of all the gas. In contrast, the existing stars can be treated as point masses, and their motion is consequently easier to follow. ■

The UK Astrophysical Fluids Facility is a high-performance computing facility dedicated to working on this sort of problem. Their website (a link is available through the S381 website) usually contains animations of some recent astrophysical simulations.

2.1.3 The Roche limit

The last part of your reading in Activity 12 discussed the tidal disruption of stars. In this way stars can provide gaseous material to feed the accretion discs in AGN. It is through tidal disruption that luminous accretion is made possible; without tidal disruption stellar material would behave as fridge-like lumps which do not generate accretion-powered luminosity.

This section explores the same underlying physics as Block 3's treatment of the Roche lobe. The star and the supermassive black hole could be thought of as a very extreme mass ratio binary. In this case, however, the star is unlikely to be in a perfectly circular orbit.

In 1850 Edouard Roche (Figure 34) calculated the radius at which a moon would be disrupted by **tidal forces** due to the gravity of the planet it orbits. His analysis applies just as well to the case of a star orbiting around a supermassive black hole. The tidal force arises because different parts of the orbiting body experience different gravitational forces, the part of the star closest to the black hole experiences the strongest gravitational force towards it. Hence the differential gravitational force will tend to elongate the orbiting star, and if the differential gravitational force is strong enough it will ultimately disrupt the star. To estimate how close to the black hole the star may approach without being disrupted, we can, like Roche, assume that

- both bodies are spherical,

- the star is non-rotating,

- disruption occurs when the differential gravitational force exceeds the self-gravitational force.

These assumptions are not strictly correct; but are good enough to get an order of magnitude estimate.

Figure 34 Edouard Roche (1820–1883).

If we consider forces acting on unit masses in the surface layers of the star shown in Figure 35, we can compare accelerations, rather than forces, simplifying the algebra slightly. The differential gravitational acceleration, Δa_{tide}, is simply the difference between the acceleration felt at distance $r - R_*$ and that felt at distance $r + R_*$:

$$\Delta a_{\text{tide}} = GM_{\text{BH}}\left(\frac{1}{(r + R_*)^2} - \frac{1}{(r - R_*)^2}\right) \tag{33}$$

while the acceleration due to self-gravity at the surface of a spherical star is:

$$a_{\text{sg}} = \frac{GM_*}{R_*^2} \tag{34}$$

where R_* and M_* are the radius and mass of the star, M_{BH} is the mass of the black hole, and r is the distance between the centre of the star and the centre of the black hole. Equation 33 can be rewritten as:

$$\Delta a_{\text{tide}} = GM_{\text{BH}} \times \frac{1}{r^2}\left(\frac{1}{\left(1 + \dfrac{R_*}{r}\right)^2} - \frac{1}{\left(1 - \dfrac{R_*}{r}\right)^2}\right)$$

or $\quad \Delta a_{\text{tide}} = GM_{\text{BH}} \times \dfrac{1}{r^2}\left(\left(1 + \dfrac{R_*}{r}\right)^{-2} - \left(1 - \dfrac{R_*}{r}\right)^{-2}\right)$

If we note that the radius of the star is much less than the distance between the two bodies, i.e. $R_*/r \ll 1$, you may now recognize the terms inside brackets as being of a form suitable for a Taylor expansion approximation, which results in

$$\Delta a_{\text{tide}} = GM_{\text{BH}} \times \frac{1}{r^2}\left[\left(1 + (-2)\left(\frac{R_*}{r}\right) + \cdots\right) - \left(1 + (-2)\left(-\frac{R_*}{r}\right) + \cdots\right)\right]$$

ignoring terms smaller than R_*/r, therefore

$$\Delta a_{\text{tide}} \approx GM_{\text{BH}} \times \frac{1}{r^2}\left(1 - 2\frac{R_*}{r} - \left(1 + 2\frac{R_*}{r}\right)\right)$$

and collecting terms we arrive at:

$$\Delta a_{\text{tide}} \approx -\frac{4GM_{\text{BH}}R_*}{r^3} \tag{35}$$

Using Equations 34 and 35, we find that the differential tidal acceleration, Δa_{tide}, is equal to the self-gravitational acceleration, a_{sg}, when:

$$\left|\frac{M_*}{R_*^2}\right| = \left|-\frac{4M_{\text{BH}}R_*}{r^3}\right| \tag{36}$$

where we have cancelled the factors of G which would have occurred on both sides, and introduced modulus signs so we don't need to worry about the two accelerations being in opposing directions.

Figure 35 A star orbiting a black hole. The distance between the centres of the two objects is r, and the radius of the star is R_*.

Question 15

(a) Manipulate Equation 36 into the form shown in Peterson Equation 3.12, i.e.

$$r_{\text{roche}} = C\left(\frac{\rho_{\text{BH}}}{\rho_*}\right)^{1/3} R_{\text{S}} \tag{37}$$

where C is a constant, ρ_{BH} is the (mean) density of the black hole, R_{S} is the Schwarzschild radius of the black hole, and ρ_* is the (mean) density of the star.

(b) What value do you obtain for the constant C? Does this agree with the value quoted in Peterson? If not, can you think of any reasons why you obtained a different result? ■

■ What makes astronomers think that AGN are fuelled by gas and not by stars swallowed whole?

❏ Stars swallowed whole would not produce significant electromagnetic radiation. Gas forming an accretion disc heated by viscous dissipation, on the other hand, will radiate approximately half the liberated gravitational potential energy. ■

Activity 14   (30 minutes)

Numbers of the beast

In this activity you will calculate the Schwarzschild radius for black holes with a variety of masses and also calculate their corresponding Roche limits for tidal interaction with solar-mass main-sequence stars and neutron stars. You will make use of logarithmic functions and logarithmic axes on graphs. Start up StarOffice and open up a new, blank spreadsheet.

1   Begin by entering the values for Newton's gravitational constant and the speed of light into a couple of cells near the top of the spreadsheet.

2   Then enter the mass and radius of (i) a solar-mass main-sequence star and (ii) a solar-mass neutron star, into pairs of cells. (Assume that a neutron star has a radius of 10 km.) Use these masses and radii to calculate the mean densities of these two stars (assuming they are spherical) either in $\mathrm{kg\,m^{-3}}$ or $\mathrm{g\,cm^{-3}}$ depending on whether you prefer to work in SI or cgs units.

3   Now, in column A, enter a range of numbers from −2.0 to 10.0 (in steps of 0.1, say) to represent the logarithm to the base 10 of a black hole mass in solar units (i.e. $\log_{10}(M/\mathrm{M_\odot})$, where M ranges from $0.01\mathrm{M_\odot}$ to $10^{10}\mathrm{M_\odot}$).

4   In column B calculate the corresponding black hole masses in solar units (10 to the power of the numbers in column A) and in column C calculate the black hole masses in grams or kilograms.

5   In column D calculate the corresponding Schwarzschild radii of these black holes, (Equation 2) in centimetres or metres.

6   In column E calculate the mean densities of the black holes within the Schwarzschild radius (again assume the black holes to be spherical).

7   Now, in columns F and G respectively calculate the Roche limit for disruption of (i) a solar-mass main-sequence star and (ii) a solar-mass neutron star, for each of the black hole masses in your table, according to Peterson Equation 3.12.

8   Now use the results of your calculation to compare the Roche limit and the Schwarzschild radius for each case. Plot a graph showing the Schwarzschild radius and the two Roche limits as a function of mass. To do this, highlight the data in columns B, D, F and G then click on Insert then Chart and produce an XY graph. The three lines corresponding to the three radii should automatically be displayed in three different colours. To make the graph easier to read, it is best to display it with logarithmic axes. To do this, select the chart once it's drawn, then click on Format then Axis then X-axis (or Y-axis) then check the Logarithmic scale box.

If you wish, refer to the completed spreadsheet for this activity, then try answering the following question.

Keywords: **Roche limit** ▪

Question 16

(a) For what mass black hole will a solar-mass main-sequence star be tidally disrupted just as it reaches the event horizon? (b) For what mass black hole will a solar-mass neutron star be tidally disrupted just as it reaches the event horizon? ▪

2.1.4 AGN accretion discs

Much of our knowledge of the physics of accretion has been derived from studying compact binary star systems. Accordingly, the next activity will be reminiscent of your work in Block 3.

Activity 15   (30 minutes)

Accretion flows around supermassive black holes

Read the remaining part of Chapter 3 of Peterson, from the beginning of Section 3.3 (pages 36–39).

You might recognize the first part of Peterson's Section 3.3 as being a summary of some of the key results you found in Section 4 of Block 3, with applications to supermassive black holes, rather than the stellar mass accretors considered in Block 3. The physics in the two cases is the same. Where Peterson says 'by setting the derivative of the Planck function to zero' you might prefer the non-algebraic alternative of looking at the appropriate curve in Figure 9 and seeing at what frequency the radiation emitted is a maximum. If you wish to attempt the mathematical challenge (which we stress is optional!), the equation to differentiate is Block 1, Equation 154 which is reprinted in the solution to Question 5. For many purposes, an estimate using $h\nu \approx kT$ is sufficient to estimate roughly at what wavelength most of the blackbody flux will emerge.

Advection refers to the process of heat energy being carried with the fluid flow. In the thin discs analysed up to now in this course, the electrons are able to efficiently radiate away the viscously generated heat, and consequently the amount of heat advected is small.

Peterson's Equation 3.22 comes directly from the virial theorem, which you first met in Block 2 (Phillips Equation 1.11). In Peterson's notation, K is the kinetic energy (Phillips used E_{KE} for the same quantity), and U is the gravitational energy (for which Phillips uses E_{GR}). In Block 1 Equation 145, we learned the average translational kinetic energy of particles is $\frac{3}{2}kT$, so considering the proton gas, $U = GMm_p/r$ per proton, while $K = \frac{3}{2}kT$ per proton.

Keywords: **accretion disc structure**, **thin disc**, **ion torus**, **advection** ▨

Question 17

(a) By writing the Eddington mass accretion rate as

$$\dot{M}_E = \frac{4\pi G m_p}{\eta c \sigma_e} M_{BH}$$

where m_p is the mass of a proton, σ_e is the Thomson cross-section, and η is the accretion efficiency, show that Peterson Equation 3.18 can be rewritten as

$$T(r) = \left(\frac{3}{16} \frac{c^5 m_p}{\eta \sigma \sigma_e} \frac{1}{GM_{BH}} \right)^{1/4} \left(\frac{\dot{M}}{\dot{M}_E} \right)^{1/4} \left(\frac{r}{R_S} \right)^{-3/4} \tag{38}$$

Hint: You should multiply Peterson Equation 3.18 by

$$\left(\frac{4\pi G m_p M_{BH}}{\eta c \sigma_e} \times \dot{M}_E^{-1} \right)^{1/4}$$

i.e. multiply by 1, expressed in this complicated way, to introduce the variable $\dot{M}_E$.

(b) By rewriting M_{BH} in units of $10^8 M_\odot$, i.e. $M_{BH} = M_8 \times 10^8 M_\odot$, where M_8 is a dimensionless number, work out what value of η was used in evaluating the numerical factor in Peterson Equation 3.20. ▪

If you got through Question 17 correctly without resorting to the solution you should feel a warm glow of accomplishment.

▪   Why does T_{vir} obtained in Peterson Equation 3.22 not agree with the temperature derived elsewhere (e.g. Peterson Equation 3.17)?

❑ Because the derivation of temperature for Peterson Equation 3.22 assumed that the protons and electrons are thermally decoupled. Elsewhere we have assumed (i) that the electrons and protons are strongly coupled, so that the gravitational energy (which is generated predominantly by the protons' mass falling in the gravitational well) is shared between the two; and (ii) that the electrons radiate efficiently, so that half of the gravitational energy is radiated rather than being advected with the flow. ■

2.2 AGN continuum emission: do we see an accretion disc?

Question 18

To what part of the electromagnetic spectrum do the following belong?

(i) A photon of energy 6 keV, (ii) an electromagnetic wave of frequency 10 GHz, (iii) an electromagnetic wave of wavelength 3 μm. ■

In Block 3 Section 4.2, and FKR Fig. 20 you saw the spectrum which would be emitted by an accretion disc radiating as a series of black bodies whose temperature is described by Equation 38. The obvious question to ask, now that we have asserted that the underlying physics is the same in the case of AGN, is 'do we see evidence of this accretion disc spectrum in our observations of AGN?' Figure 36 summarizes the observations of the continuum spectral energy distribution of AGN. The feature which reaches a maximum at about 1000 Å is called the **big blue bump**, and is often attributed to thermal emission from an accretion disc. The wavelength of this feature is roughly as predicted by Peterson Equation 3.21.

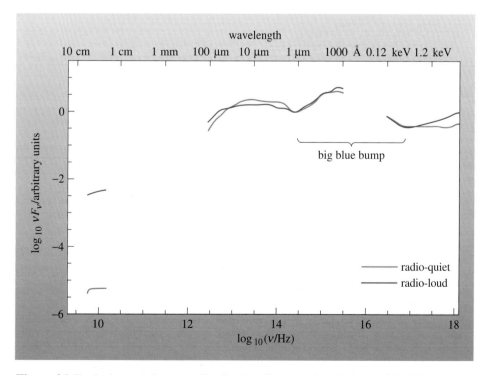

Figure 36 Typical spectral energy distributions for typical radio-quiet (blue line) and radio-loud (red line) quasars.

The emission we see compared to what we expect

Read Section 4.1 of Peterson up to and including the second paragraph on page 45 which ends '… entire spectral range.'

From the second paragraph of Section 4.1 up to Peterson Equation 4.6, the material revises Block 3 Section 4.3, and conveniently Peterson uses the same notation as FKR's Section 5.5.

The **small blue bump** is a feature which is attributed to overlapping emission lines, and is illustrated in Peterson Fig. 5.2 (Peterson page 71).

Keywords: **accretion disc spectrum**, **AGN continua**

To summarize:

- the answer to the question 'Do we see evidence of this accretion disc spectrum in our observations of AGN?' is 'Perhaps'.
- It is clear that irrespective of whether we see an accretion disc spectrum, we certainly see emission from other things.

Example 5

This example will show you how Peterson uses the substitution given by his Equation 4.5 in his Equation 4.4 to arrive at his Equation 4.6.

Rewrite

$$L_\nu = \frac{4\pi^2 h\nu^3 \cos i}{c^2} \int_{r=R_{\text{in}}}^{r=R_{\text{out}}} \frac{r\,\mathrm{d}r}{\mathrm{e}^{h\nu/kT(r)} - 1} \qquad \text{(Peterson 4.4)}$$

using the substitution

$$x = \frac{h\nu}{kT(r)} = \frac{h\nu}{kT_*}\left(\frac{r}{R_{\text{S}}}\right)^{3/4} \qquad \text{(Peterson 4.5)}$$

and hence evaluate an expression for L_ν.

Solution

In order to substitute into Peterson Equation 4.4, we need expressions for both r and $\mathrm{d}r$ in terms of x and $\mathrm{d}x$. So first we rearrange Peterson 4.5 to make r the subject

$$r = \left(\frac{kT_*}{h\nu}\right)^{4/3} x^{4/3} R_{\text{S}}$$

To find an expression for $\mathrm{d}r$, we differentiate this expression to give

$$\frac{\mathrm{d}r}{\mathrm{d}x} = \frac{4}{3}\left(\frac{kT_*}{h\nu}\right)^{4/3} x^{1/3} R_{\text{S}}$$

so $\qquad \mathrm{d}r = \frac{4}{3}\left(\frac{kT_*}{h\nu}\right)^{4/3} x^{1/3} R_{\text{S}}\,\mathrm{d}x$

Now having expressions for both r and $\mathrm{d}r$ in terms of x and $\mathrm{d}x$, we can substitute both of these into Peterson 4.4

$$L_\nu = \frac{4\pi^2 h\nu^3 \cos i}{c^2} \int_{r=R_{\text{in}}}^{r=R_{\text{out}}} \frac{\left(\dfrac{kT_*}{h\nu}\right)^{4/3} x^{4/3} R_{\text{S}}\,\dfrac{4}{3}\left(\dfrac{kT_*}{h\nu}\right)^{4/3} x^{1/3} R_{\text{S}}}{\mathrm{e}^x - 1}\,\mathrm{d}x$$

Peterson shows that at $r = R_{in}$, $x = 0$ and that at $r = R_{out}$, $x = \infty$. So, changing the limits of the integration and moving the constants outside the integral this gives

$$L_\nu = \frac{16\pi^2 h\nu^3 \cos i}{3c^2}\left(\frac{kT_*}{h\nu}\right)^{8/3} R_S^2 \int_{x=0}^{x=\infty} \frac{x^{5/3}}{e^x - 1}\,dx$$

Now, we note that the integral is a 'standard' one which may be found in calculus textbooks and has a value of simply $3\pi/5$. So collecting together all the constant terms we have

$$L_\nu = \left[\frac{16\pi^2 h}{3c^2}\left(\frac{k}{h}\right)^{8/3}\frac{3\pi}{5}\right]R_S^2 \cos(i)\,T_*^{8/3}\,\nu^{1/3}$$

We now evaluate this by putting in the cgs values for the various constants, giving

$$L_\nu = \left[\frac{16\pi^2 \times 6.63\times10^{-27}}{3\times(3.00\times10^{10})^2}\left(\frac{1.38\times10^{-16}}{6.63\times10^{-27}}\right)^{8/3}\frac{3\pi}{5}\right]R_S^2 \cos(i)\,T_*^{8/3}\,\nu^{1/3}\,\text{erg s}^{-1}$$

so $L_\nu = 2.4\times10^{-18}R_S^2 \cos(i)\,T_*^{8/3}\,\nu^{1/3}\,\text{erg s}^{-1}\,\text{Hz}^{-1}$ (Peterson 4.6)

This is Peterson's Equation 4.6 as required, and shows that $L_\nu \propto \nu^{1/3}$. ∎

Question 19

(a) Starting from Peterson Equation 3.21

$$\nu_{max} = \frac{2.8kT}{h} \tag{39}$$

show that emission at 5000 Å corresponds to a temperature $T \sim 10^4$ K.

(b) A particular AGN accretes via a standard optically thick, geometrically thin disc in which each annulus emits as a black body, i.e. Peterson Equation 3.18 holds, so

$$T(R) = \left(\frac{3GM_{BH}\dot{M}}{8\pi\sigma R_S^3}\right)^{1/4}\left(\frac{r}{R_S}\right)^{-3/4}$$

The AGN harbours a black hole of mass $M_{BH} = 10^8 M_\odot$ and is accreting at the Eddington limit. Work out the radius r_{5000} at which $T(r) = 10^4$ K, giving your answer in units of R_S, the Schwarzschild radius for the $10^8 M_\odot$ black hole. (*Hint*: It may be easiest to use Peterson Equation 3.20 as your starting point.)

(c) Write down or derive an expression for the Keplerian angular speed, ω_{Kep}, as a function of r. (*Hint*: Use Block 1, Example 30 if you don't know where to start.) Consequently derive an expression for the Keplerian frequency, $f_{Kep}(r)$, which measures how may times per second a particle at radius r will complete a full circle. Hence for material orbiting at $r = r_{5000}$, calculate the angular speed ω_{5000} and the corresponding Keplerian frequency.

(d) What time-resolution and duration of observations would be required to search for periodic variability associated with orbital motions of material emitting at 5000 Å? ∎

2.3 Summary of Section 2

1 When an object (such as an old fridge) of mass m is accreted by a black hole of mass M_{BH}, with Schwarzschild radius R_S, the amount of energy liberated as radiation depends on whether the object has any angular momentum with respect to the black hole. If its angular momentum is zero, the kinetic energy gained by the object by the time it crosses the Schwarzschild radius is identical in magnitude to the gravitational potential energy it loses:

$$\Delta E_{KE} = \Delta E_{GR} = GM_{BH}m\left(\frac{1}{R_S} - \frac{1}{r_0}\right)$$

where r_0 is the initial distance of the object from the black hole.

2 The Eddington limit is the maximum luminosity that can be produced by an object as a result of spherical accretion. It occurs when the outward force of radiation pressure is exactly balanced by the inward force of gravity. It is given by

$$L_E = \frac{4\pi Gcm_p}{\sigma_e} M = 1.26 \times 10^{38}(M/M_\odot)\,\mathrm{erg\,s^{-1}}$$

where M is the mass of the accreting object. Hence for a typical quasar luminosity of $10^{46}\,\mathrm{erg\,s^{-1}}$, a central mass in excess of $10^8 M_\odot$ is required.

3 If the efficiency of extracting energy from mass during accretion is η, the mass accretion rate necessary to sustain the Eddington luminosity is

$$\dot{M}_E = \frac{L_E}{\eta c^2} = 2.2M_8 M_\odot\ \mathrm{yr^{-1}} \quad \text{(assuming } \eta = 0.1)$$

where M_8 is the mass of the central object in units of 10^8 solar masses.

4 The major problem to solve in fuelling an AGN by accretion is how the angular momentum is removed from the in-falling material. Gravitational interactions with other galaxies may provide a mechanism for removing this angular momentum, or alternatively the fuel may be stars which are tidally disrupted before being accreted, rather than being swallowed whole by the black hole.

5 A star of density ρ_* near a black hole of density ρ_{BH} contained within the Schwarzschild radius R_S can approach no closer than the Roche limit:

$$r_{\mathrm{roche}} = 2.4\left(\frac{\rho_{BH}}{\rho_*}\right)^{1/3} R_S$$

without being tidally disrupted. As a result stars are tidally disrupted outside the Schwarzschild radius of black holes with mass less than about $10^8 M_\odot$. For black holes more massive than this, the stars are not tidally disrupted and so the black hole grows without emitting much electromagnetic radiation.

6 The temperature structure of an accretion disc around a black hole is given by

$$T(r) = \left[\frac{3GM\dot{M}}{8\pi\sigma R_S^3}\right]^{1/4}\left(\frac{r}{R_S}\right)^{-3/4}$$

For a disc surrounding a black hole of mass $10^8 M_\odot$ accreting at the Eddington rate, the temperature is of the order of 10^5–10^6 K and the emission from it reaches a peak at a wavelength of around 100 Å in the extreme ultraviolet or soft X-ray part of the spectrum.

7   The emitted spectrum from the accretion disc is a composite of optically thick thermal emission spectra, corresponding to the different temperatures at different radii in the disc. X-ray emission arises in the innermost, hottest parts.

8   At high accretion rates, greater than the Eddington rate, radiation is partially trapped by inflowing material and the disc expands vertically into a thick torus. In this case, energy is advected (i.e. transported without loss of energy) inwards much more quickly than the disc can cool and the emitted spectrum is close to that of a single temperature black body.

9   At very low accretion rates, the disc becomes optically thin and an ion torus can develop. Such structures are suspected of playing a part in the production of jets because they are believed to be able to anchor strong magnetic fields. The virial temperature of the disc in this case is

$$T_{\mathrm{vir}} = 2 \times 10^{12} (r/R_S)^{-1} \text{ K}$$

10   Alternative theories to supermassive black holes in the centres of AGN are mostly now discarded, although the nuclear starburst scenario has not been entirely abandoned. Strong evidence for the existence of supermassive black holes is provided by dynamical studies of gas, the detection of gravitationally redshifted X-ray emission lines, and reverberation mapping of the broad-line regions in AGN.

11   A simple model for a thin accretion disc has a luminosity at a frequency ν given by

$$L_\nu = 2.4 \times 10^{-18} R_S^2 \cos(i) \, T_*^{8/3} \, \nu^{1/3} \text{ erg s}^{-1}$$

where R_S is the Schwarzschild radius of the black hole, T_* is the temperature of the disc at the Schwarzschild radius and i is the inclination angle between the disc and the plane of the sky. The prediction of this simple model is not in accord with the UV/optical continuum of AGN which typically show a SED proportional to $\nu^{-0.3}$ not $\nu^{1/3}$. However, a cool thermal spectrum in the infrared, plus an accretion disc spectrum in the UV and optical *can* successfully model the continuum spectrum of AGN over this range.

3 THE HITCH-HIKER'S GUIDE TO ACTIVE GALAXIES

Don't panic. This chapter contains a lot of observational detail, please do not be dismayed if you find it difficult to quickly organize all this new information into a coherent whole. This is probably your first real taste of a rapidly developing field in observational astronomy. If you rush, you may experience mental indigestion.

Like most empirical sciences, observational astronomy generally begins by making classifications of objects and phenomena, grouping similar examples together. This is known as **taxonomy**. The classification of living things into kingdoms, phyla, subphyla, class, subclass and species in biology is the archetypal example of taxonomy. Taxonomic characterization is necessary before attempting to understand the general principles behind the empirical findings. In Block 2 the characterization of stars based on the Hertzsprung–Russell diagram quickly led to identification of the main sequence and other luminosity classes. The study of stars was greatly expedited by these discoveries which came directly from making a graph showing the two most basic observational properties of stars (brightness and colour). The study of AGN is more challenging.

The readings from Peterson in this section of Block 4 first describe the properties of the various subclasses of AGN, and then begin to elucidate some of the possible reasons behind their differences. As a counterpoint to this observational material, we will examine some interesting consequences of applying special relativity to AGN.

> If you begin to feel overwhelmed by the readings in this section please consider using the following as motivation.
>
> Open Peterson on page 125. This is as far as we will follow Peterson's detailed treatment in this course, and corresponds to the end of Section 7 in this Study Guide.
>
> Flip through Peterson up to page 125; rest assured the most difficult readings are those associated with Chapter 2.
>
> Skip ahead in this Study Guide to Activity 51 at the end of Section 7.4. If you follow the course, you will, by then, be able to read the condensed abstracts of contemporary research articles and make sense of them. Much of the new vocabulary you will need to do this is introduced in these early readings.

3.1 Types of AGN

In the following readings from Peterson you will learn about various types of AGN, and how their spectra are used to distinguish between them.

> Self-study suggestion: As you work through this section, draw a block diagram indicating the classes and subclasses of AGN. Annotate your diagram with their distinguishing features. There is no definitive right or wrong answer for this activity. Making the block diagram should help you organize the many facts you read in this section. To demonstrate the sort of diagram we expect, take a look at Block 3 Figure 19 which shows the taxonomy of binary stars.

To supplement the examples of spectra given in Peterson, Figure 39 to Figure 44 show some examples taken from recently published research papers. The first type of AGN which Peterson will consider are Seyfert galaxies. Figure 37 and Figure 38 show images of Seyfert galaxies. Superficially these look like normal spiral galaxies, but with brighter central nuclei, as we saw in Figure 1.

Figure 39 shows a very high quality optical spectrum of a Seyfert 1 galaxy. If you compare this with the example shown in Peterson Fig. 1.1, you should be able to pick out the similarities which lead to both these objects being classified as type 1 Seyferts:

• the same emission lines appear in both spectra
• both sets of emission lines show broad bases

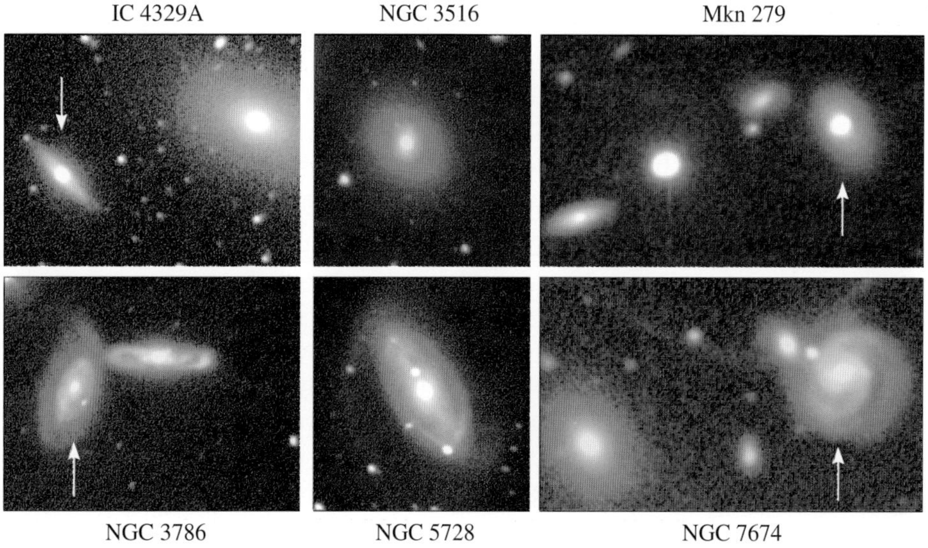

Figure 37 A montage of wide-field V band images of Seyfert galaxies. All these galaxies harbour an intense point-like nucleus, but they are seen at a range of orientations, in a range of environments, and include a range of spiral, barred spiral and lenticular (S0) galaxy types. Where more than one galaxy is included in the field of view, the Seyfert is indicated with an arrow.

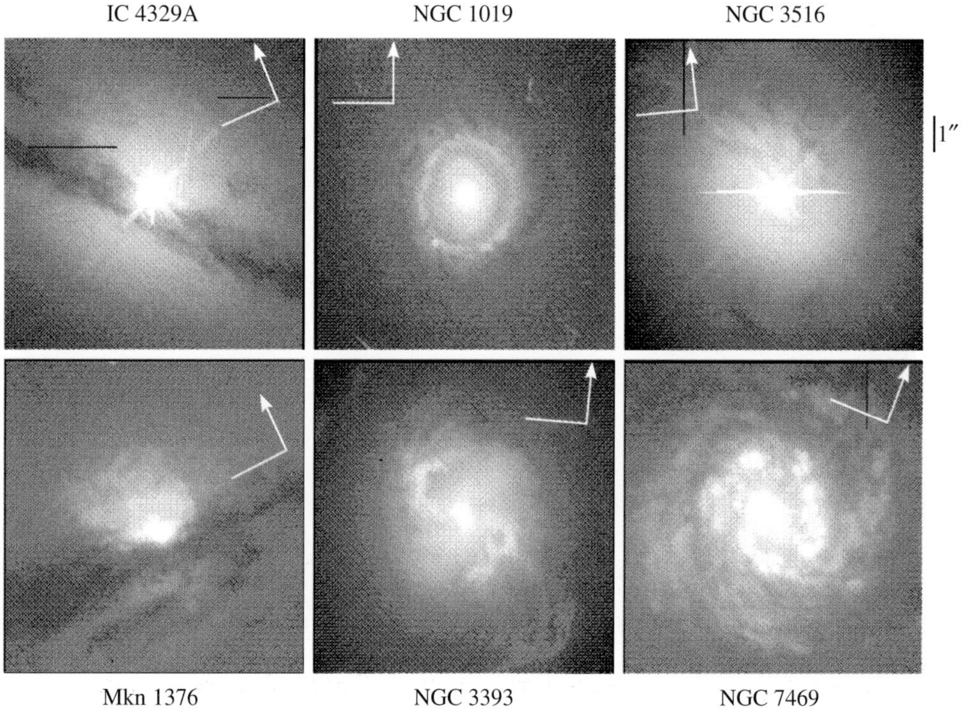

Figure 38 A montage of close-up red images of Seyfert nuclei obtained with the Hubble Space Telescope's Planetary Camera. In each case the arrow gives the direction of North, and the straight vertical and horizontal dark lines are imperfections in the detector. In some Seyferts the bright central nucleus is surrounded by bright young stars (e.g. the ring apparent in NGC 1019). In others regions of ionized gas shine brightly in emission line radiation (e.g. the spiral structure in NGC 3393). In IC 4329 and Mkn 1376 the nuclei peek out from behind dust in the disc of spiral galaxies seen edge-on.

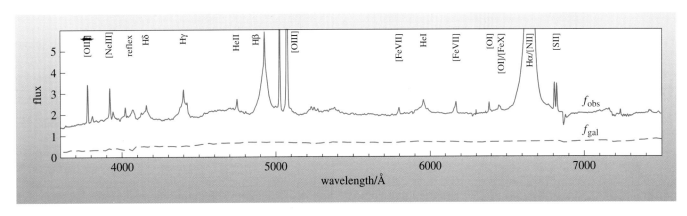

Figure 39 The spectrum of the Seyfert 1 galaxy Fairall 51, observed using the European Southern Observatory's Very Large Telescope. f_{gal} shows the contribution to the spectrum of the light emitted by stars in the galaxy surrounding the active nucleus.

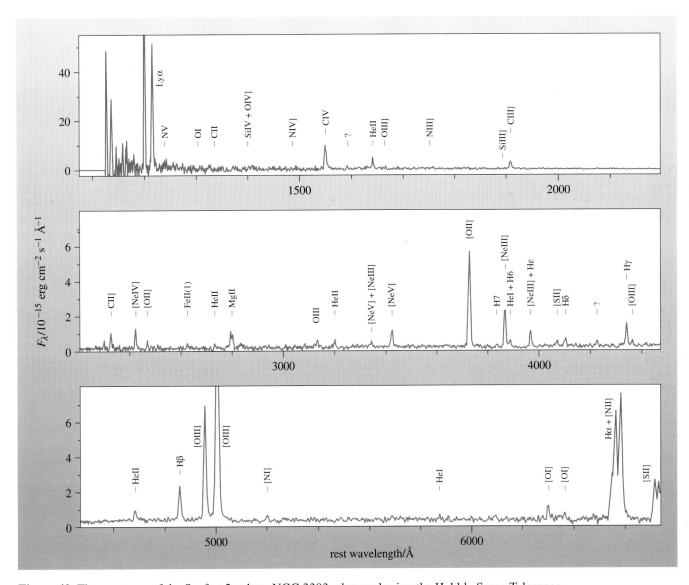

Figure 40 The spectrum of the Seyfert 2 galaxy NGC 3393, observed using the Hubble Space Telescope.

as well as the differences between the spectra of Fairall 51 and NGC 5548:

- the shapes of the broad lines are different
- the relative strengths of the various lines are different
- the underlying continuum shape appears different.

In contrast, Figure 40 shows an example of the other type of Seyfert galaxy: NGC 3393, which is a Seyfert 2 galaxy.

■ Why does the Hα line appear at a longer wavelength in Figure 39 than it does in Figure 40?

❑ Figure 39 has wavelength on the horizontal axis. In this case the authors are referring to the observed wavelength, so the line appears redshifted, due to the cosmological redshift of the galaxy observed. In contrast, Figure 40 has **rest wavelength** on the horizontal axis. In this case the authors have corrected for the redshift of the galaxy and the lines all appear at the wavelength an observer moving with that galaxy would observe. ■

■ What is the most obvious difference between the Hβ lines in the Seyfert 1 and Seyfert 2 spectra shown in Figure 39 and Figure 40?

❑ The Hβ line is much broader in the Seyfert 1 spectrum than in the Seyfert 2 spectrum. ■

Activity 17   **(40 minutes)**

Seyfert galaxies

Read Chapter 2 of Peterson up to and including Section 2.1. Then skip forwards to Peterson page 28 and read Section 2.6.

The criterion for dividing AGN between Seyferts and quasars, absolute magnitude $M_B > -21.5 + 5 \log h_0$, may at first appear mysterious. Refer back to Block 1, Equation 53 for the definition of the distance modulus, which gives the relationship between the (observed) apparent magnitude, and the absolute magnitude (which specifies the luminosity of the source). Clearly any classification scheme is only sensible if it is based on the intrinsic properties of the sources, hence the criterion refers to absolute magnitudes. However, in order to calculate the absolute magnitude of a typical AGN from its apparent magnitude, the estimate of its distance given by Hubble's law must be used, as Peterson Equation 1.4 shows. Consequently the value adopted for the Hubble constant, affects the deduced absolute magnitude. Therefore, the criterion dividing the two classes is specified for *any* value of h_0, so the dividing line between the two classes remains fixed, even though different researchers may have different preferred values of h_0.

As Section 1 outlined, spectral line radiation is governed by the rules of quantum mechanics. The most likely transitions are those which occur with the emission or absorption of 'electric dipole radiation' these are the so-called **permitted lines**. Sometimes atoms can be excited to quantum states from which there are no electric dipole transitions available: the atom would be stuck indefinitely if permitted transitions were the only way to reach another (lower energy) quantum state. Though permitted transitions are the most likely when available, there are also less-likely transitions which occur with the emission or absorption of 'electric quadrupole radiation' these are the so-called **forbidden lines**. If no permitted transition is possible, the atom will remain in the excited state until one of two things happen:

- it may be caused to make a transition by a collision with a free electron, atom, or ion

- or eventually it will make a low-probability, forbidden transition.

In high-density regions, collisions will be frequent and few atoms will remain in the excited state for long enough to make a forbidden transition. Conversely, in low-density regions, collisions will be infrequent and so the atoms will eventually make a forbidden transition. This is how 'the absence of broad forbidden-line emission indicates the broad-line gas is of high density'. This is a further example of the way that astronomers can deduce a wealth of information, some of it not immediately obvious, from the light they collect.

Keywords: **type 1 and type 2 Seyferts**, **Seyfert 1.5**, **1.8**, **1.9 subclasses**, **narrow-line X-ray galaxies (NLXGs)**

- Which component of the spectrum is used to distinguish between Seyfert 1 and Seyfert 2 galaxies?

- The broad-line emission: Seyfert 1 galaxies have both broad and narrow emission lines, superimposed on each other; Seyfert 2 galaxies emit only the narrow emission lines.

- Why is the classification between Seyfert 1 and Seyfert 2 galaxies sometimes problematical?

- Because the broad lines are sometimes found to be highly variable, and occasionally almost disappear.

Figure 41 to Figure 43 show spectra of quasars. As for Seyfert galaxies, the most obvious feature of quasar spectra is the prominent emission lines. Unlike Seyfert galaxies, however, there is no appreciable contribution to the spectrum from star light.

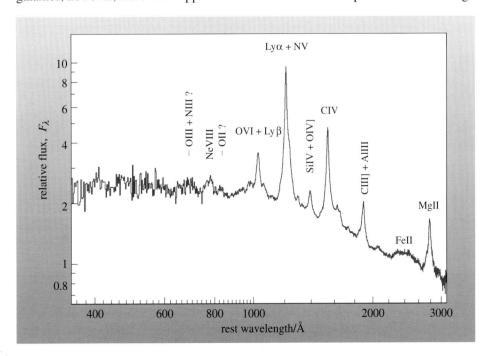

Figure 41 An 'average' quasar spectrum formed by averaging together Hubble Space Telescope observations of 101 quasars with redshifts $z > 0.33$.

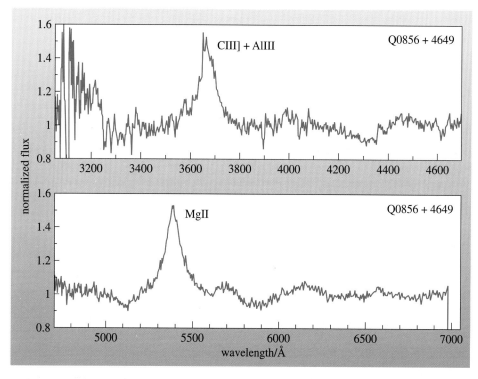

Figure 42 A spectrum of Q0856+4649, a reasonably typical quasar with redshift $z = 0.924$. The observations were made using the 5 m Hale telescope and show the CIII], AlIII and MgII emission lines which have all been redshifted into the optical part of the spectrum.

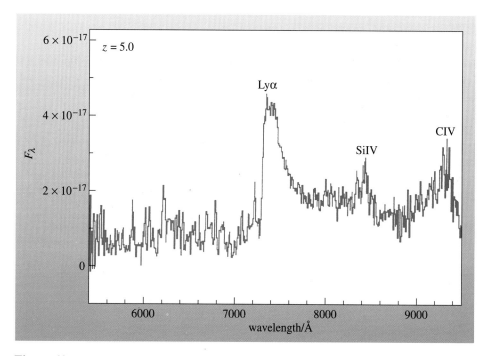

Figure 43 The spectrum of this quasar, at redshift $z = 5.0$ shows the same emission lines as the relatively nearby quasars in Figure 41. The main difference is that the quality of the data is poorer as this distant quasar appears very faint.

Quasars and radio galaxies

Read Sections 2.2 and 2.3 of Peterson (pages 23 and 24).

The Palomar Sky Survey (see Collins) served for about four decades as a widely used reference to the optical sky. Recently it has been digitized to produce the Hubble Guide Star Catalogue, which (as its name suggests) was developed to provide reliable guide stars for observations using the Hubble Space Telescope. A link to the Hubble Guide Star Catalogue is given in the Course resources section of the S381 website.

You have already seen several examples of quasar fuzz in Figure 5.

Keywords: **quasar fuzz**

- What is 'quasar fuzz'?

- It is the faint, low surface brightness emission of the galaxy surrounding the quasar.

- What do the abbreviations NLRG and BLRG stand for?

- Narrow-Line Radio Galaxy and Broad-Line Radio Galaxy respectively.

In Figure 44 some recent high quality spectra of a '**low-ionization nuclear emission line region (LINER)**' galaxy are shown. Though similar to Seyfert galaxies, LINERs have relatively strong **low-ionization** lines: for example the [OI] $\lambda6300$ line is relatively strong in Figure 44 compared to Figure 40. Low-ionization species are those which have only had weakly bound electrons removed, or as in the case of OI, are neutral atoms.

In the next reading you will learn about the interpretation of the spectra of LINERs, Seyfert galaxies and quasars in more detail. One of the key methods used in this interpretation is the comparison of **line ratios**. A line ratio is simply the flux in one line divided by the flux in another line (lines in general and line flux in particular are discussed in Section 1.8.3), and is often referred to with notation like:

([OIII] $\lambda5007$)/(Hβ $\lambda4861$)

which indicates the flux in the forbidden line of O^{2+} at 5007 Å divided by the flux in the Hβ line. Line ratios are useful because they are independent of distance, especially if the two lines have similar wavelengths (i.e. suffer the same reddening), so they allow the intrinsic properties of objects to be straightforwardly compared.

Figure 44 Spectra of the LINER NGC 4450 (a) taken with the Palomar 5 m telescope. The dotted line shows a normal galaxy spectrum, and the lower solid line shows the AGN emission in NGC 4450 after correcting by subtracting the contribution of star light to the observed spectrum. The aperture used to collect light for these observations was 2 arcsec by 4 arcsec in size. (b) and (c) taken with the Hubble Space Telescope, using an aperture of size 0.2 arcsec by 0.15 arcsec. Because of the smaller aperture used in the Hubble Space Telescope observations, the total amount of flux in the optical region is smaller than that of the Palomar observations, and the very broad-line emission apparent in panel (b) is attributed to emission coming from a disc within $\lesssim 2000 R_{\mathrm{S}}$ of the central black hole.

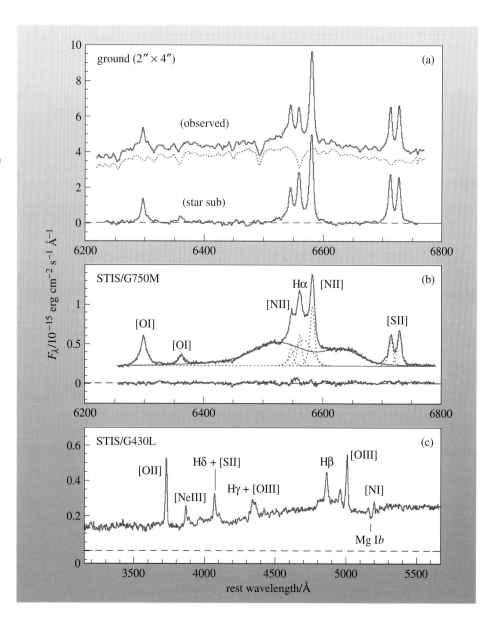

Activity 19 (20 minutes)

LINERs and line ratios

Read Section 2.4 of Peterson (pages 24 to 27).

A **HII region** is a region of ionized hydrogen close to a source of ultraviolet radiation. They are also more poetically referred to as **emission nebulae** (see Collins). There are several examples of these **photoionized** nebulae in the Image Archive.

Ionizing continuum radiation was explained in Section 1.8.

Keywords: **Strömgren sphere** ▪

Question 20

What is meant by 'the systematic effects of reddening' referred to in Peterson's footnote on page 26? ▪

The next section in Peterson introduces **blazars**. A blazar is an AGN which is thought to eject jets of material moving at relativistic velocities (i.e. $v_{jet} \sim c$), with the jets oriented so that the approaching jet velocity is in a direction close to our line of sight. In Section 3.4 we will look at the relativistic physics of blazars.

Activity 20

Beamed AGN

Read Section 2.5 of Peterson (page 27).

Keywords: **Blazars**, **OVVs**, **BL Lacs** ■

■ What is the primary observed difference between BL Lac objects and OVVs?

❑ BL Lacs have weak spectral line features, while OVVs generally have prominent broad emission lines. ■

3.2 Taxonomy and interrelations

Activity 21   **(25 minutes)**

Taxonomy and interrelations

Read Section 2.7 of Peterson including all its subsections (pages 28 and 29). When you reach the end of Section 2.7.1 take a look at the Cartwheel galaxy image and accompanying caption in the Image Archive. The Cartwheel is one of the most famous examples of a starburst galaxy.

Section 2.7.4 on 'Ultraluminous far-infrared galaxies' heralds an area of extragalactic astronomy which is enjoying a golden era in the early 21st century. These sources are now commonly known as **ULIRGs** (or ULIGs), which stands for ultraluminous infrared galaxies. It is speculated that many of the supermassive black holes which are postulated to be at the centres of most normal galaxies grew during an early ULIRG phase, when the young active nucleus was shrouded in dust. The next generation space telescope (NGST), and other powerful new infrared observatories will test this hypothesis.

Keywords: **starbursts**, **ULIRG**, **Markarian galaxies**, **Zwicky galaxies**, **N galaxies** ■

■ Is the Cartwheel galaxy an example of a nuclear starburst?

❑ No, the starburst in the Cartwheel is clearly a ring towards the outside of the galaxy. ■

■ Are the two small galaxies to the right-hand side of the Cartwheel image examples of nuclear starbursts?

❑ Perhaps the lower of the two is: it shows the blue colour of new massive star formation in its centre. The upper of the two is much redder, and shows no evidence of starburst activity. ■

Question 21

Write a short paragraph (no more than 250 words) explaining how selection effects led to the first astronomers studying AGN to make an artificially strong division into two entirely separate classes: Seyferts and QSOs. ■

3.3 Radio properties of AGN

For the remainder of this section we will focus on the radio properties of AGN, beginning with the compact central sources. We will then explore the physics of relativistic jets, with an analysis of Doppler boosting and apparent faster-than-light (**superluminal**) motion. For the last part of this section we summarize the properties of blazars.

So far we have learned:

- radio-loud quasars are a small subset of AGN, which often exhibit powerful radio jets

- these objects show unusually dramatic variability

- radio-loud quasars generally have power-law spectra which are interpreted as synchrotron emission

- synchrotron self-absorption (SSA) becomes important at low frequencies, where the emitting material becomes optically thick

- inverse Compton scattering can increase the energy of synchrotron photons before they leave the cloud of electrons which produced them. This process is known as synchrotron self-Compton (cf. Section 1.7.4).

Activity 22   (20 minutes)

Cosmic radio emitters

Read the first part of Section 4.4 of Peterson, up to and including Section 4.4.1 (pages 57 to 59).

The **flat spectra** for compact sources are attributed to regions with varying dependences of optical depth on photon frequency, as discussed in Section 1.7.3.

The **brightness temperature** T_B is calculated by essentially pretending that the radio emission arises from the Rayleigh–Jeans tail of a thermal blackbody spectrum. A black body of a given temperature always produces the same amount of radiation per unit emitting area. Thus by measuring the intensity of radiation at a particular frequency, ν, and measuring the size of the source (through the angular size θ) a corresponding Planck curve (Figure 9), with a particular value of temperature, T_B, is defined. For compact extragalactic radio sources the values of T_B this leads to are far higher than the more reliable temperature indicators derived from other parts of the spectrum. Consequently the pretence that the radio emission can be attributed to a blackbody spectrum is clearly not correct. If it were, the compact cores would be far more luminous emitters of higher energy radiation: the observed radio emission is dominated by non-thermal emission, generally attributed to the synchrotron mechanism.

The last paragraph of Section 4.4.1 uses the result expressed in Equation 25.

Keywords: **brightness temperature** ■

■   Why are temperatures $T \lesssim 3\,\mathrm{K}$ not realizable in the Universe?

❏   This is the temperature of the cosmic microwave background radiation (see Collins if this term is not familiar to you). Anything cooler than this would be heated by absorption of this radiation until it reaches thermal equilibrium at $T = 3\,\mathrm{K}$. ■

3.4 Relativistic boosting

To rigorously examine the effects caused by relativistic velocities we must, of course, use Einstein's special theory of relativity. You may be relieved to read that we will *not* be deriving the fundamental equations of special relativity here, instead we will assume these, and simply apply them to the problem of emission from relativistic jets. If you are disappointed in not having the fundamental derivations presented to you, please consult the 'Course resources' section of the S381 website.

3.4.1 Aberration of light: the non-relativistic limit

Before delving into the mathematics of relativistic beaming, let us first discuss the **aberration of light**. This effect arises because motion of the observer changes the apparent direction of a luminous object. This, like other effects described in special relativity, is caused by the finite speed of light, and is ubiquitous though imperceptibly small to the naked eye. A more obvious analogous effect arises when driving a car in the rain. Generally rain falls in a direction close to vertical, and the number of raindrops which hit the (also almost vertical) windscreen is small if the car is stationary at a traffic light. When the car speeds up, the apparent velocity (as observed by the driver of the car) of the raindrops has a component towards the windscreen. Because of this, the rate at which the raindrops hit the windscreen increases. Next time you are driving in the rain, see if you notice this effect. One senior astrophysicist reported that when he was young he used to think it was odd that the rain seemed to get heavier whenever he joined a motorway.

In the case of light the effect is more subtle. Figure 45 illustrates a telescope, pointed in the exact direction of a particular star, moving with speed v at angle θ to the direction to that star. The light from the star is moving at speed c so it will take a time $t = l/c$ to traverse the length, l, of the telescope. During this time interval, the telescope will have travelled a distance vt. The component of this motion perpendicular to the light beam from the star will be $vt \sin \theta$, hence the light beam will strike the primary mirror of the telescope at a distance $x = vt \sin \theta$ from the axis of the telescope. This means that the observed direction to the star is shifted by a small angle α (called the aberration angle)

$$\alpha = \frac{x}{l} = \frac{vt \sin \theta}{ct} = (v/c)\sin \theta \qquad (40)$$

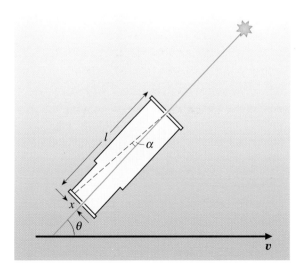

Figure 45 A telescope on the surface of the moving planet Earth is pointed to the sky. Aberration causes the light from a star to appear to emanate from a direction slightly different from the true direction to the star.

■   What are the units of α in Equation 40?

❑ α is in radians. As a radian is a length divided by a length, it has null dimensions, as does the right-hand side of Equation 40. ■

The relative motion of the source and the detector is what is important in determining the aberration angle. We could draw a diagram analogous to Figure 45 in which the telescope was fixed and the star was moving. The angle α would be the same in both cases.

We have implicitly assumed that α is small, because strictly speaking the left-hand side of Equation 40 should read tan α. For small α, tan $\alpha \approx \alpha$, where α is measured in radians.

Question 22

(a) The maximum possible value of aberration due to the Earth's orbital motion around the Sun is $21''$. Assuming that the orbit of the Earth is a perfect circle, calculate the Earth's orbital speed.

(b) The maximum shift due to the Earth's daily rotation is $0.3''$, calculate the speed at which a telescope at the equator moves due to the Earth's rotation. ■

The method used to derive Equation 40 implicitly used the **Galilean transform**, the common-sense everyday idea that the length of an object is the same irrespective of whether or not it is moving. Special relativity actually demonstrates that this is *not* the case, though for $v \ll c$, the change in length is imperceptibly small. Because the motion of the Earth is at speeds $v \ll c$, Equation 40 is perfectly adequate to calculate the effects of aberration on the observed position of any object in the sky.

■   What happens when astronomers observe distant galaxies which have velocities with respect to Earth which do not satisfy $v \ll c$?

❑   In this case the true aberration would require a relativistic calculation, but except for the component due to the Earth's motion through space, the velocity is unlikely to have changed measurably during the time people have been accurately charting the skies. Because this relativistic aberration will, therefore, have remained constant, the charted right ascension and declination of the object (i.e. its position in the sky) will be the sum of the true direction plus a constant aberration correction. There will be smaller, constantly changing adjustments to the aberration caused by the small changes in the net velocity due to the Earth's motion. These smaller adjustments will be accurately predicted by Equation 40. ■

3.4.2 Aberration of light: the relativistic case

Special relativity is based on the postulate that the speed of light in empty space, c, is constant and the same for all observers. From this experimentally based postulate, simple mathematics and relentless logic, Einstein showed that the Galilean transform must, in general, be replaced by the **Lorentz transform**. Figure 46 shows two frames of reference, F, and F', which are moving towards each other with relative velocity $\boldsymbol{v}$. The coordinate frames are defined so that the relative velocity is in the x-direction.

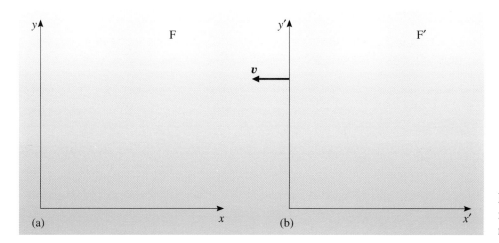

Figure 46 Two frames of reference moving towards each other with relative velocity $\boldsymbol{v}$.

The Lorentz transform relates the quantities x, y, z, t, etc. measured in frame F, to the quantities x', y', z', t', etc. measured in frame F$'$. The Lorentz transform is defined by the Equations 41a to 41d.

$$x' = \gamma(x + vt) \tag{41a}$$
$$y' = y \tag{41b}$$
$$z' = z \tag{41c}$$
$$t' = \gamma\left(t + \frac{v}{c^2}x\right) \tag{41d}$$

We recall the **Lorentz factor**, γ, is defined by

$$\gamma \equiv \frac{1}{\sqrt{1 - \dfrac{v^2}{c^2}}} \tag{14}$$

Most textbooks give the Lorentz transform equations slightly differently, wherever we have v they have $-v$.

■ How can both these versions of the Lorentz transform be correct?

❑ Most textbooks would have the two frames of reference moving away from each other, rather than towards each other. Both are correct, but we must be aware of which convention is being adopted. ■

In general throughout this block and the rest of the course, we will adopt the convention that recessional velocities, i.e. velocities away from the Earth, are positive. For the discussion of aberration of light, and relativistic beaming, we are primarily concerned with the observed properties of the approaching jet, so here we will use the definition of v shown in Figure 46 and implicit in Equations 41. For the whole of this section, v is the velocity of the jet material.

Since we wish to examine the aberration of light in the relativistic case, we need to consider the relationships between velocities measured in each frame. We begin by considering any object moving with velocity $\boldsymbol{u}$ in frame F. To simplify the algebra, we will choose to orient the y-axis so that the velocity $\boldsymbol{u}$ is in the x-y plane, i.e. we choose coordinates so that $u_z = 0$. Whatever the direction of $\boldsymbol{u}$, we could always do this, so our working remains perfectly general. As Figure 47 shows, the velocity of the moving object makes an angle θ with the x-axis and an angle θ' with the x'-axis.

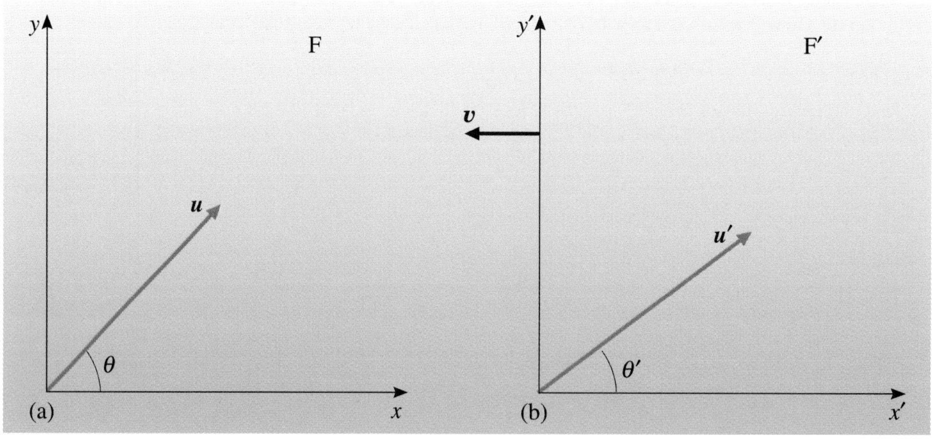

Figure 47 The velocity **u** measured in frame F and the corresponding velocity **u′** which would be measured in frame F′. The angles θ and θ' which the velocity makes with the x- and x'-axes are indicated.

Differentiating Equations 41 we obtain:

$$dx' = \gamma(dx + v\,dt) \tag{42a}$$

$$dy' = dy \tag{42b}$$

$$dz' = dz \tag{42c}$$

$$dt' = \gamma\left(dt + \frac{v}{c^2}dx\right) \tag{42d}$$

Note: Here we are using physicist's mathematics. If you are of a pure maths outlook, then you might prefer to differentiate with respect to time, so that in place of Equation 42a you have $\dfrac{dx'}{dt} = \gamma\left(\dfrac{dx}{dt} + v\right)$ and similarly for Equations 42b to 42d. You will arrive at the results in Equations 45a and 45b.

Using these equations we can then work out the relationships between velocities, **u** and **u′** measured in the two frames, noting

$$u_x = \frac{dx}{dt} \tag{43a}$$

$$u_y = \frac{dy}{dt} \tag{43b}$$

and similarly

$$u_x' = \frac{dx'}{dt'} \tag{44a}$$

$$u_y' = \frac{dy'}{dt'} \tag{44b}$$

Substituting into Equations 44 successively using Equations 42 and 43 we obtain

$$u_x' = \frac{dx'}{dt'} = \frac{\gamma(dx + v\,dt)}{\gamma\left(dt + \dfrac{v\,dx}{c^2}\right)} = \frac{u_x + v}{1 + \dfrac{vu_x}{c^2}} \tag{45a}$$

$$u_y' = \frac{dy'}{dt'} = \frac{dy}{\gamma\left(dt + \dfrac{v\,dx}{c^2}\right)} = \frac{u_y}{\gamma\left(1 + \dfrac{vu_x}{c^2}\right)} \tag{45b}$$

■ Write down an expression for u_z' in terms of γ, u_z, u_x, v and c.

❏ Since Equations 41b and 41c giving y' (in terms of y) and z' (in terms of z) are of exactly the same form, the equations for u_z can be obtained from Equations 44b and 45b by simply replacing every occurrence of y with z, hence obtaining

$$u_z' = \frac{u_z}{\gamma\left(1 + \dfrac{vu_x}{c^2}\right)} \; ■$$

We chose our coordinate system so that $u_z = 0$, and $u_z' \propto u_z$, which means $u_z' = 0$. Referring to Figure 48, we can now use our expressions for the components of $\boldsymbol{u}$ and $\boldsymbol{u'}$ and some trigonometry to derive expressions giving θ and θ'.

$$\tan\theta = \frac{u_y}{u_x} \tag{46a}$$

$$\tan\theta' = \frac{u_y'}{u_x'} \tag{46b}$$

So substituting Equations 45a and 45b into Equation 46b we obtain

$$\tan\theta' = \frac{u_y}{\gamma\left(1 + \dfrac{vu_x}{c^2}\right)} \frac{\left(1 + \dfrac{vu_x}{c^2}\right)}{u_x + v} = \frac{u_y}{\gamma(u_x + v)} \tag{47}$$

or, if we express u_x and u_y in terms of the magnitude of the velocity, u, so that $u_x = u\cos\theta$, $u_y = u\sin\theta$, we have

$$\tan\theta' = \frac{u\sin\theta}{\gamma(u\cos\theta + v)} \tag{48}$$

While working through all that algebra you may have lost sight of what we were doing, and why! Our purpose is to derive the special relativistic version of the formulae describing the aberration of light. So far, the velocity transform is perfectly general. To apply it to light, we need to consider the special case where the object whose motion we are following is a photon or a beam of light. In this case, $u = c$, and we know that u' is also equal to c, because the speed of light must be the same in both frames. Substituting in Equation 48 for $u = c$, we obtain

$$\tan\theta' = \frac{\sin\theta}{\gamma\left(\cos\theta + \dfrac{v}{c}\right)} \tag{49a}$$

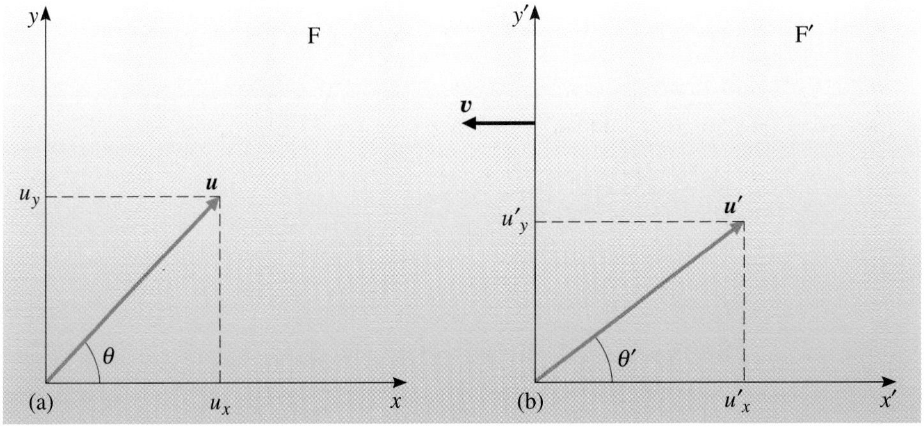

Figure 48 Vector velocities $\boldsymbol{u}$ and $\boldsymbol{u'}$ resolved into components u_x and u_y.

Question 23

For the case $u' = u = c$, derive an expression for $\cos\theta'$ in terms of v, c and θ only. ∎

Gathering the expressions for $\tan\theta'$ and $\cos\theta'$ we now have the relativistic equations describing the aberration of light:

$$\tan\theta' = \frac{\sin\theta}{\gamma\left(\cos\theta + \dfrac{v}{c}\right)} \qquad (49a)$$

$$\cos\theta' = \frac{\cos\theta + \dfrac{v}{c}}{1 + \dfrac{v}{c}\cos\theta} \qquad (49b)$$

∎ Why isn't Equation 49a sufficient to specify the value of θ'?

❑ Two equations are required because there are two values of θ' corresponding to any value of $\tan\theta'$. For any angle, β (in radians), $\tan\beta = \tan(\beta + \pi)$. The values of $\cos\beta$ and $\cos(\beta + \pi)$, are, however, different: $\cos\beta = -\cos(\beta + \pi)$. Hence with equations which give both $\tan\theta'$ and $\cos\theta'$, the value of θ' *is* uniquely specified. ∎

Whenever we derive a relativistic result, it is essential to verify that the non-relativistic limit is consistent with that obtained through a non-relativistic derivation. Therefore the Equations 49a and 49b must be equivalent to Equation 40 in the case $v \ll c$. In order to show this, we must first express the angle α, which appears in the non-relativistic equation, in terms of θ'.

The telescope and star shown in Figure 45 correspond to those in Figure 49 (imagine Figure 45 upside down). In Figure 49, coordinate frames moving with the star and the telescope are shown. Figure 50 shows the relevant geometry, and we have defined another angle, ϕ, at the apex of the right-angled triangle ABC. Since there are 180° in a triangle, then considering triangle ABC, $\phi + \theta = 90°$. Similarly considering triangle ABC′, $(\phi + \alpha) + \theta' = 90°$. Therefore we have $\phi + \theta = (\phi + \alpha) + \theta'$, which simplifies to $\alpha + \theta' = \theta$, or equivalently

$$\theta' = \theta - \alpha \qquad (50)$$

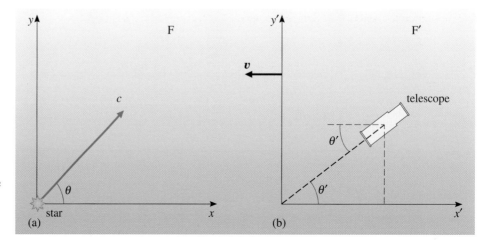

Figure 49 Figure 45 showed a telescope on the surface of a moving planet, and light being emitted from a distant star. Here we see how this can be redrawn with coordinates that can be related to those in Figure 46 and Figure 47.

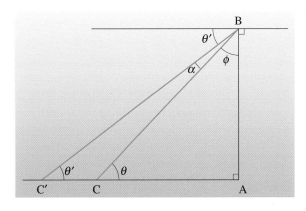

Figure 50 The angle θ' in Figure 49 is equal to $\theta - \alpha$, where α is the angle of aberration shown in Figure 45. (See text for details of the derivation proving this.)

Example 6

Show that Equation 49b reduces to Equation 40 in the non-relativistic limit, i.e. when $v \ll c$.

Solution

The first step is to express Equation 49 in terms of α, which occurs in Equation 40, eliminating θ' which does not occur in Equation 40. Equation 50 allows us to do that, yielding:

$$\cos(\theta - \alpha) = \frac{\cos\theta + \dfrac{v}{c}}{1 + \dfrac{v}{c}\cos\theta} \tag{51}$$

We must now use a standard trigonometric result:

$$\cos(\theta - \alpha) = \cos\theta\cos\alpha + \sin\theta\sin\alpha \tag{52}$$

Note: If Equation 52 is completely new to you, you might want to check that it holds for any value of α and θ by picking values at random and working out the numerical value of both sides of the equation. Don't worry if this is unfamiliar to you, we will not expect you to memorize or derive this result unaided.

Substituting Equation 52 into Equation 51,

$$\cos\theta\cos\alpha + \sin\theta\sin\alpha = \frac{\cos\theta + \dfrac{v}{c}}{1 + \dfrac{v}{c}\cos\theta} \tag{53}$$

We now need to use the fact that in the non-relativistic limit, α is small, so

$$\cos\alpha \approx 1 \quad \text{and} \quad \sin\alpha \approx \alpha$$

where α is measured in radians. Using these small-angle approximations in Equation 53, we obtain

$$\cos\theta + \alpha\sin\theta \approx \frac{\cos\theta + \dfrac{v}{c}}{1 + \dfrac{v}{c}\cos\theta}$$

Multiplying both sides by $(1 + (v/c)\cos\theta)$ and then multiplying out terms we find for the left-hand side:

$$(\cos\theta + \alpha\sin\theta)\left(1 + \frac{v}{c}\cos\theta\right) \approx \cos\theta + \alpha\sin\theta + \frac{v}{c}\cos^2\theta + \alpha\frac{v}{c}\cos\theta$$

so equating this to the new right-hand side:

$$\cos\theta + \alpha\sin\theta + \frac{v}{c}\cos^2\theta + \alpha\frac{v}{c}\cos\theta \approx \cos\theta + \frac{v}{c}$$

This can be simplified by subtracting $\cos\theta$ from both sides, and by noting that both α and v/c are small quantities (i.e. they are both $\ll 1$), so that the term $\alpha(v/c)\cos\theta$ can be neglected because it must be much smaller than all the other terms in the equation. After this simplification we obtain:

$$\alpha\sin\theta + \frac{v}{c}\cos^2\theta \approx \frac{v}{c}$$

which can be rearranged to give

$$\alpha\sin\theta \approx \frac{v}{c}(1-\cos^2\theta)$$

We must make use of another standard trigonometric result (this one comes more or less directly from Pythagoras's theorem):

$$\cos^2\theta + \sin^2\theta = 1$$

to obtain $\alpha\sin\theta \approx (v/c)\sin^2\theta$, which further simplifies by dividing through by $\sin\theta$ to give (Equation 40)

$$\alpha \approx \frac{v}{c}\sin\theta$$

Therefore we have shown that the relativistic equations for the aberration of light, which we derived from the Lorentz transform, reduce to the result we derived from the Galilean transform if we impose the conditions $v \ll c$ and $\alpha \ll 1$, where α is expressed in radians. Since Equation 40 shows that $\alpha \propto v/c$, these two conditions are consistent and required by each other (since the equation is valid for any value of θ). ∎

3.4.3 The beaming effect

We now have the equations needed to understand the relativistic beaming effect, which is highly relevant to AGN which eject relativistic jets in a direction close to our line of sight. To address this, we need to consider the case of light being emitted from a source which is moving at a relativistic speed, v towards us. We can use Equations 49 to compare how the angular distribution of emission will appear in the rest frame of the jet and the rest frame of an observer here on Earth. To do this it is interesting to consider the case of a photon which is emitted by the jet at an angle $\theta = \pi/2$, i.e. a photon which is emitted perpendicular to the velocity v. If we insert this value of θ into the equations, noting that $\sin(\pi/2) = 1$, and $\cos(\pi/2) = 0$, we obtain:

$$\tan\theta' = \frac{c}{\gamma v} \tag{54a}$$

$$\cos\theta' = \frac{v}{c} \tag{54b}$$

which means that $\sin\theta' = (\tan\theta' \times \cos\theta') = 1/\gamma$. Since all quantities on the right-hand sides of Equations 54 are positive (we set up our coordinates so that v would be positive for frames of reference with relative velocities towards each other), we can immediately see that $0 < \theta' < \pi/2$, (because either $\tan\theta'$ or $\cos\theta'$ are negative for any angle $\theta' \geq \pi/2$). For highly relativistic velocities, the Lorentz factor,

$$\gamma = \frac{1}{\sqrt{1-(v^2/c^2)}} \gg 1,\text{ hence } \sin\theta' \ll 1,\text{ and we can use the small-angle}$$

approximation to give:

$$\theta' \sim \frac{1}{\gamma} \qquad\qquad (55)$$

This means that a photon emitted in the rest frame of the jet with a velocity perpendicular to the jet motion appears to an observer on Earth to be moving in a direction which is only slightly different from the direction of the jet motion! This is a remarkable result. If the jet material emits light uniformly in all directions, (i.e. **isotropically**) half of that emission appears to an observer on Earth to be beamed into a narrow emission cone which has an opening angle $\theta' \sim 1/\gamma$! Figure 51 illustrates this **beaming** effect.

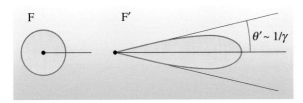

Figure 51 Radiation emitted isotropically in F, the rest frame of the jet, appears to be highly concentrated around the direction of the jet velocity in F′, the rest frame of an observer on Earth.

■   Which would appear brighter, an ordinary 60 W light bulb, or a 60 W light bulb which emits light only in a direction towards the observer?

❑   The light bulb which emits only towards the observer will appear much more luminous. ■

Because of this relativistic beaming, jets which are moving towards us appear much brighter than jets which are moving away from us.

Equation 55 shows that for a relativistically approaching source like this one, all the radiation emitted in the approaching hemisphere in the rest frame of the source appears concentrated in a cone of opening angle γ^{-1} in the rest frame of the observer.

Example 7

Estimate how much the observed flux per unit area is increased by beaming for a source approaching with velocity $v = 0.9c$.

Solution

Assuming the source emits isotropically in the rest frame, the emitted energy per unit area at a distance, d, in a comoving frame is the emitted energy, E, divided by the surface area of a sphere of radius d. In the rest frame, therefore, we have energy per unit area = $E/4\pi d^2$. In the observer's frame, all the energy in the approaching hemisphere is concentrated into the cone shown in Figure 52 (overleaf) and is thus spread over a circle of radius $r_{\text{circ}} = d/\gamma$. In the observer's frame, therefore, we have energy $E/2$ (because we are considering the energy emitted by an isotropic source into one hemisphere), and area πr_{circ}^2, so we have energy per unit area = $E/2\pi r_{\text{circ}}^2$. Comparing these we have a beaming enhancement of a factor, f:

$$f = \frac{E}{2\pi r_{\text{circ}}^2}\frac{4\pi d^2}{E} = 2\left(\frac{d}{r_{\text{circ}}}\right)^2 = 2\gamma^2 \qquad\qquad (56)$$

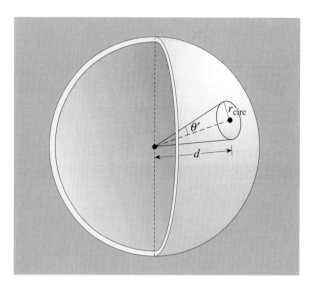

Figure 52 The beamed radiation appears concentrated into a cone so the flux emitted into an entire hemisphere is concentrated into an area approximated by a circle of radius $r_{circ} = d/\gamma$.

Therefore beaming gives an enhancement of a factor $\sim\gamma^2$. (Since we are asked for an estimate, we have not taken into account the fact that radiation is not uniformly spread over the cone, and we will drop the factor of 2.) We are asked to estimate the enhancement for a source moving towards us with velocity $v = 0.9c$, so we evaluate f:

$$f \approx \gamma^2 = \left(\frac{1}{\sqrt{1 - \dfrac{v^2}{c^2}}} \right)^2 = \frac{1}{1 - 0.81} = 5.3$$

Thus we see for a source approaching with velocity $0.9c$ relativistic beaming reduces the area the radiation is spread over by a factor of approximately 5, and hence increases the flux per unit area by a factor of approximately 5. ■

Beware! We are not yet quite ready to apply our work on the relativistic aberration of light to observations of AGN, we must also take into account the relativistic Doppler shift!

3.4.4 Relativistic Doppler shift

If you want to know more about how these special relativistic effects arise, consult the 'Course resources' on the S381 website.

Before we are ready to quantitatively tackle the observed emission from jets approaching us at relativistic speeds, there are two further factors which we must consider, both of which are a consequence of the Doppler shift (e.g. Block 1, Equation 44). The Doppler shift is familiar to most people in terms of the shift in pitch (i.e. frequency) of sound which is perceived when a vehicle recedes from us or approaches towards us at high speed. A similar effect occurs in the jets of AGN. However, the relativistic Doppler shift affects both the observed frequency (or wavelength) of the emitted radiation *and* the rate at which photons are detected. We consider this second factor first.

The luminosity of a jet is the amount of energy carried by the photons per unit time, that is it depends on the *rate* at which photons are emitted or detected. As a result of the Doppler shift, the rate of emission of photons measured in a frame of reference moving with the jet *differs* from the rate at which photons are detected by an observer on the Earth. In fact the Doppler shift introduces a factor γ between the two rates. For the approaching jet considered in Section 3.4.3, this will cause the apparent luminosity of the jet to be boosted by a factor γ.

This Doppler shift effect on the luminosity is independent of the beaming effect discussed in Section 3.4.3, and both will occur simultaneously. Beaming affects the solid angle (or area) over which radiation is distributed, while the Doppler shift affects the rate at which photons are detected.

> boosting due to beaming: $\sim\gamma^2$
>
> boosting due to Doppler shift of photon rate: $\sim\gamma$

The Doppler shift of the photon rate increases the apparent luminosity of an approaching source by a factor γ, while we saw earlier in Section 3.4.3 that relativistic beaming of the radiation from an approaching source increases the apparent energy per unit area by a factor γ^2.

Finally we need to consider the effects of the Doppler shift on the wavelength of the photons and what effect this has on the observed luminosity. If the photons detected at wavelength $\lambda = \lambda_0 + \Delta\lambda$ exactly replaced those which were emitted at wavelength λ, but not detected because they were Doppler shifted out of the observed waveband, the Doppler shift would have no additional effect on the detected luminosity. In general, however, extragalactic radio sources have power-law spectra described by $F_\nu \propto \nu^{-\alpha}$, and in this case the detected luminosity is enhanced by a further factor of γ^α

> boosting due to Doppler shift of wavelength: $\sim\gamma^\alpha$

Therefore, overall the apparent luminosity of a source which is approaching us is boosted by a factor $\gamma^{3+\alpha}$

> overall boosting of an approaching source $\sim\gamma^2 \times \gamma \times \gamma^\alpha = \gamma^{3+\alpha}$ (57)

This overall effect is referred to by various writers somewhat loosely as relativistic beaming, Doppler boosting, Doppler favouritism, or relativistic boosting. The formulae presented here assume that the jet is emitted in a direction close to our line of sight. If approaching jets at significant angles to our line of sight are considered, boosting will still occur, but these formulae will not accurately estimate how much the luminosity is enhanced.

Question 24

An active galaxy ejects a pair of diametrically opposed jets, each with speed $v = 0.9c$. The axis of jet ejection is aligned with the direction to the Earth, and each jet emits isotropically with power-law index $\alpha = 0.7$ in its own rest frame. Estimate how much brighter the approaching jet appears to an observer on Earth, compared to a stationary, isotropically emitting source with the same luminosity and distance. You may neglect the recessional velocity of the AGN itself. ∎

3.4.5 Superluminal motion

■ Recalling the reading from Activity 22, why do flat radio spectra imply structure on small scales in the radio source?

❑ The flat spectrum is thought to arise from a superposition of many distinct self-absorbed synchrotron spectra, each with differing magnetic field and particle density, consequently each with a distinct value for the low-frequency cutoff. All of these distinct spectra come from an unresolved source, meaning that this unresolved source has a variety of physical conditions. Hence the physical conditions must vary from place to place (i.e. exhibit structure) within the unresolved (hence small) source. ■

Activity 23   **(1 hour)**

Faster than light?

Read Section 4.4.2 of Peterson (pages 59–63).

Note: The word 'diagrammed' used near the bottom of page 59, is an Americanism, rather than an accepted scientific usage. British astronomers sometimes use 'graph' as a verb, but even this is rather informal, and the verb 'to plot' is more correct (though perhaps it has undesirable overtones of espionage). Note that in his Fig. 4.6, Peterson uses $\Delta\varphi$ (i.e. an alternative lower-case 'phi' character) to label the angle at the left-hand side of the diagram, while in the text he uses $\Delta\phi$ to refer to the same angle.

As we saw in Block 1, **proper motion** refers to motion of a source in the plane of the sky. Combining this with the distance to the source allows the corresponding **transverse velocity**, v_T, to be deduced, as shown in Figure 53. The transverse velocity is simply the angular velocity multiplied by the distance, i.e.

$$v_T = D\frac{d\phi}{dt} \tag{58}$$

Some notes concerning Peterson's derivation on pages 61 and 62 are given following this activity.

Keywords: **proper motion, apparent transverse velocity, superluminal motion** ■

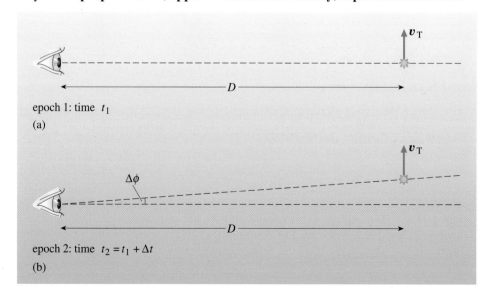

Figure 53 The diagram shows the relationship between the measured proper motion (the rate of change of the angle) and the inferred transverse velocity.

When following through the argument on Peterson page 61, note that the derivation assumes that the angle $\Delta\phi$ is small, i.e. that the distance D is much greater than $v\delta t$. For an extragalactic source this will be the case because the light travel time from source to observer will greatly exceed the duration of the observations. The diagram (Peterson Fig. 4.6) shows $\Delta\phi$ as a much larger angle, otherwise the triangle on the left of the diagram would be too long and flat for the diagram to be legible. Because the source moves to position B' with velocity v in time $\delta t = t_2 - t_1$, the measured time interval Δt is given by

$$\Delta t = t_2' - t_1'$$

and substituting for t_2' and t_1' from Peterson Equations 4.18 and 4.19 we have

$$\Delta t = t_2 - t_1 + \frac{D}{c} - \frac{D}{c} - \frac{v\delta t \cos\theta}{c} = \delta t - \frac{v\delta t \cos\theta}{c}$$

$$= \delta t\left(1 - \frac{v\cos\theta}{c}\right) = \delta t(1 - \beta\cos\theta) \qquad \text{(Peterson 4.20)}$$

where β is the velocity of the moving source divided by the speed of light, v/c, as is normal in discussions involving special relativity. The same convention is used in Peterson Equation 4.21 where he sets up the algebra to calculate β_T rather than v_T. The working shown in Peterson Equation 4.21 is simple substitution from Equation 58 above, and Peterson Equations 4.17 and 4.20, followed by replacing velocity v with βc, and cancelling c.

The step used to obtain Peterson Equation 4.22 may, at first glance, be mystifying. Don't panic, all that has happened is that the function $\dfrac{\beta\sin\theta}{1 - \beta\cos\theta}$ has been differentiated using the product rule (Block 1, Equation 76), with the functions p and q being set to: $p = \beta\sin\theta$ and $q = (1 - \beta\cos\theta)^{-1}$ exactly as in Block 1, Question 64.

Question 25

Differentiate $p = \beta\sin\theta$, and $q = (1 - \beta\cos\theta)^{-1}$ with respect to θ, i.e. derive expressions for $\partial p/\partial\theta$ and $\partial q/\partial\theta$, assuming the variable β is independent of θ. Note this working is an intermediate step to get to Peterson Equation 4.22. ∎

Peterson Equation 4.23 simplifies to

$$\cos\theta(1 - \beta\cos\theta) = \beta(1 - \cos^2\theta) \qquad (59)$$

and the intermediate step used the result from Pythagoras's theorem that for any value of θ, $\sin^2\theta + \cos^2\theta = 1$.

Hence Equation 59 becomes

$$\cos\theta(1 - \beta\cos\theta) = \beta - \beta\cos^2\theta$$

and multiplying out the bracket on the left-hand side and subtracting $\beta\cos^2\theta$ from both sides we obtain

$$\cos\theta_{max} = \beta \qquad (60)$$

Here we introduced the subscript 'max' to indicate that we have solved an equation which allows us to find the value of θ at which β_T is maximized (i.e. when $d\beta_T/d\theta = 0$). This means that for any value of jet velocity, v, the maximum

Note that

$$\frac{1}{\cos\beta} = (\cos\beta)^{-1}$$

$$\neq \cos^{-1}\beta$$

transverse velocity v_T will be inferred when the direction of motion of the emitting source makes an angle, θ_{max}, with the line of sight such that Equation 60 is satisfied. Equation 60 can be rewritten in Peterson's form by using the notation '$\cos^{-1}\beta$', which should be read as 'the angle whose cosine is β'.

Peterson Equation 4.25 comes from his Equation 4.21 by inserting the values appropriate to $\theta = \theta_{max}$, i.e. replacing $\cos\theta$ with β, and replacing $\sin\theta$ with $(1 - \beta^2)^{1/2}$. This value for $\sin\theta$ arises from the right-angled triangle with one angle equal to θ, a hypotenuse of length 1, and other sides of length β, and (from applying Pythagoras's theorem) $\sqrt{(1^2 - \beta^2)}$.

Once this is done we have an equation for the maximum value of the transverse velocity, which Peterson calls β_T^{max}. (Note this has nothing to do with raising β to the power 'max'.) The intermediate step between this and the final expression for β_T^{max} is to cancel top and bottom by a factor of $(1 - \beta^2)^{1/2}$, to give

$$\beta_T^{max} = \frac{\beta}{(1 - \beta^2)^{1/2}}.$$

which can be further simplified by substituting from Equation 14, for the Lorentz factor, γ.

- Why was the VLBI needed to discover superluminal motion?

- Because very high spatial resolution is required to be able to separate the individual sources. ■

Activity 24 (30 minutes)

Faster than a speeding bullet: Superluminal cartoon

From *The Energetic Universe* MM guide, view the animation 'Faster than a speeding bullet'. ■

Activity 25 (30 minutes)

Do-it-yourself superluminal motion

In this activity you will use a spreadsheet to reproduce Peterson's Fig. 4.7 and see the power of a spreadsheet to calculate literally hundreds of numbers from a single formula input. Start up StarOffice and open up a new, blank spreadsheet.

1   Type the word 'gamma' into cell A1 and enter the following values of gamma into cells B1 to K1: 1.25, 1.50, 2.00, 3.00, 4.00, 5.00, 6.00, 7.00, 8.00, 9.00. These represent the various gamma factors for which we will calculate curves of apparent transverse speed versus ejection angle.

2   Type the word 'beta' into cell A2 and in cells B2 to K2 calculate the beta values (ejection speeds) corresponding to the gamma values in the row above. Remember, by definition

$$\gamma = \frac{1}{\sqrt{1 - \beta^2}}$$

where $\beta = v/c$. You will need to rearrange the formula above to make β the subject rather than γ.

3   In cell A4 type 'theta/degrees' and then fill column A (cells A5 to A95) with ejection angles from 0° to 90°.

4   Now, for each of the cells from B5 in the top-left corner to K95 in the bottom-right corner, you should calculate the value of the apparent transverse speed β_T (according to Peterson Equation 4.21) corresponding to the ejection angles θ in column A and values of ejection speed β in row 2. You should be able to do this by entering the appropriate formula into cell B5 (corresponding to $\theta = 0°$ and $\gamma = 1.25$, $\beta = 0.60$) then dragging this cell to fill column B, then dragging column B to fill columns C to K. The spreadsheet trigonometric functions work in radians, so you will also have to convert the angles from degrees to radians in your formula.

5   Finally select all the data in your spreadsheet (cells A5 to K95) and then click on **Insert** then **Chart** to produce an XY graph containing 10 lines (corresponding to ten different values of ejection speed β) showing the variation of apparent transverse speed (β_T) versus ejection angle (θ). Confirm that this resembles Peterson's Fig. 4.7.

If you need help with how to do any of these steps, consult the Comments on activities, then answer the following question. ▦

Question 26

(a) Of the various values of β for which lines have been plotted in Activity 25, what is the minimum value of β for which apparent superluminal motion (i.e. $v_T > c$) occurs? (b) For this value of β, over what range of ejection angles will apparent superluminal motion be observed? ■

3.5 Blazar spectra

Activity 26   (20 minutes)

Emission pointed at us

Read Section 4.5 of Peterson (pages 63 to 66).

Čerenkov imaging is briefly explained in the Collins entry for 'Čerenkov counter'. The **big blue bump**, the **1 μm minimum** and the **submillimetre break** will be discussed when you reach Activity 27. (Don't forget 'SED' is the spectral energy distribution.)

Keywords: **microvariability** ▦

■   What is the primary observed difference between BL Lac objects and OVVs?

❑   BL Lacs have weak (or undetected) spectral line features, while OVVs generally have prominent broad emission lines. ■

■   Are there any radio-quiet blazars?

❑   No. By definition blazars are all radio-loud. ■

Figure 54 (overleaf) shows some results from multiwavelength monitoring of BL Lac. The variability mentioned in Peterson Equation 4.5 is clearly evident in the optical and the γ-ray light curves.

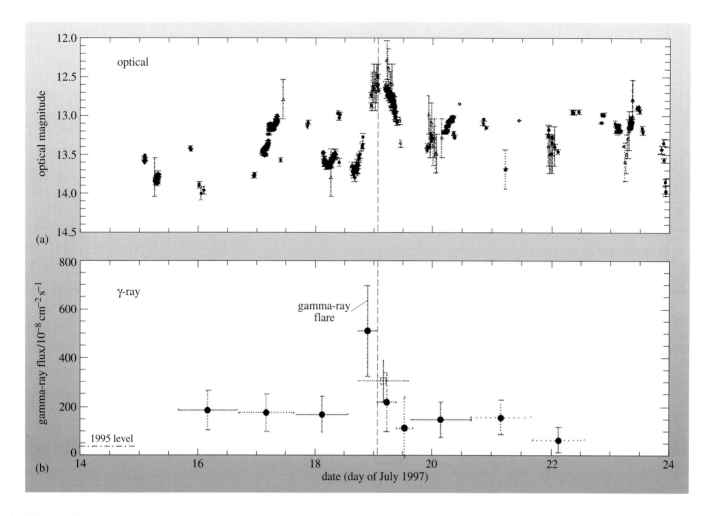

Figure 54 The optical and γ-ray variability of BL Lac.

Suggest a reason for the observation that the apparent transverse velocities in superluminal BL Lac objects tend to be lower than those for superluminal quasars. ■

In this section we have exhaustively studied radio-loud AGN. It is important to note that all AGN have *some* radio emission (see Figure 36). Even radio-quiet objects have weak non-relativistic jets.

You should by now have a completed block diagram summarizing the taxonomy of AGN which you started at the beginning of Section 3. An example diagram is given in Appendix A5.

3.6 Summary of Section 3

1   Seyfert galaxies are low-luminosity AGN with an absolute magnitude of $M_B > -21.5 + 5 \log h_0$ (where $h_0 = H_0/100 \, \text{km s}^{-1} \, \text{Mpc}^{-1}$). They have quasar-like nuclei, but a host spiral galaxy is clearly detectable.

2   The spectra of Seyfert 1 galaxies show narrow emission lines (widths of a few hundred km s^{-1}) as well as broad lines (widths up to $10^4 \, \text{km s}^{-1}$) from permitted transitions only. The narrow lines originate in low-density ionized gas ($n_e = 10^3 - 10^6 \, \text{cm}^{-3}$) whilst the broad lines come from high-density gas ($n_e \sim 10^9 \, \text{cm}^{-3}$). The spectra of Seyfert 2 galaxies contain only the narrow emission lines.

3   Quasars are the most luminous subclass of AGN with $M_B < -21.5 + 5 \log h_0$. Around 5–10% of quasars are radio-loud, and all quasars are spatially unresolved on optical survey photographs. Their spectra are similar to those of Seyfert galaxies.

4   Strong radio sources are usually identified with giant elliptical galaxies or with quasars. The radio-loud analogues of Seyfert 1 and Seyfert 2 galaxies are the broad-line radio galaxies (BLRGs) and narrow-line radio galaxies (NLRGs) respectively.

5   Low-ionization nuclear emission-line region galaxies (LINERs) resemble Seyfert 2 galaxies, except their low-ionization lines are relatively strong. They may be present in nearly half of all spiral galaxies. Some LINERs may be simply very low luminosity Seyfert 2 galaxies.

6   A BPT (Baldwin, Phillips and Terlevich) diagram plots line ratios against one another, such as the [OIII] $\lambda5007$/Hβ $\lambda4861$ line ratio against the [NII] $\lambda6583$/Hα $\lambda6563$ line ratio for a sample of emission line galaxies. Such a diagram enables narrow line AGN (Seyfert 2 and NLRGs) to be distinguished from HII regions and LINERs.

7   Related to AGN are starburst galaxies (which show signatures of recent star formation), Markarian galaxies (UV excess objects), Zwicky galaxies (blue compact galaxies), N galaxies (with a bright nucleus) and ultraluminous far-infrared galaxies (ULIRGs). Some members of each of these categories have turned out to be AGN of various types.

8   The properties of quasars and Seyfert galaxies show considerable overlap and most astronomers now accept that they form a continuous sequence in luminosity. The original distinction arose largely because the first members of each class to be discovered were the extremes of their type.

9   The radio spectra of the cores of AGN are flat ($\alpha \sim 0$) and assumed to be due to synchrotron emission. Low-frequency cutoffs due to synchrotron self-absorption are sometimes seen, but the spectral slope is not as steep as expected, probably due to a complex source structure.

10   The brightness temperature of a radio source is the equivalent temperature the source would have if it were radiating like a black body with the same intensity at the specified frequency.

11 Relativistic beaming is the effect whereby light emitted isotropically from a rapidly moving source is beamed into narrow emission cones which are aligned with the motion of the source. The opening angle of the emission cone is $\theta \sim 1/\gamma$ where γ is the Lorentz factor of the emitter. This effect causes an enhancement of the emission in the direction of the motion by a factor of γ^2. Relativistic Doppler shifting introduces another factor of γ: the luminosity of a source of emission which is approaching us with a Lorentz factor of γ is therefore enhanced by a factor of γ^3. If the emission has a synchrotron spectrum with power-law index α, Doppler shifting of the wavelength gives a further boost and the total enhancement is by a factor of $\gamma^{3+\alpha}$.

12 Material ejected from the cores of AGN is sometimes seen to undergo apparent superluminal motion (i.e. it appears to travel faster than the speed of light). The effect can arise if material is travelling close to the line of sight at an appreciable fraction of the speed of light. The material 'catches up' somewhat the light it has emitted earlier. The transverse speed inferred by an observer is given by

$$\beta_T = \frac{\beta \sin \theta}{1 - \beta \cos \theta}$$

where $\beta_T = v_T/c$ and v_T is the observed transverse speed, $\beta = v/c$ and v is the actual speed of the material ejected at an angle θ to the line of sight.

13 Blazars constitute a small subset of AGN. They are characterized by a featureless continuum spectrum, rapid (timescales of days) variability of their optical flux and polarization, and strong variable radio emission. They are all radio-loud and core dominated, have infrared brightness temperatures $>10^6$ K and radio brightness temperatures of $>10^{12}$ K. Some exhibit apparent superluminal motion.

14 Subclasses of blazars are BL Lacs objects, with weak emission and absorption lines, and optically violent variables (OVVs), with strong broad emission lines.

15 The peak in blazar spectral energy distributions (SEDs) is at different wavelengths in different sources, and the characteristic features of other AGN SEDs (big blue bump, submillimetre break and 1 μm minimum) are absent. The continuum is non-thermal.

16 The strength of flux variations in blazars is higher for brighter sources and for those with stronger polarization. Variations in the UV continuum have been seen to lag behind similar variations in the X-ray continuum with a delay of 2–3 hours; this rules out the SSC mechanism in which the opposite would be expected.

4 HIGH-ENERGY AND THERMAL EMISSION

So far we have undertaken overviews of the observations, taxonomy, and theory of AGN, and have had a detailed look at their radio properties. In this and the next two sections we will study what the various components of the electromagnetic radiation we detect from AGN can tell us about the conditions in which the light was generated. After doing this we will bring what we have learnt together, summarizing how the different emission components interrelate and how the different AGN properties we observe might be understood in terms of a self-consistent 'unified model' for all active galaxies.

The first component of the emission from AGN we will study is the continuum emission. The underlying physical processes were outlined in Section 1.7, and we'll begin here with a reading which will deal with the different parts of the electromagnetic spectrum.

4.1 Overview of continuum emission

Before undertaking the following activity you should make sure you remember the continuum emission physics you learned in Section 1.7. For example, do you remember what the inverse Compton process is?

Activity 27   **(30 minutes)**

The spectral energy distribution (SED)

Read the first part of Chapter 4 of Peterson, up to but not including Section 4.1 (pages 40–43).

If you have forgotten the significance of the **Maxwell–Boltzmann distribution**, you may wish to revise Section 4.7 of Block 1, including the MM activity 'Sharing out energy in gases' (Activity 6).

Where Peterson says '**several decades of frequency**', he means several factors of 10 on the frequency axis.

Keywords: **big blue bump**, **soft X-ray excess**, **IR bump**, **1 μm minimum**, **submillimetre break**, **primary emission**, **secondary emission** ▆

■ What generally happens to photons with wavelengths between 100 Å and 912 Å which are emitted by an AGN?

❏ They are absorbed by neutral hydrogen close to where they are emitted because neutral hydrogen has a large cross-section for absorbing these ionizing photons. ■

■ Do all AGN show a submillimetre break? If not, which do and which do not?

❏ No. The submillimetre break is the rapid drop in the SED at long wavelengths exhibited by radio-quiet AGN. Radio-loud AGN do not show this feature. ■

Sketch the SED of a radio-quiet AGN labelling the following features:

*   the big blue bump
*   the soft X-ray excess
*   the IR bump
*   the submillimetre break ■

Explain the statement 'optically thin thermal radiation is isotropic' using only words which you could reasonably expect to be familiar to someone with no science higher education. ■

■   What is a blazar? Why are blazar's SEDs different to those of normal AGN?

❑   A blazar is an AGN in which our line of sight is close to the direction of motion of an approaching relativistic jet. Because the non-thermal emission from the jet is highly beamed in our direction (see Section 3.4), while emission from the central engine is not, the jet emission appears to us to be a far larger fraction of the total AGN luminosity than it truly is. ■

4.2 High-energy emission

ELEMENTS, ELECTRONS AND SHELLS

As you learned in Block 2 Section 7.3, the most stable atomic nucleus is iron with 26 protons and 30 neutrons. An iron atom will have 26 electrons so that it is electrically neutral. Each of these electrons must have distinct sets of quantum numbers, and for an iron atom in the ground state these electrons will occupy the 26 lowest quantum states available. Other chemical elements have different numbers of protons in their nuclei, and consequently differing numbers of electrons in the neutral atom. In each case, the ground state of the neutral atom will correspond to the lowest energy quantum states in Figure 55 being filled until the atom has the number of electrons required for charge neutrality. The chemical properties of matter are determined by the outermost electrons, which can interact with other atoms forming chemical bonds.

In the high-energy environments which produce the X-ray and γ-ray emission from AGN, most of the matter is not in the form of neutral atoms in the ground state. Instead, the abundant high-energy photons cause multiple ionizations to occur, and the electrons which are lost in ionization events often come from the innermost, most strongly bound subshells. The $n = 1$ level shown in Figure 55 is known as the **K-shell** by X-ray spectroscopists,

similarly they call the $n = 2$ level the **L-shell**. Thus when a high-energy photon is absorbed in the process of removing an $n = 1$ electron from an atom or ion, this is known as a **K-shell absorption**. For the $n = 2$ and higher levels, the shells are subdivided into subshells which correspond to different angular momentum and magnetic quantum numbers for the electron removed: thus there are **LI, LII and LIII-subshells**.

■   How many L-shell electrons are there in a neutral iron atom?

❑   8: a neutral iron atom has 26 electrons, so will fill the 2s and 2p levels (which comprise the L-shell), and beyond. There will be 2 electrons in the 2s subshell and 6 in the 2p subshell, making 8 L-shell electrons in all. ■

Figure 56 shows the absorption cross-section for X-rays passing through silver. The sharp features in the curve (labelled K edge, LI edge, etc.) correspond to the ionization energies of electrons in each of the K, LI, LII and LIII-shells. These features appear in the curve because the absorption cross-section is particularly high when the photon energy only just exceeds the ionization energy.

electron capacity of subshell

s	p	d	f
2	6	10	14

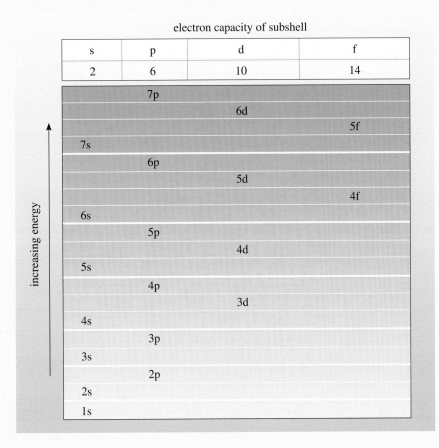

Figure 55 The quantum states available to electrons in an atom. Each electron occupies a state described by a distinct set of quantum numbers. The principal quantum number, n, is 1 for the lowest energy state. The s, p, d and f subshells correspond to differing values of the electron's orbital angular momentum quantum number, and have the capacities shown (each electron in a subshell has a distinct magnetic and spin quantum number). The two electrons in the 1s quantum state are known as K-shell electrons by X-ray spectroscopists. Similarly electrons in either the 2s or the 2p quantum states are known as L-shell electrons.

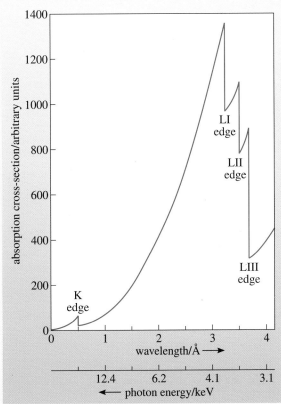

Figure 56 The absorption coefficient of silver.

The K-shell electrons can be excited to higher energy levels within the atom, as well as being completely removed from the atom by photoionization. For example if a K-shell electron is excited to the $n = 2$ (L-shell) by absorbing an X-ray photon, the corresponding spectral feature is known as the Kα line (by analogy with the Hα line in neutral hydrogen which appears in the optical part of the spectrum).

Much of our knowledge of the energy levels in multielectron atoms comes from X-ray absorption measurements made in the laboratory. In astrophysics we are able to see the same energetic ionization processes in nature's high-energy laboratories. Figure 57 shows examples of X-ray spectral line features in AGN.

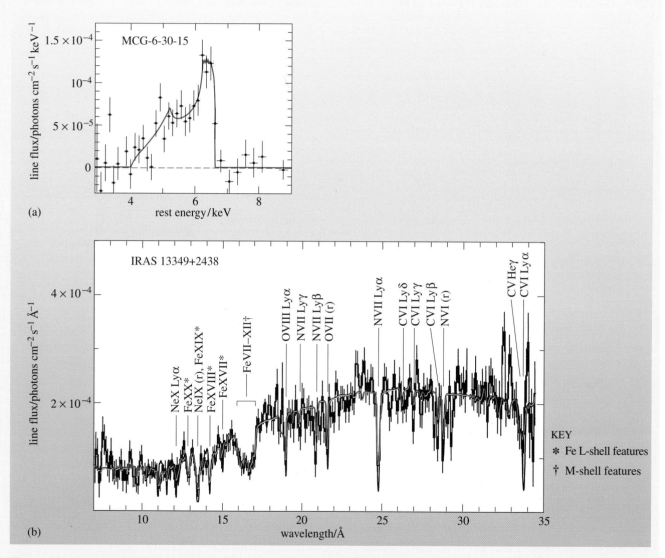

Figure 57 (a) The iron Kα emission line from the Seyfert 1 galaxy MCG-6-30-15. (b) An X-ray spectrum of IRAS 13349+2438 showing several L-shell and M-shell absorption features.

PAIR PRODUCTION

The interactions between photons and matter which we have considered so far have generally involved the exchange of energy between an electron and a photon. For the highest energy photons, there is a fundamentally new type of interaction possible: energy from a pair of γ-ray photons can be used to *create* an electron and a positron; the γ-rays are destroyed in the process. This process is called **pair production**. For pair production to happen there must be sufficient energy in the two γ-rays to provide the rest mass energy of the electron and the positron, i.e. if the two γ-rays have energies E_1 and E_2 respectively, pair production requires

$$E_1 E_2 > (m_e c^2)^2$$

Pair production cannot occur from an isolated highly energetic photon because it would be impossible for both energy and momentum to be conserved. *Note*: If the energetic photon is being scattered by the electric field of a nucleus then the nucleus can carry away momentum, and pair production is possible from a single photon. The reverse reaction to pair production, in which an electron and a positron (or indeed another particle–antiparticle pair) interact to create a pair of γ-ray photons is called **annihilation** because the electron and positron are annihilated in the process.

Activity 28

The X-ray continuum

Read the first part of Section 4.2 of Peterson, up to and including the first paragraph on page 50 which ends 'i.e., with $\alpha \approx 0.9$–1.'

Keywords: **soft X-rays**, **hard X-rays**, **γ-rays**, **photon index** Γ ■

■ How much of the bolometric luminosity of an AGN is typically radiated in the X-ray part of the electromagnetic spectrum?

❑ ~10% (see Peterson page 49). ■

■ Why does rapid variability in the X-ray emission from AGN indicate that X-rays originate in the innermost regions of AGN?

❑ Because rapid variability indicates a short light travel time, hence a small region, which we assume (by symmetry) is central to the AGN. ■

■ What is the K-shell?

❑ The innermost $n = 1$ shell in a multielectron atom is known as the K-shell by X-ray spectroscopists. ■

Question 30

Figure 57a shows the Fe Kα emission line in MCG-6-30-15. At the peak of the line, the flux is approximately 1.3×10^{-4} photons cm^{-2} s^{-1} keV^{-1}. What is the value of this peak flux in units of erg s^{-1} cm^{-2} Hz^{-1}? ■

Extreme energies from extreme objects

Read the next part of Section 4.2 of Peterson, from the second paragraph on page 50 which begins 'Observations of faint sources …', up to and including the second paragraph on page 51 which ends 'from hot gas.'

Where Peterson talks about a '**high energy cutoff**' he means the photon energy at which the emission from the source begins to fall to zero. For any emitter there will be a photon energy which is too great to be powered by the emission mechanisms operating. For Seyfert galaxies this threshold is at a few hundred keV.

Keywords: **K-correction, Comptonization, optical/X-ray spectral index α_{ox}** ▪

■ Why might we expect blazars to be preferentially detected at very high photon energies ($\lesssim 300$ keV)?

❏ Because, as observed by us, the photons emitted by the approaching jet will be blueshifted to higher energies than their energy in the rest frame of the jet. ▪

■ What is the 'K-correction'?

❏ The correction which must be made to the observations to derive fluxes at specific wavelengths in the rest frame of the source. ▪

■ Why is the high-energy emission in AGN not directly attributable to an accretion disc, as it was in the interacting binary stars studied in Block 3?

❏ Because the scaling of the temperature for a disc around a supermassive black hole shows that the innermost regions of the disc will only have $T \sim 10^5$ K as shown in Peterson Equation 3.20. ▪

Pairs, edges lines and reflection

Read the next part of Section 4.2 of Peterson, from the third paragraph on page 51 which begins 'Compton-scattering …', up to and including the sentence which ends with Peterson Equation 4.12, then skip to the second paragraph on page 52 which begins 'In addition to …' and continue to the end of the first paragraph on page 54 5 which ends '… unification models (Chapter 7).' to within a few days or less?

In the discussion of **electron–positron pair production** Peterson says 'the cross-section for pair production reaches a maximum value … just above the energetic threshold for the reaction'. To paraphrase, this means that pair production is most likely to occur if the two photons have energies which only just exceed the minimum required; the probability of pair production occurring decreases as the available energy increases beyond this.

The most common astrophysical example of an **ionization front** is given in Collins' definition of the **Strömgren sphere**. Unlike the central star producing a Strömgren sphere, the source of high-energy radiation in an AGN does not simply turn on and stay on. The ionizing source in an AGN varies, so the ionization fronts in the surrounding clouds will move in and out as the continuously changing balance between ionization and recombination is established. (We will return to this in Section 5.3.)

The **equivalent width** quoted for the 6.4 keV Fe Kα line is given in units of eV (Peterson has a typographical error and erroneously says keV rather than eV!) rather than Å, since X-ray astronomers usually plot their spectra with photon energy in keV on the horizontal axis. Optical astronomers generally show their spectra with wavelength in Å on the horizontal axis. In either case the equivalent width gives the measure of the length on the horizontal axis needed to give an equivalent rectangular area under the continuum spectrum (cf. Collins and Figure 25).

By '**the direction of the causal relationship**' Peterson is referring to the issue of whether:

- the X-ray variations drive the longer wavelength variations by, for example irradiating the outer regions. If the UV and optical emission is powered by this X-ray heating, then the amount of reprocessed UV and optical light should be approximately proportional to the amount of X-ray flux reaching the UV and optical emitting regions. In this case the X-ray variations should *lead* the UV–optical variations by the light travel time between the X-ray and UV–optical emitting regions, which depends on the geometry of the source.

or alternatively whether:

- the local viscous dissipation is the primary source of optical and UV radiation, so that variations in the mass transfer rate through the UV and optical emitting regions cause the UV and optical variability. Later the same mass transfer fluctuations will affect the innermost, X-ray emitting, disc regions. In this case the X-ray variations should *lag* the UV–optical variations by the viscous timescale required for accretion rate fluctuations to propagate between the two regions.

Keywords: **pair production**, **compactness parameter** *l*

Question 31

Describe the physical conditions needed for pair production to be important.

Why does blueshifted absorption indicate material which is flowing outwards?

Because the absorbing material must be between us and the continuum source, and blueshifted features indicate motion towards us, therefore away from the continuum source.

What is a 'Comptonized Wien tail'?

The Wien tail is the high-energy end of the Planck (blackbody) spectrum, and if the feature is Comptonized, it means the initial photons have undergone Compton scattering off electrons, and therefore had their energies changed (by upscattering or downscattering).

Why does the exact rest energy of the Fe Kα line depend on the ionization state?

Because the more highly ionized the iron is, the greater its net positive charge, hence the more difficult it is to move electrons away from the nucleus. The energy required to move electrons between the K-shell ($n = 1$) and the L-shell ($n = 2$) will, therefore, depend on the ionization state.

X-RAY UPDATE: *CHANDRA* AND XMM-NEWTON

At the time of writing this course two new X-ray observatories, *Chandra* and XMM-Newton, are superceding the results from previous X-ray missions. Figure 57b shows an example of a spectrum taken by the XMM-Newton satellite in which there are many well-resolved X-ray line features. The technological advances embodied in the new X-ray observatories will undoubtedly substantially improve our understanding of the central regions of AGN. See the links from the Course resources section of the S381 website for the latest information.

4.3 Ultraviolet–optical continuum

Photons with wavelengths just shorter than 912 Å (the wavelength of the Lyman limit) cause photoionization, and are strongly absorbed by neutral hydrogen. Because the cross-section for this absorption is so high, thermally emitting sources in which the temperature varies along the typical path followed by observed photons generally show a discontinuous feature at 912 Å, which is known as the **Lyman discontinuity** or **Lyman edge**. This feature would be expected to be present in the emission from an accretion disc, but only ambiguous evidence has been found for it to date. This might be explained by noting that an accretion disc in an AGN is likely to have a corona of hot electrons above and below it. Photons emitted by the accretion disc would traverse the corona, and would consequently be likely to undergo inverse Compton scattering. The energy gained will differ for each individual photon, so any feature in the spectrum will be blurred out and shifted. Hence, considerations of the Lyman edge do not change the conclusion we reached in Section 2.2, i.e. UV and optical continuum emission from AGN may or may not originate in an accretion disc.

Activity 31   **(15 minutes)**

Variability in the emission we would see

In Section 4.1 of Peterson, read from the second paragraph of page 46, which begins 'While the basic physics …' to '… completely irregular.' at the end of the following paragraph. Then skip to the last paragraph on page 47 'In principle, continuum …' and read down to '… temperature is high ($\sim 10^6$ K).' at the top of page 49.

Like Figure 30 in this Study Guide, the horizontal axis of Peterson's Fig. 4.2 is labelled by **Julian Date**, which is a calendar system allowing time to be specified by a single number rather than year, month and day. For data like that shown, which spans years or decades, this is obviously an advantage.

The Collins entry for **gravitational lens** will explain what is meant by **microlensing**. We will discover some exciting recent work using microlensing in Section 4.3.2.

Keywords: **continuum emission** ■

- What happens to the spectral index, α, when a continuum spectrum gets 'harder'?

- A harder spectrum has proportionally more emission at high energies, i.e. α decreases (cf. Equation 21). ■

Question 32

Referring to Fig. 4.2 in Peterson, how fast are the changes in the flux at 5100 Å in the active galaxy NGC 5548? Derive a maximum size for the region emitting at 5100 Å, fully explaining any assumptions you make. ■

- Can you think of any mechanism which might cause 'near-simultaneity of the UV and optical continuum variations' (cf. Peterson page 48, paragraph 3) in a geometrically thin accretion disc?

- If the innermost, hottest parts of the accretion flow emit radiation which shines on the outer disc, heating it, the variations at different wavelengths might have delays due only to the light travel time across the disc. If this were the case, the UV and optical continuum variations would be 'near-simultaneous', i.e. delayed by much less than the sound travel time. ▦

4.3.1 Gravitational lensing

Einstein's general theory of relativity (see Collins) describes how matter and energy curve space. Gravitational lensing is a natural consequence of general relativistic curved spacetime. We are used to the idea that light travels in straight lines. In our everyday world the general relativistic curvature of spacetime is imperceptible, and there is only one straight line between two points. In general relativistic curved spacetime there may be more than one path which a light ray could follow between two points, just as there are in Figure 58, which shows a gravitational lens. The line of sight

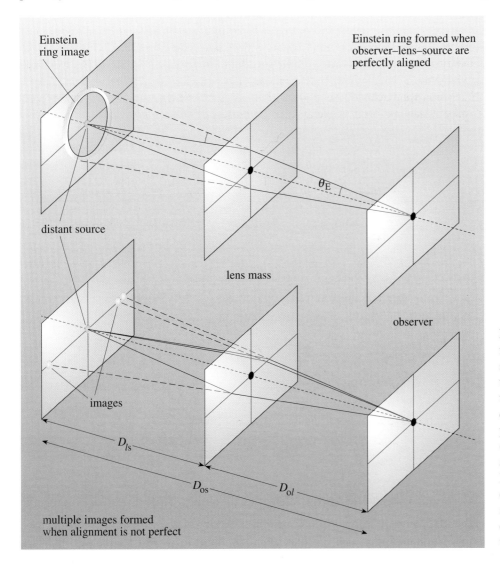

Figure 58 A gravitational lens is formed by the curvature of spacetime caused by the mass of the lensing object. (Top diagram) If the lensing mass is symmetrically distributed and the alignment is perfect, an Einstein ring is formed. (Bottom diagram) Generally the alignment is imperfect, and the lensing mass is a galaxy or cluster of galaxies, so the curvature of space is complex. In this case, the observer sees multiple images of the more distant lensed object.

from the observer to the distant object on the extreme left of the figure closely coincides with a massive object at intermediate distance. Because of the curvature of spacetime, the rays of light shown are bent so that both end up reaching the observer. Consequently the observer sees more than one image of the distant object.

It is important to note that the angles in Figure 58 are shown much larger than they are in reality. The gravitationally lensed images are generally only separated by an arc second or so if the lens has the mass of a typical galaxy. This, of course, helps in identifying what we see as being gravitationally lensed images, rather than distinct objects. Other characteristics of the images which are used to confirm that gravitational lensing is taking place are similar spectra, and similar time variability.

While a full treatment of the gravitational lensing process clearly requires the general theory of relativity, which is beyond the scope of this course, we can go some way to understanding when we might expect it to occur, and how large the deflection of the light ray will be.

Figure 59a shows the angle θ between the directions to the lensing mass and the lensed image. We will assume for now that these can both be regarded as point-like. Whether or not gravitational lensing will be seen depends on how strong the effects of gravity are along the path taken by light from the lensed source. Obviously the curvature of space is an effect which varies gradually and continuously along the light ray. For the purposes of our discussion we will make the simplifying approximation that all of the apparent bending of the light ray occurs at the closest approach to the lensing mass, where the strongest gravitational effects occur. The consequent approximate light path, with an abrupt bend when the light is at the shortest distance r_1 from the lens mass, is shown in Figure 59b. At this point of maximum bending, the gravitational potential is

$$\frac{GM_l}{r_1}$$

Figure 59 (a) How small must the angle θ, measured between the directions to the lensing mass and to the distant light source, be for gravitational lensing to be seen? (b) Light rays passing within the Einstein ring radius are lensed. (c) The Einstein ring radius could be thought of as the apparent angular size of the 'magnifying glass' of the gravitational lens.

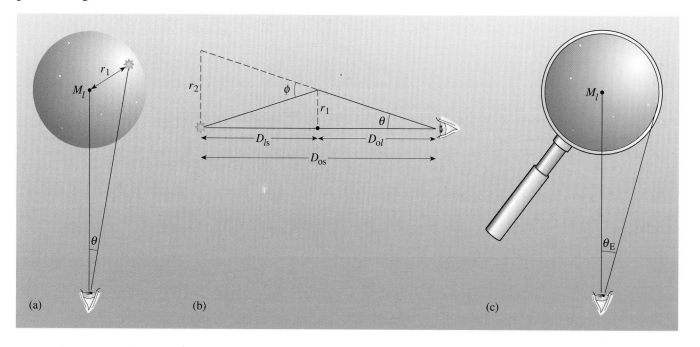

where M_l is the mass of the lensing object, and G is the (usual) Newtonian constant of gravity. The deflection (measured as an angle in radians) which the light ray undergoes, ϕ, is proportional to this gravitational potential, so we can say

$$\phi \propto \frac{GM_l}{r_1} \qquad (61)$$

We are just stating this: proof is beyond the scope of this course.

We can also use the small-angle approximations for the triangles in Figure 59b to say

$$r_1 \approx D_{ol} \times \theta \qquad (62)$$

and $$r_2 \approx D_{ls} \times \phi \approx D_{os} \times \theta$$

Thus we know the two small angles, θ and ϕ are related by

$$\phi \approx \theta \times \frac{D_{os}}{D_{ls}} \qquad (63)$$

If we substitute for r_1 and ϕ from Equations 62 and 63 into Equation 61 we obtain

$$\theta \times \frac{D_{os}}{D_{ls}} \propto \frac{GM_l}{D_{ol}\theta}$$

i.e. $$\theta^2 \propto GM_l \frac{D_{ls}}{D_{ol}D_{os}}$$

or $$\theta \propto \left(GM_l \frac{D_{ls}}{D_{ol}D_{os}} \right)^{1/2} \qquad (64)$$

This expression for θ contains everything we require except for the constant of proportionality. The full general relativistic calculation gives us this constant. The complete formula for the angular size of the **Einstein ring radius**, θ_E is:

$$\theta_E = \left(\frac{4GM_l}{c^2} \times \frac{D_{ls}}{D_{ol}D_{os}} \right)^{1/2} \qquad (65)$$

Here the distances D_{ls}, D_{ol} and D_{os} are shown in Figure 59b, and θ_E could be thought of as the apparent angular size of the magnifying glass through which substantial gravitational lensing occurs, as shown in Figure 59c. You may recognize (from Section 1.2) the quantity

$$\frac{4GM_l}{c^2}$$

as being twice the **Schwarzschild radius** of a black hole of mass M_l. We shouldn't be surprised that the Schwarzschild radius is an important length scale in determining the geometry of the gravitational lens.

If we put in values for the quantities in Equation 65 estimated for the lensing mass being a typical galaxy, and the distances being 'cosmological', i.e. a large fraction of the distance across the observable Universe, we might use $M_l = 10^{12} M_\odot$, and $D_{ol}D_{os}/D_{ls} = 1 \times 10^9$ pc. Using these values, with the appropriate conversions to cgs units, so

$$M_l = 10^{12} M_\odot = 10^{12} \times 2 \times 10^{33}\,\text{g}$$

$$\frac{D_{ol}D_{os}}{D_{ls}} = 1 \times 10^9\,\text{pc} = 1 \times 10^9 \times 3 \times 10^{18}\,\text{cm}$$

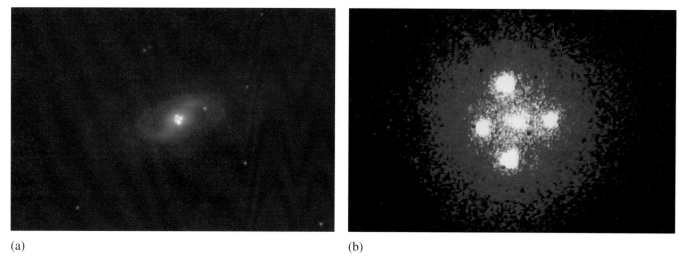

(a)   (b)

Figure 60 (a) The four bright spots at the centre of this galaxy are in fact four images of a more distant quasar. The light from the quasar is gravitationally lensed by the mass of the intervening galaxy. (b) A close-up higher-resolution image showing the four images of the lensed quasar surrounding the fainter, more extended nucleus of the lensing galaxy.

and substituting in values for the constants, G and c, in Equation 65 we have:

$$\theta_E = \left(\frac{4 \times (6.7 \times 10^{-8}) \times (10^{12} \times 2 \times 10^{33})}{(3 \times 10^{10})^2} \times \frac{1}{(10^9 \times 3 \times 10^{18})} \right)^{1/2} \text{radians}$$

$$= (2 \times 10^{-10})^{1/2} \text{ radians}$$

$$= 1.4 \times 10^{-5} \text{ radians} = 1.4 \times 10^{-5} \times \frac{360}{2\pi} \text{degrees}$$

$$= 8.0 \times 10^{-4} \text{ degrees} = 8.0 \times 10^{-4} \times 60 \times 60 \text{ arcsec}$$

$$\theta_E = 3 \text{ arcsec} \tag{66}$$

Thus we have learned that a gravitational lens caused by the mass of a galaxy at cosmological distances will form images of an even more distant object provided that their angular separations are of the order of an arc second.

In 1985 the discovery of a close alignment of a galaxy and a more distant quasar was published. The composite object was given the catalogue name Q 2237+0305, and the quasar is at redshift $z = 1.7$ with the foreground galaxy at $z = 0.04$. This discovery naturally caused excitement, because it seemed a gravitational lens might operate in this system. High-resolution optical images clearly show that a gravitational lens is indeed present, and four images of the distant quasars are found around the centre of the lensing galaxy (Figure 60). The separation of the four images of the distant quasar is roughly 1 arc second, just as our estimate in Equation 66 predicted.

4.3.2 Gravitational lens mapping of quasar accretion flows

In the last section we considered a distant quasar being gravitationally lensed by a galaxy at intermediate distance, and found that a number of images of the quasar are seen. The multiple images are caused by the general relativistic curving of space as a result of the mass of the lensing galaxy. This form of gravitational lensing is known as **macrolensing**, it is the mass of the entire intervening galaxy which produces macrolensed images.

The macrolensing galaxy is, of course, composed of individual stars. Consequently its mass is not uniformly distributed, but instead comes in highly concentrated stellar particles. There is a second type of gravitational lensing, **microlensing**, which occurs when an individual star in the macrolensing galaxy is exactly lined up with one of the light-paths to the lensed quasar. When this exact conjunction occurs, the macrolensed image is brightened by the microlensing effect. Because stars orbit around the centre of mass of the galaxy they belong to, the exact conjunction is transient: the microlensing star will drift across the line of sight to the lensed quasar. This leads to a transient brightening of the macrolensed image, which is known as a **microlensing event**. The time duration of the microlensing event depends on size of the quasar being lensed, on the speed with which the foreground, microlensing star is moving, and on the Einstein ring radius.

It is possible to calculate the time-dependent brightening due to the microlensing event if the relative distances between the observer, the microlensing star, and the lensed quasar are known. The results of these general relativistic calculations show that light curves of microlensing events are independent of colour, *unless the size of the lensed quasar is different at different wavelengths*. This is potentially very interesting, because as we have seen, an accretion disc should produce short-wavelength radiation in the innermost regions and increasingly longer wavelength radiation further out. That is to say, the quasar should be a more compact source of violet radiation than of red radiation. Figure 61 shows how the microlensed light curve depends on the size of the lensed source. In principle, therefore, microlensing may allow us to derive the size of the continuum source in the lensed quasar, even though this source is far too small to be directly resolved. It may ultimately even allow the colour dependence of the size of the continuum source to be detected.

In Activity 31 we read that, in principle, an upper limit to the size of the emitting region might be obtained by the gravitational microlensing method explained above. In the intervening years since Peterson wrote the text, this has been accomplished. Figure 62 shows a microlensing event in the quasar Q 2237+0305, along with the calculated gravitational microlensing light curve. By matching the shape of the calculated curve to the observations, the size of the V-band continuum source in Q 2237+0305 can be deduced. The result found is that the source is smaller than 2000 AU.

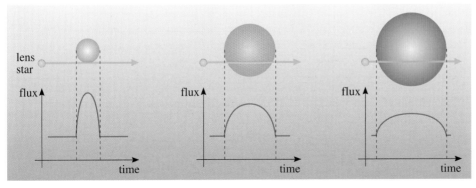

Figure 61 Schematic illustration of how the size of the source affects the microlensed light curve. Small sources have shorter microlensing events because the alignment required to produce lensing does not last so long.

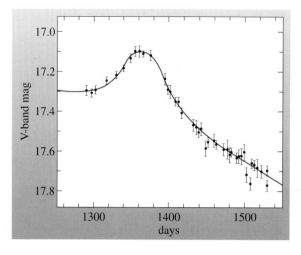

Figure 62 An observed microlensing event in the light curve of Q 2237+0305 is shown by the points with error bars. A calculated microlensing light curve which matches these observations is shown by the solid line curve.

4.4 Reprocessing in dust

If your eyes were sensitive to infrared (IR) radiation, you would see everything around you glowing in its own infrared light. This glow would continue even when no optical light was present to illuminate your surroundings. In the infrared, therefore, it never gets truly dark anywhere on Earth. This has obvious drawbacks for infrared astronomy, and demands careful subtraction of background IR emission, and telescopes designed to stay as cool as possible. The past two decades have seen great advances, driven by advancing technology, being made in IR astronomy, and it is likely to be one of the most informative areas of AGN astronomy in the first decade of the 21st century, as we shall see later.

Note: The dust in space is NOT thought to have the same composition as house dust!

Astronomers refer to solid particles in space as **dust**. The study of the infrared emission from dust is an entire sub-field of astronomy, which we will briefly mention here. The dust in space can have a variety of chemical compositions, including the silicate and graphite grains which Peterson will discuss in the reading in Activity 32. These can be unambiguously identified by spectral emission and absorption features.

Activity 32   (15 minutes)

Glowing dust and how the nucleus keeps itself dust-free

Read Section 4.3 of Peterson (pages 56 and 57).

Sublimation is the state change from solid to gas. Dust grains in AGN will be destroyed by sublimation at temperatures $T \gtrsim 2000 \, \mathrm{K}$.

In the paragraph entitled '**The submillimeter break**' Peterson describes the consequences of the sensitive dependence on photon frequency, ν, of the emitting efficiency of small grains. This sensitive dependence arises when the grain size becomes comparable to the wavelength, λ. Ultimately the emission of electromagnetic radiation is described by Maxwell's equations, a full treatment of which is beyond the scope of this course. If, however, we remember that a source of electromagnetic radiation requires an oscillation of electric charge at the appropriate frequency, we can arrive at a simplified understanding of emission from dust. Clearly when the size, a, of the emitting dust grain becomes as small as the wavelength, λ, of the radiation which is emitted, such oscillations are difficult to sustain. Hence radiation is inefficient at wavelengths $\lambda \lesssim a$, even when the temperature of the dust is such that the Planck function (see Figure 9) predicts the emission should peak at this wavelength. As the dust grains cannot radiate efficiently at $\lambda \geq a$, emission shifts to shorter wavelengths, and the emitting efficiency becomes a steep function of wavelength.

Keywords: **sublimation radius**, **grain emitting efficiency Q_ν** ▧

Question 33

Outline an argument in support of the hypothesis that the IR continuum in non-blazar AGN arises from thermal emission from dust grains. Your answer should include and define the sublimation radius, and include specific observational evidence. ▪

Question 34

(a) Would an X-ray astronomer consider a gas of temperature 10^4 K hot or cold?

(b) Would an IR astronomer consider a gas of temperature 10^4 K hot or cold?

Give reasons for your answers. ▪

4.5 Summary of Section 4

1   Important features in the broad band continuum of an AGN spectral energy distribution (SED) include the following:

   - A big blue bump between 4000 Å and 1000 Å (possibly extending to shorter wavelengths where it is seen as a soft X-ray excess) which is probably due to thermal emission – either optically thick black body or optically thin bremsstrahlung.

   - Superimposed on the big blue bump is a small blue bump due to a combination of overlapping emission lines.

   - A local minimum around 1 μm between the big blue bump and a cool thermal spectrum due to emission by warm dust grains. The emission towards wavelengths longer than 1 μm is known as the IR bump.

   - A submillimetre break in the spectrum of radio-quiet AGN below which the SED decreases rapidly.

2   X-ray emission accounts for around 10% of the luminosity of an AGN and its rapid variability indicates that it originates in regions close to the centre of the AGN.

3   X-ray SEDs are generally of the form P_E (photons s^{-1} keV^{-1}) $\propto E^{-\Gamma} \propto \nu^{-\Gamma}$ where the photon index Γ is related to the usual energy index α by $\Gamma = \alpha + 1$. The power-law slope of the X-ray spectra of AGN typically has $\alpha \sim 0.7$ in the 2–20 keV range, steepening to $\alpha \sim 0.9$–1.0 at lower energies. The spectral index in the γ-ray regime is typically $\alpha \sim 1.2$, with a high-energy cutoff around a few hundred keV.

4   The optical/X-ray spectral index between 2500 Å and 2 keV is defined as

$$\alpha_{ox} = -0.384 \log_{10} [F_\nu(2\,\text{keV})/F_\nu(2500\,\text{Å})]$$

   and typically found to be $\alpha_{ox} \sim 1.4$.

5   In most models of AGN, the X-ray and γ-ray emission is thought to be produced by inverse Compton scattering of UV–optical photons from the accretion disc off hot electrons in a corona surrounding the disc.

6   Electron–positron pair production can occur for a pair of photons if the product of their energies exceeds $(511 \text{ keV})^2$. The condition can be met in AGN.

7   The $n = 1$ and $n = 2$ shells of an atom are also known as the K-shell and L-shell respectively. Absorption features in the X-ray spectra of AGN correspond to K- or L-shell absorption edges from heavy metals such as iron. The amount of absorption is seen to vary in time implying that the ionization fronts vary in position.

8   The low-energy X-ray spectra (<2 keV) of many AGN show a soft X-ray excess which may be the tail of the big blue bump seen in the optical–UV spectrum, or a blend of soft X-ray line emission.

9   The high-energy X-ray spectra (>10 keV) sit above the power-law extrapolation at lower energies and are generally assumed to be due to Compton scattering off cold gas, perhaps in the accretion disc.

10 Iron Kα emission lines at 6.4 keV are seen in the X-ray spectra of many AGN. Their widths of up to a few hundred eV imply velocities of around 10^4 km s^{-1}.

11 The X-ray spectra of AGN can be modelled in terms of a reflection model. In such a model, an initial power-law continuum of photons (with $\alpha \sim 0.7$) irradiates cold gas ($T < 10^6$ K). The reflected X-ray spectrum contains iron and nickel emission lines, and absorption edges. Higher energy photons are Compton scattered to lower energies, whilst lower energy photons undergo photoelectric absorption, resulting in broad hump in the reflected continuum between about 20 and 100 keV.

12 One indication of the large distances to AGN is that some of them are subject to gravitational lensing, whereby their light is 'bent' by the gravitational field of an intervening galaxy such that we see multiple images of the distant AGN. When an AGN is directly in line with its lensing galaxy, a complete ring image is seen, known as an Einstein ring, whose angular size is typically a few arc seconds.

13 A significant variation in flux on a timescale Δt implies that a significant amount of the emitting material must be contained within a distance $r < c\Delta t$. Such variations limit the size of the emitting region in AGN to $\lesssim 10^{16}$ cm . Limits on the emitting size are also found from microlensing of quasars, which arises dues to gravitational lensing by individual stars in the intervening lensing galaxy.

14 The IR emission from AGN is believed to be due to thermal emission from dust which is heated by the optical–UV emission from the central source. The IR bump in the spectrum at wavelengths longer than 1μm is attributed to dust with a maximum temperature of 2000 K outside the sublimation radius.

15 The minimum distance from an AGN at which dust grains can exist without sublimating is the sublimation radius:

$$r = 1.3 L_{\text{uv46}}^{1/2} T_{1500}^{-2.8} \text{ pc}$$

(Peterson 4.15)

where L_{uv46} is the UV luminosity of the central source in units of $10^{46} \text{ erg s}^{-1}$ and T_{1500} is the grain sublimation temperature in units of 1500 K.

16 The IR continuum shows the same variability as the UV–optical continuum but with time delays of hundreds of days. This is interpreted as the light travel time between the central source and the IR emitting region. The implied separation agrees well with the estimated sublimation radius.

5 BROAD EMISSION LINES

5.1 Interpretation of spectral lines

In this section we reveal some of the interpretative tools optical and UV astronomers use to make surprisingly robust and far-reaching deductions about the distant objects whose light they collect. While the most obvious aim here is to illuminate our understanding of the broad-line region of AGN, the approach and techniques have been applied in many different areas of astrophysics.

Emission lines are produced when an atom or an ion in an excited state undergoes a transition to a lower state, and emits a photon which carries away the difference in energy between the initial and final states. This energy, and hence the wavelength of the emitted photon, is determined in the rest frame of the emitting atom or ion, so that the overall emission line profile from a gas cloud has a profile which is broadened by the Doppler shifts due to the thermal motions of all the individual emitting particles, as shown in Figure 63a (overleaf). This **thermal broadening** causes spectral lines to have appreciable **thermal width**. For a gas with $T = 10^4$ K, the magnitude of the thermal velocity of a typical particle is $v_{th} \sim 10\,\mathrm{km\,s^{-1}}$, so the thermal width of the line is the Doppler shift appropriate to this value of v_{th}. For obvious reasons, line widths are often given in velocity units, rather than units of wavelength.

- How would you estimate the thermal velocity of a typical particle in gas of temperature T?

☐ By following Block 1 Equation 145, we can say

$$\frac{1}{2} m v_{th}^2 \approx \frac{3}{2} kT$$

so putting in values for the mass of the particle, m, and the temperature, T, the thermal velocity, v_{th}, can be estimated. ■

This section will build on the ideas explored in the Block 1 interactive multimedia activities, 'Sharing out energy in gases' (Activity 6) and 'Atomic energy levels' (Activity 7). Now might be a good time to review these packages.

Question 35

(a) Estimate the temperature required to produce a thermal width of $5000\,\mathrm{km\,s^{-1}}$.

(b) Comment on your answer. In particular would you expect a gas at this temperature to emit the Balmer series? Give a reason. ■

The broad emission lines Carl Seyfert noted in his spectra of Seyfert galaxies have widths of order $5000\,\mathrm{km\,s^{-1}}$. These widths are too wide to be attributed to thermal broadening. Instead, the profiles are predominantly broadened by bulk motions of entire gas clouds, as illustrated in Figure 63b (overleaf).

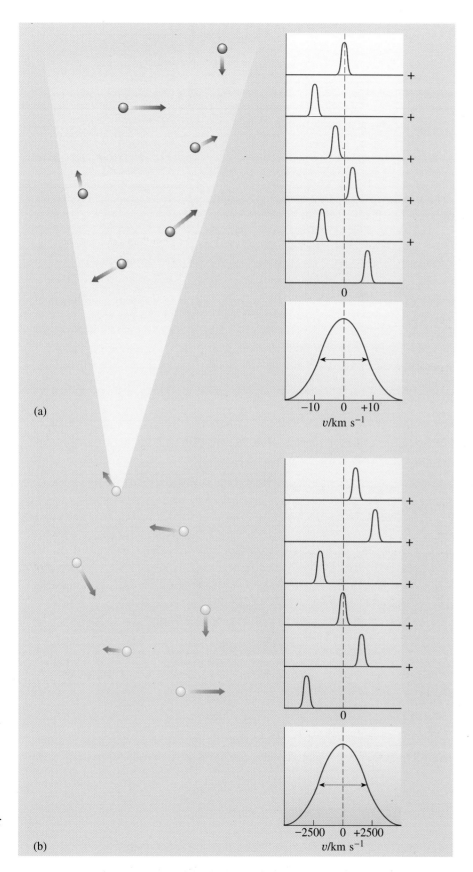

Figure 63 (a) Doppler broadening due to the random motions of gas molecules. (b) Doppler broadening due to the random motions of gas clouds. Each cloud in (b) has a narrower line profile due to the thermal motions of its constituent molecules. The clouds have large velocities, leading to large Doppler shifts and hence a broad line profile.

Activity 33 builds on Block 1 Activity 6 and Block 1 Activity 7 and will introduce and explain the atomic physics you need to interpret the emission lines from AGN. It is important that you cover this material before doing the readings which follow. If this is absolutely impossible, an abbreviated discussion of some of this material is given in Peterson Section 6.2.

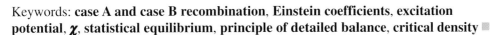

Activity 33   **(2 hours)**

Photons and particles

From *The Energetic Universe* MM guide, start the activity entitled 'Photons and particles'.

Keywords: **case A and case B recombination, Einstein coefficients, excitation potential, χ, statistical equilibrium, principle of detailed balance, critical density** ▪

5.2 Broad-line spectra and what we deduce from them

We will now examine what has been learnt about the **broad-line region (BLR)** which first drew attention to AGN.

Activity 34   **(25 minutes)**

Overview of broad-line spectra

Read Peterson Section 5.1 (pages 67–70). This reading will give you an opportunity to practise applying some of the material and new terminology from Section 5.1.

At the top of page 68, Peterson mentions the **Balmer decrement**. This is a measure of the relative fluxes in the Balmer series lines. Peterson makes the point that the shapes of the various lines in the emission from a single object differ, e.g. the Hα line has a different shape to the Hβ line and so on. For a broad emission line, the shape arises because of the Doppler shift: regions with differing velocities contribute to differing observed wavelengths. Since the Balmer series lines do not all have the same profile (shape), regions with differing velocities must emit with differing flux ratios. For example, some regions will emit relatively more Hα, so the Hα profile will be enhanced relative to the other lines at the corresponding velocity. This in turn means that the physical parameters (e.g. temperature, density, ionizing flux, etc.) must vary from place to place within the broad-line emitting region.

Keywords: **emission lines, Balmer decrement, photoionization, line profile, variability** ▪

▪   What does the abbreviation FWHM stand for?

❑   Full width at half maximum. ▪

▪   What is the range of values observed for the widths, Δv_{FWHM}, of AGN broad lines?

❑ $500\,\mathrm{km\,s^{-1}} < \Delta v_{\mathrm{FWHM}} \lesssim 10^4\,\mathrm{km\,s^{-1}}$. ▪

▪   For a given AGN, do all the broad lines have the same width?

❑   No, typically the He lines are broader than the Balmer lines. ▪

5.2.1 Estimating the mass of the broad-line region

Interpreting the broad lines: (i) the mass of the BLR

Read the next part of Chapter 5 of Peterson, up to and including the paragraph containing Peterson Equation 5.9 which ends '… gas is required' (on page 73). This reading will give you further practise in applying the material and new terminology from Section 5.1 above.

Note: There is an error in the units given for Peterson Equation 5.3. While the luminosity must be in erg s^{-1}, the right-hand side of the equation should include units cm^3 erg s^{-1}, because the quantity $r^3 n_e^2$ has units cm^{-3}. Hence the correct version should read

$$(4 \cdot 6 \times 10^{-23} \text{ cm}^3 \text{ ergs}^{-1}) \, \epsilon \, r^2 n_e^2$$

$$L(\text{CIV}) \approx \epsilon r^3 n_e^2 \, 4.6 \times 10^{-23} \text{ cm}^3 \text{ erg s}^{-1} \qquad \text{(Peterson 5.3)}$$

In the beginning of Section 5.2 Peterson says '**forbidden lines are collisionally suppressed**'; as explained in Section 1.8.3, this means that before a relatively low probability, forbidden, radiative de-excitation can take place, the excited species undergoes a collision with a free electron, and consequently makes a transition to a different state, as we saw in Activity 33.

On pages 72 and 73 Peterson presents a calculation which allows the mass of the gas in the broad-line region to be estimated from the observed line flux. The starting point for this is the **line emissivity**, j, which is the amount of energy per unit time per unit volume per unit solid angle carried away from the emitting gas by emission line photons. Notes on the derivation leading to Peterson Equation 5.9 follow this activity. h_0 is the Hubble constant in the form introduced in Equation 9.

Keywords: **broad-line clouds, filling factor, line emissivity** ■

■ Why do astronomers think that the electron density in AGN broad-line regions exceeds 10^8 cm^{-3}?

❏ Because the forbidden oxygen lines [OIII] $\lambda\lambda 4363, 4959, 5007$ are weak or absent in broad-line spectra. If $n_e \leq 10^8$ cm^3 we would expect these emission lines to be clearly present. ■

■ What is the approximate value of the ratio: (number of carbon atoms in the Universe)/(number of hydrogen atoms in the Universe)?

❏ From the numbers quoted in Peterson half way down page 72 the value of the ratio is $10^{-3.48} \approx 1/3000$. ■

Peterson states

$$j(\text{CIV}) = n_e n_{C^{3+}} q(2s \, ^2S, \, 2p \, ^2P) \frac{h\nu}{4\pi} \qquad \text{(Peterson 5.2)}$$

without justification. Firstly do not be alarmed by the notation ($2s \, ^2S, \, 2p \, ^2P$) which is used to denote the two levels involved in the transition referred to by the collisional transition rate q. This notation is used by atomic physicists and spectroscopists to describe the quantum mechanical configuration of the electrons within an atom. You do not need to know the details, and here you can mentally substitute i for $2s \, ^2S$ which denotes the lower energy level and j for $2p \, ^2P$ which denotes the upper level.

Hence the equation could be rewritten as

$$j(\text{CIV}) = n_e n_{\text{C}^{3+}} q_{i,j} \frac{h\nu}{4\pi}$$

where $q_{i,j}$ is just the collisional transition rate which was defined in Activity 33. The same spectroscopic notation system appears in Peterson Figs. 6.1 and 6.3. Peterson Equation 5.2 assumes that the upper level of the CIV $\lambda1549$ line is populated exclusively by collisional excitation, and depopulated exclusively by radiative de-excitation, so that every collisional excitation leads to an emitted line photon. As we saw in Activity 33, the probability of a collision between a particle of species A and a particle of species B is proportional to both the number densities, hence the rate of collisional excitations is clearly $\propto n_e n_{\text{C}^{3+}}$. The **collisional excitation rate**, q, for the transition in question is the constant of proportionality:

number of collisional excitations per unit time $= n_e n_{\text{C}^{3+}} q$

The factor $h\nu$ on the right-hand side of Peterson Equation 5.2 is the energy of the emitted photon, by which we must multiply because the emissivity is measured in $\text{erg s}^{-1} \text{cm}^{-3} \text{ster}^{-1}$, rather than $\text{photons s}^{-1} \text{cm}^{-3} \text{ster}^{-1}$. The factor $1/4\pi$ accounts for the fact that the photon will be emitted in a random direction, hence the energy will be uniformly spread over the 4π steradians of a full sphere. The trickiest part of this calculation would be determining the appropriate value of the collisional excitation rate, q. We will not go into this in this course, but will supply you with information for these rates as you need it.

Peterson Equation 5.3 calculates the luminosity of the CIV line emission, using Equation 5.2 as a starting point. The definition of luminosity requires that we integrate over the 4π steradians of a full sphere ($\int d\Omega$), and of course we must integrate over the whole of the emitting object ($\int dV$). These two integrations are independent of each other because all regions of the emitting object contain ions which will emit uniformly in all directions: none of the CIV ions have preferred directions. Hence, in this case, it makes no difference in which order we choose to do the two integrations. The integral over the solid angle is:

$$\int j(\text{CIV}) d\Omega = 4\pi j(\text{CIV})$$

The integral over volume could be more complicated, because we might expect the physical conditions to vary with position within the emitting volume: for example some parts might be hotter and/or denser than others. We will treat the emitting gas as uniform, so that n_e and $n_{\text{C}^{3+}}$ are constant, and we will take a single value of q. The assumption that the broad-line region is a single uniform emission region is, however, a poor one. Consequently Peterson introduces the **filling factor**, ϵ, to describe the proportion of the space which is filled with line-emitting gas. Rather than considering a complex and realistic gas cloud with gradients in temperature and density, this approach assumes that any position is either filled with emitting material or not, and that all the emitting material is identical (see Figure 64, overleaf). The final step in reaching Peterson Equation 5.3 involves substituting in values of q and $n_{\text{C}^{3+}}$.

Peterson Equation 5.8 arises from setting the two expressions (i.e. Peterson Equations 5.3 and 5.5) for $L(\text{CIV})$ equal to each other, then dividing the resulting equation through by (n_e^2 $4.6 \times 10^{-23} \text{erg s}^{-1}$). The '**mass density**' is simply the total

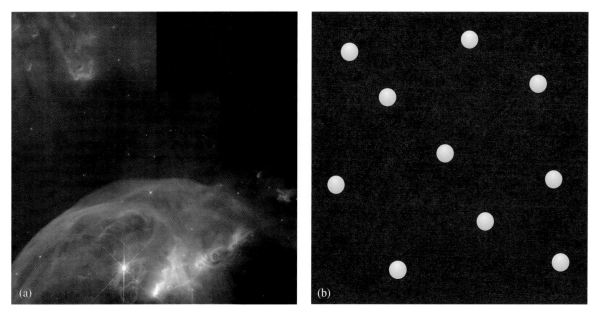

Figure 64 (a) The bubble nebula: an emission line nebula around a hot star in our own Galaxy. The hot emitting gas has a range of densities and line emissivities. (b) The approximation used in deriving Peterson Equation 5.3: the region is populated with clumps of gas, all with the same physical conditions. The fraction of the total volume occupied by this emitting gas is ϵ.

mass divided by the total volume, i.e. the density, ρ, with which we are thoroughly familiar. Peterson uses the approximation $\rho \approx n_e m_p$, where the term m_p gives 'mass' and n_e gives 'per unit volume'. This expression would be almost exactly correct for a gas which was solely composed of fully ionized hydrogen. If the gas is only partially ionized, or if the gas contains any heavier nuclei (i.e. has neutrons as well as protons contributing appreciably to the mass), the true density will be higher than this estimate. This section of Peterson is an example of one of the basic skills any physicist must develop: an ability to decide where to make approximations. In extragalactic astronomy often we require only order-of-magnitude estimates, so using $\rho \approx n_e m_p$, which for any highly ionized gas is unlikely to introduce a discrepancy bigger than ~2, is a sensible and useful approximation.

5.2.2 Estimating the covering factor, *f*

Activity 36   (40 minutes)

Interpreting the broad lines: (ii) absorption of continuum light

Read the remainder of Section 5.2 of Peterson, from 'Another important quantity …' half way down page 73.

In this reading, Peterson estimates how much of the continuum emission is absorbed by the broad-line region. Notes on the derivations follow.

Keywords: **covering factor, *f*** ■

In deriving Peterson Equation 5.10 the notation $\Phi(H)$ is introduced for the number flux of ionizing photons emitted by the source. The 'H' stands for hydrogen, and indicates that we are considering photons which are capable of ionizing hydrogen. $\Phi(H)$ has units photons s^{-1} cm^{-2}, and the first step in evaluating it is to say the number flux of photons of frequency v is simply F_v divided by the energy carried by a single photon, hv. Then

$$\Phi(\mathrm{H}) = \int_{v_1}^{\infty} n_v \, \mathrm{d}v = \int_{v_1}^{\infty} \frac{F_v}{hv} \, \mathrm{d}v$$

Figure 65 illustrates the spectrum in units of F_v, n_v and F_λ.

The next step uses the assumption that F_v can be expressed as a power law: $F_v = F_0 (v/v_0)^{-\alpha_{\mathrm{ox}}}$. F_0 and v_0 can be taken as the frequency and continuum flux at the Lyman α line. Thus in the expression on the right-hand side of the second equation down on Peterson page 74 everything is a constant, except for frequency, v. Taking the constants out of the integral, we are left to integrate

$$\int_{v_1}^{\infty} v^{-1-\alpha_{\mathrm{ox}}} \, \mathrm{d}v = \left[\frac{v^{-\alpha_{\mathrm{ox}}}}{-\alpha_{\mathrm{ox}}} \right]_{v_1}^{\infty} \qquad \text{where } \alpha_{\mathrm{ox}} \neq 0$$

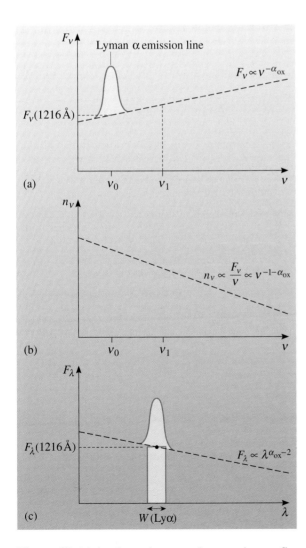

Figure 65 (a) A schematic power-law continuum flux and the Lyman α emission line, (b) the corresponding continuum photon flux, (c) the equivalent width of the Lyα line, $W(\mathrm{Ly}\alpha)$. All axes of this schematic figure are logarithmic ie log F_v, log F_λ, log n_v log v and log λ.

for the case $\alpha_{ox} = 0$ we have

$$\int_{v_1}^{\infty} v^{-1}\, dv = [\log_e v]_{v_1}^{\infty} \qquad \text{where } \alpha_{ox} = 0$$

which is infinite, so the analysis in Peterson does not apply in this case. Restricting ourselves to $\alpha_{ox} > 0$, we have:

$$\int_{v_1}^{\infty} v^{-1-\alpha_{ox}}\, dv = \left[\frac{v^{-\alpha_{ox}}}{-\alpha_{ox}} \right]_{v_1}^{\infty} = \left[0 - \left(-\frac{v_1^{-\alpha_{ox}}}{\alpha_{ox}} \right) \right] = \frac{v_1^{-\alpha_{ox}}}{\alpha_{ox}} = \frac{1}{\alpha_{ox}} \frac{1}{v_1^{\alpha_{ox}}}$$

- Why is this only valid if $\alpha_{ox} > 0$?

- Because the upper limit to be evaluated is infinite for $\alpha_{ox} \leq 0$. ■

Combining the results from the integral with the constants taken outside the integral, we obtain

$$\Phi(H) = \frac{F_v(1216\,\text{Å})v_0^{\alpha_{ox}}}{h} \frac{1}{\alpha_{ox}} \frac{1}{v_1^{\alpha_{ox}}} = \frac{F_v(1216\,\text{Å})}{h\alpha_{ox}} \left(\frac{v_0}{v_1} \right)^{\alpha_{ox}}$$

which is the same as Peterson's fourth equation on page 74. The final trick is to note that the ratio of the two frequencies inside the bracket will be the inverse of the ratio of the two wavelengths, since $v_1\lambda_1 = v_0\lambda_0 = c$. Hence

$$\frac{v_0}{v_1} = \frac{\lambda_1}{\lambda_0} = \frac{912\,\text{Å}}{1216\,\text{Å}}$$

where in the last step we have inserted the values of the two wavelengths in question, both wavelengths in Å.

In the second step in Peterson Equation 5.11, $v_0\lambda_0 = c$ has been used to substitute for v_0 and then the value of λ_0 has been inserted. At the same time the expression derived for $\Phi(H)$ in Peterson Equation 5.10 has been substituted, and factors of h on the numerator and denominator have been cancelled.

Peterson Equation 5.12 is simply the definition of the equivalent width, expressed in the notation of this section. Then $F(\text{Ly}\alpha)$ is replaced with the right-hand side of Peterson Equation 5.11 and the general result

$$F_v = \frac{\lambda^2 F_\lambda}{c} \qquad\qquad \text{(Peterson 1.6)}$$

is used to evaluate the ratio F_v/F_λ.

Question 36

(a) Describe the overall structure and kinematics of the broad-line region.

(b) Why can't the continuum source at ionizing UV wavelengths be observed directly?

(c) How does reddening affect the values of line ratios such as Lyα/Hβ? ■

5.3 Photoionization

The simplest and best known consideration of photoionization in astrophysics is the calculation of the radius of the sphere around a hot star which is photoionized as a result of the ionizing radiation from the star. This region is known as the **Strömgren sphere**, after Strömgren who published the calculation in 1939. The size of the Strömgren sphere is determined by the balance between photoionization and recombination (as you have seen in Activity 30). We will not reproduce this classic calculation here, as the subject of this block is AGN rather than stars, but the next reading will deal with the same processes in the context of AGN.

NUMBER DENSITY AND COLUMN DENSITY

The **column density** is the integral of the number density along the line of sight (Figure 66). It is generally denoted by the symbol N, and it is crucial to distinguish between column densities and number densities. Table 2 summarizes the differences.

The mathematical definition of column density is

$$N = \int n \, dl \qquad (67)$$

where the integral is performed along the path travelled by a photon, and is generally the line of sight of the observer.

Table 2 Number density and column density.

	Number density	Column density
standard notation	n	N
cgs units	cm^{-3}	cm^{-2}
definition	number per unit volume	number passed along path

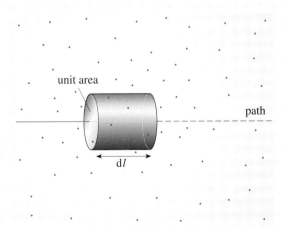

Figure 66 The column density is obtained by integrating the number density along the path travelled by a photon. It gives a measurement of the total number of particles encountered along the way by a cylinder of unit cross-sectional area.

RECOMBINATION COEFFICIENTS

Many of the emission lines from AGN are powered by photoionization followed by **recombination** to an excited state. As you saw in Activity 33, the atoms or ions in the excited state return to the ground state by emitting spectral lines. For a recombination to occur, an ion and an electron must collide, and the probability of this occurring is proportional to the number densities of each. If we are considering a highly ionized pure hydrogen gas, then each H+ ion has a corresponding free electron , so $n_H = n_e$. In this case the recombination rate $\propto n_H n_e = n_e^2$. The **recombination coefficient α** is the constant of proportionality which multiplies the densities to give the total number of recombinations per unit volume per unit time.

The recombination can lead to an atom or ion in its ground state, or in one of its excited states. The symbol α_A is generally used for the recombination coefficient summed over all levels. Those recombinations which lead directly to the ground state obviously do not lead to subsequent spectral line emission. For each emission line there will be contributions from (i) recombinations directly to the higher state involved in the transition and (ii) recombinations to even higher states, which then decay (by emission of other spectral lines) to the upper level of the emission line in question. When analysing **recombination lines**, the book-keeping of all the possible contributing paths to a particular emission line is hidden by the use of an effective recombination coefficient for the emission line in question. Peterson considers the Hβ line and the effective recombination coefficient for this line is $\alpha_{H\beta}^{eff}$. Another specific recombination coefficient Peterson will use is α_B, which was described in Activity 33, and is the recombination coefficient summed over all levels above the ground level (i.e. all levels which can lead to emission-line production).

When considering ionization equilibrium in an optically thick nebula (i.e. one in which no ionizing photons escape), α_B is the most important recombination coefficient. Recombinations which proceed directly to the ground state emit an ionizing photon, which will cause a subsequent photoionization elsewhere in the nebula, and hence will have no net effect on the ionization balance.

You do not need to worry about how to determine the value of any of the recombination coefficients. It is sufficient for you to know that they are constants of proportionality leading from the densities to the emission-line production being considered.

Activity 37 (1 hour)

The ionization parameter

Read Section 5.3 of Peterson (pages 75 to 78).

In deriving the equation for the **ionization parameter, *U*,** in Peterson Equation 5.15, the photon number density, n_{ph}, is used. The working to arrive at this from the number of ionizing photons emitted per second, $Q(H)$, is given in Section 5.3.1 following this activity. The 'H' indicates we are considering photons capable of ionizing hydrogen.

The final step to obtaining the expression for the ionization parameter, *U*, is simply to use the definition of *U*, which is

$$U = (\text{density of photons}, n_{ph})/(\text{density of particles}) \tag{68}$$

The density of particles can be taken as simply the number density of hydrogen nuclei, n_H, hence

$$U = \frac{n_{ph}}{n_H} = \frac{Q(H)}{4\pi r^2 c n_H} \tag{69}$$

We will not expect you to be able to perform a full ionization calculation yourself, but it is important that you read the (long) caption for Peterson Fig. 5.3.

By **fiducial** values, Peterson means the values which have been derived to be typical. He gives fiducial values of U and n_e at the top of page 77, and later uses these values for his Equation 5.19.

On page 77 Peterson presents some mathematical working to derive the radial ionization structure of the broad-line region (BLR). Some notes concerning this are given in Section 5.3.2.

H^0 is just another way of representing neutral atomic hydrogen (usually referred to as simply H).

Keywords: **ionization structure**, **ionization front** ▪

▪ What is special about the value $h\nu \geq 13.6\,\text{eV}$?

❏ 13.6 eV is the ionization energy of hydrogen, so photons with energy exceeding this are capable of ionizing hydrogen. This threshold is known as the Lyman edge. ▪

5.3.1 The number density of photons, n_{ph}

Each second the number of photons emitted is $Q(H)$. These photons are assumed to move radially outwards from the source. After a second has elapsed, the first ones will have travelled a distance equal to 1 light-second. Therefore the volume of the sphere occupied by photons emitted during that second is $V_1 = (4/3)\pi(c \times 1\,\text{second})^3$, and consequently the average number density of ionizing photons within that sphere is simply:

$$\frac{Q(H)}{V_1} = \frac{3Q(H)}{4\pi(c \times 1\,\text{second})^3}$$

As these particular photons move further away from the central source, the volume they occupy becomes a spherical shell, as shown in Figure 67. At time t the radius of this shell is given by

$$r = ct \qquad (70)$$

The volume of an infinitesimally thin spherical shell of thickness dr (Block 2, Section 1.2) is given by

$$dV = 4\pi r^2 dr$$

The number of photons occupying this volume element will be $Q(H)dt$, the number of photons emitted by the central source during the time interval, dt, required to cross the thickness dr of the shell. We know photons travel at speed c, so d$r = c$dt (formally we could derive this by differentiating Equation 70 above).

Hence the density of ionizing photons is number divided by volume:

$$n_{ph} = \frac{Q(H)dt}{4\pi r^2 \, dr} = \frac{Q(H)}{4\pi r^2 c}$$

where in the second step we have replaced dr/dt with c.

5.3.2 The radial ionization structure of the BLR

Figure 68 (overleaf) shows the geometry which is used to derive Peterson Equation 5.16. The fraction of the emitted photons which hit the cloud is simply the ratio of the cloud's area as viewed from the source to the total surface area of the sphere at the same distance from the source. (Another more technical way of expressing this

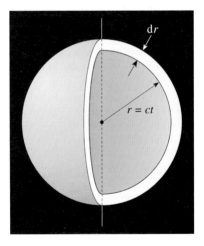

Figure 67 Photons leaving a central source at a constant rate occupy progressively more distant spherical shells as they travel at speed c.

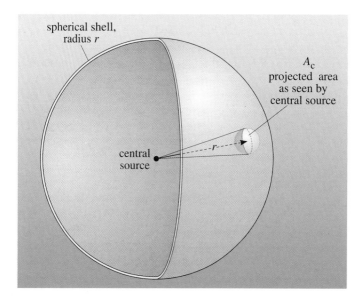

Figure 68 A broad-line cloud of area A_c at a distance r from the central source. The solid angle, Ω, subtended by the cloud is A_c/r^2.

would be to say that the fraction of the emitted photons which hit the cloud is the **solid angle** (A_c/r^2) subtended by the cloud divided by the 4π steradians in a full sphere.) The fraction of photons which hit the cloud is, substituting in expressions for the two areas:

$$\frac{A_c}{4\pi r^2}$$

so the number hitting the cloud per second is

$$\frac{A_c}{4\pi r^2} \times Q(H)$$

and the final step to get Peterson Equation 5.16 simply involves substituting from Peterson Equation 5.15 or equivalently our Equation 68.

The quantity α_B used to evaluate the number of recombinations per second per unit volume is explained in the box on 'Recombination coefficients'. Note that the recombination rate is proportional to the square of the electron density, n_e^2 – there is a typographical error in the statement of this in Peterson's text between his Equations 5.16 and 5.17. For a recombination to occur, an ion and an electron must collide, and the probability of this occurring is proportional to the number densities of each. For highly ionized pure hydrogen gas $n_H = n_e$. The recombination coefficient, α_B is the constant of proportionality needed to calculate the net number of recombinations per unit volume per unit time in an optically thick nebula. Hence

net number of recombinations in volume V_c per second $= n_e^2 \alpha_B V_c$

Ionization equilibrium requires this to be equal to the number of ionizations per second, as expressed in Peterson Equation 5.17. The **Strömgren depth** is simply the depth into the cloud to which complete ionization is maintained by the incident photon flux. Assuming the cloud to have a cylindrical shape, the Strömgren depth, r_1, is the ionized volume V_c divided by the cross-sectional area of the cylinder as in Figure 69.

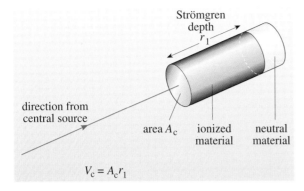

Figure 69 The broad-line cloud is ionized to a depth r_1, and is assumed to have a cylindrical shape.

Question 37

For an ionization parameter of $U = 10^{-2}$ and $n_e = 10^{11}$ cm^{-3}, how would the strengths of the CIV and CIII] lines shown in Fig. 5.3 of Peterson compare? ▪

Question 38

(a) Explain why the CIII] intensity first increases then decreases as U increases.

(b) Can you think of an analogous phenomenon in stellar physics? ▪

Question 39

(a) What does the abbreviation PIZ stand for?

(b) How does absorption cross-section depend on energy for ionizing photons?

(c) Why is there an extended PIZ in broad-line region clouds but not in the Strömgren sphere surrounding an O star? ▪

In Activity 37 we read that the Strömgren depth for a broad-line cloud is typically only about $0.7R_\odot$. This means that complete ionization is achieved only for the first $0.7R_\odot$ of the distance into the cloud. Beyond this extends the PIZ.

▪   How might selection effects have biased the determination of the fiducial parameters for the physical properties of broad-line clouds?

❑   The clouds which are most amenable to analysis are those which produce strong lines. For any given AGN the CIV emission will be dominated by the clouds with physical conditions leading to strong CIV emission, and so on for all other species. Consequently an analysis based on CIV emission is likely to derive physical properties conducive to CIV emission, and similarly for other species. ▪

Question 40

Can you suggest any way to assess whether selection effects have biased the determination of the physical parameters of broad-line clouds? For example, if an ionization calculation has been performed which reproduces the observed CIV emission, can you think of a way to independently test whether the broad-line clouds actually have the determined parameters? ▪

5.4 Broad-line profiles

Dynamics deduced from line profiles

Read the first and last paragraphs of Section 5.4.1 of Peterson (on pages 78 and 81). Between these two paragraphs is an algebraic derivation. This derivation shows that for a broad-line region populated by clouds which are being propelled radially outwards by radiation pressure, a logarithmic line profile would be expected. You do not need to read the derivation.

Read Section 5.4.2 of Peterson (page 81).

To summarize this subsection of Peterson: the broad-line region is complicated and non-homogeneous. The spectra contain a lot of information, and there is no simple model which can neatly explain it all. The two mechanisms illustrated in Figure 70 are possible ways of forming a redward asymmetric line profile. In Figure 70a all the clouds are flowing radially inwards and the more distant clouds are obscured, so we detect more redshifted emission (from the nearer clouds flowing away from us) than blueshifted emission (from the more distant, partially obscured clouds flowing towards us). In Figure 70b the clouds are flowing radially outwards, and are illuminated by the central source. Hence we detect more redshifted emission (from the bright inner faces of the more distant clouds moving away from us) than blueshifted emission (from the dim outer faces of the nearer clouds moving towards us). These two mechanisms, and the two complementary mechanisms which cause bluewards asymmetries, seem to operate in combinations which vary from line to line, source to source, and over time within a particular source.

Keywords: **logarithmic line profiles**, **broad-line region structure** ■

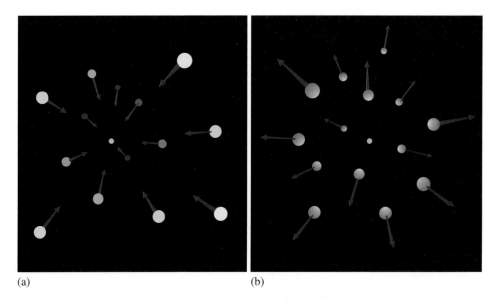

(a)   (b)

Figure 70 Two possible ways of forming a line profile which is redward asymmetric (a) clouds flowing towards the centre with the more distant ones being more obscured by intervening material, (b) clouds flowing outwards and radiating predominantly from the inwards-facing illuminated surfaces.

Sketch the two mechanisms complementary to those shown in Figure 70, which would produce blueward asymmetric line profiles. ∎

In Activity 35 we learned that the broad lines in a given AGN do not all have the same width. In general the higher ionization potential lines are broader than the lower ionization potential lines. This is probably understandable within the context of the virial theorem which we examined in Example 1. As Equation 6 shows, material closer (i.e. with smaller r) to the central mass, M, will typically have larger velocity. The ionization parameter is also higher for smaller r (Equation 69) consequently the lines formed at large ionization parameters will typically be broader.

The **ionization potential** is simply another name for the **ionization energy**, which was defined in Block 1.

We have seen in Activity 38 that the emission-line profiles, though containing much information, do not allow a unique determination of the dynamics of the broad-line region. There are many different combinations of cloud motions and line radiation properties which could produce the same line profile. This is not really surprising because the line profiles are only sensitive to the radial velocity component of the potentially complex three-dimensional broad-line region dynamics. To go from the observed line profile to deduce the underlying dynamics, which is of course what astronomers would like to do, would require additional information or assumptions. This is an example of a **data inversion problem**; you have already met other examples in Block 3 (eclipse mapping, Doppler tomography and Roche tomography). In AGN the interpretation of emission-line profiles is less informative than Doppler tomography of interacting binary stars.

Why is Doppler tomography more informative for interacting binary stars than analogous studies of emission lines in AGN? (*Hint*: In medical tomographic imaging, the equipment is moved in a circular path around the patient between exposures to provide images from each viewpoint.) ∎

5.5 Reverberation mapping

In Section 5.4 we saw that line profiles from broad-line regions cannot give us definitive results for the structure and dynamics of broad-line regions. In this section we will introduce reverberation mapping, another tool which can in principle allow us to make some progress with this problem. Peterson has been one of the leaders in developing reverberation mapping as a tool for probing the structure of AGN. His textbook gives a fairly rigorous discussion of the underlying mathematics, which you are of course free to read. In S381, however, we will skip most of the mathematics and aim for an understanding of the concepts and the principal results to date. We begin with an Earth-bound analogy, and then examine a particularly simple extragalactic astrophysics example, before considering AGN.

5.5.1 The echo-mapping idea

A submarine's sonar equipment uses sound reflections, echoes, to locate objects underwater. In a similar way **reverberation mapping** uses **light echoes** to probe the reprocessing structures surrounding the central source in an AGN.

In the case of sound echoes, it is easiest to interpret the reflected signal if the initial sound is a short sharp pulse, like a hand clap or the intense pulses (pings) produced by sonar. In this case the reflected signal will also be a short sharp pulse, which will be delayed by the sound travel time difference between the direct and reflected signals.

Figure 71 shows the principle used in sonar. By measuring the time delay, τ, between the clap and its echo, the distance to the cliff, d, can be determined:

$$2d = c_s \tau \tag{71}$$

where c_s is the sound speed. More generally a similar method could be used by two people, one providing the sound, and the other measuring the sound travel time delay between the direct and the reflected signal, as shown in Figure 72.

Light echoes are also easiest to interpret if the initial signal is a short sharp pulse of light. To see how this method works in an astronomical context, consider applying it to the light generated by a supernova explosion. Compared to the light travel time across even a small galaxy, the time taken for a supernova to brighten and fade is short. Consequently, one of the most impressive applications of reverberation mapping so far is its application to the study of the region surrounding SN 1987A, which is in a nearby galaxy called the Large Magellanic Cloud (LMC).

■ Why this particular supernova?

❑ Because this is the closest one which has been discovered in the era of modern astronomy. More distant supernovae have low apparent brightness, and the spatial resolution of optical telescopes is too low to be able to detect their light echoes. ■

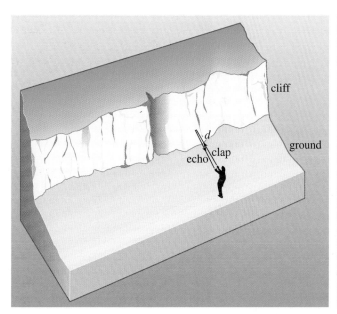

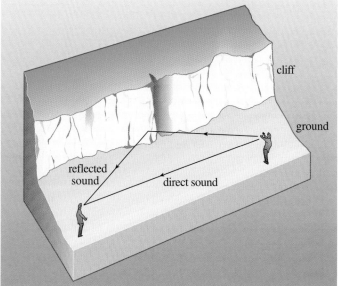

Figure 71 A person claps his hands near a cliff. He hears two claps: the first is immediate, the second is delayed by the time taken for sound to travel from him to the cliff, where the sound is reflected, and back. If he measured the time delay, then knowing the speed of sound, he could calculate the distance to the cliff from the sound travel time delay. This is the basis of the method used in sonar.

Figure 72 The sound travel time delay between the direct and the reflected sound depends on the difference in the lengths of the two paths travelled.

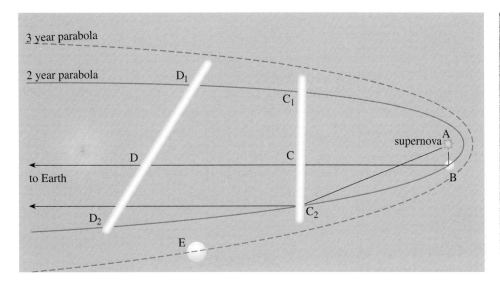

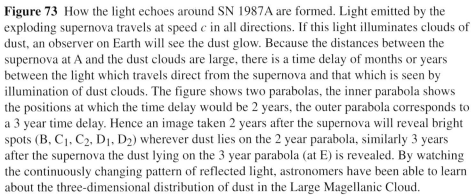

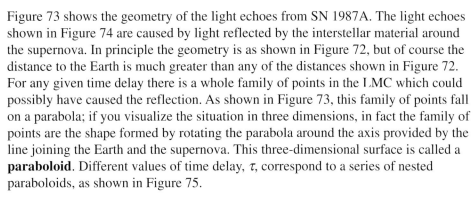

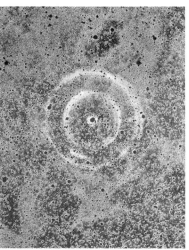

Figure 73 How the light echoes around SN 1987A are formed. Light emitted by the exploding supernova travels at speed c in all directions. If this light illuminates clouds of dust, an observer on Earth will see the dust glow. Because the distances between the supernova at A and the dust clouds are large, there is a time delay of months or years between the light which travels direct from the supernova and that which is seen by illumination of dust clouds. The figure shows two parabolas, the inner parabola shows the positions at which the time delay would be 2 years, the outer parabola corresponds to a 3 year time delay. Hence an image taken 2 years after the supernova will reveal bright spots (B, C_1, C_2, D_1, D_2) wherever dust lies on the 2 year parabola, similarly 3 years after the supernova the dust lying on the 3 year parabola (at E) is revealed. By watching the continuously changing pattern of reflected light, astronomers have been able to learn about the three-dimensional distribution of dust in the Large Magellanic Cloud.

Figure 74 The bright rings are light echoes from supernova 1987A. The mottled appearance is because an image of the same area of the LMC without the light echo has been subtracted, to remove most of the light due to stars. Because the image quality of the two images was not identical, mottling is created when one image is subtracted from the other. Each of the bright rings is caused by light reflected by a sheet of dust, as shown in Figure 73.

Figure 73 shows the geometry of the light echoes from SN 1987A. The light echoes shown in Figure 74 are caused by light reflected by the interstellar material around the supernova. In principle the geometry is as shown in Figure 72, but of course the distance to the Earth is much greater than any of the distances shown in Figure 72. For any given time delay there is a whole family of points in the LMC which could possibly have caused the reflection. As shown in Figure 73, this family of points fall on a parabola; if you visualize the situation in three dimensions, in fact the family of points are the shape formed by rotating the parabola around the axis provided by the line joining the Earth and the supernova. This three-dimensional surface is called a **paraboloid**. Different values of time delay, τ, correspond to a series of nested paraboloids, as shown in Figure 75.

Reflecting material at any point on the paraboloid will cause a light echo to be observed at time τ after the time the supernova itself was seen. By combining the position on the sky of the light echo with the time τ, we can locate the reflecting material's three-dimensional position in space. Note that this is a completely new piece of information – usually astronomers can only definitely measure the direction to objects, and have almost no direct information on relative distances.

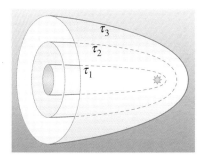

Figure 75 The surfaces corresponding to differing time delays, τ, are nested paraboloids.

5.5.2 Reverberation mapping applied to AGN

Section 5.51 showed that light echoes can, in principle, lead to novel information on the relative positions of structures in distant objects. Consequently it could be beneficial in solving some of the mysteries about the structure of AGN, particularly the nature of the broad-line region.

■ Why is the broad-line region in particular suitable for reverberation mapping?

❑ Because it is easy to isolate light which comes from this region (i.e. the broad emission lines), and the emission line fluxes vary with time in a way that is highly correlated with the continuum fluxes, suggesting they may be powered by absorbing and reprocessing the illuminating continuum. ■

■ Suggest two reasons why the application of reverberation mapping to AGN may be more difficult than its application to SN 1987A.

❑ Firstly the illuminating continuum is not a short sharp pulse of light, instead it is continuously varying. Secondly we can't spatially resolve the broad-line region in the way that we can spatially resolve the dust clouds in the LMC. ■

The basic method used in reverberation mapping of AGN is illustrated in Figure 76. The light curves of both continuum light and broad emission lines are observed. The continuum light from the central source illuminates the broad-line region, causing photoionization which powers the line emission. Sharp changes in the luminosity of the central source appear directly in the continuum light curve, and cause changes in the line emission. Consequently, blurred and delayed echoes of the features in the continuum light curve should appear in the emission line light curves. By measuring the typical delay time, τ, between the direct feature in the continuum light curve and the delayed feature in the light curve for a particular emission line, we can estimate the size of the region in which that particular emission line is produced. In Activity 40 we will measure for ourselves the delay, τ, between two light curves. The method for doing this is called **cross-correlation**. A cross-correlation analysis reveals whether two light curves have the same features, and the value of the time delay, τ, between them.

Activity 39

Reverberation mapping of broad-line regions

Read the first two paragraphs of Section 5.5 of Peterson, down to Peterson Equation 5.34 (page 82). Then read from the bottom paragraph on Peterson page 83 (which begins 'The reverberation-mapping technique …') to the end of the numbered list at the top of page 84. Then skip to the bottom of page 85 and begin reading at the last paragraph ('One of the most …') and continue to the end of Section 5.5.

A **δ-function** is a mathematical description of a sharp pulse. By considering a continuum outburst to be a **δ-function in time**, Peterson is specifying a sudden, sharp, short-lived flash of light at time $t = t_0$, like that indicated in Figure 77 (overleaf).

Note: There is a precise (though abstract) mathematical definition of a δ-function, such that $\delta(x) = 0$, $x \neq 0$, and $\int_{-\infty}^{\infty} \delta(x)\,dx = 1$. For any function $f(x)$, $\int_{-\infty}^{\infty} f(x)\delta(x)\,dx = f(0)$.

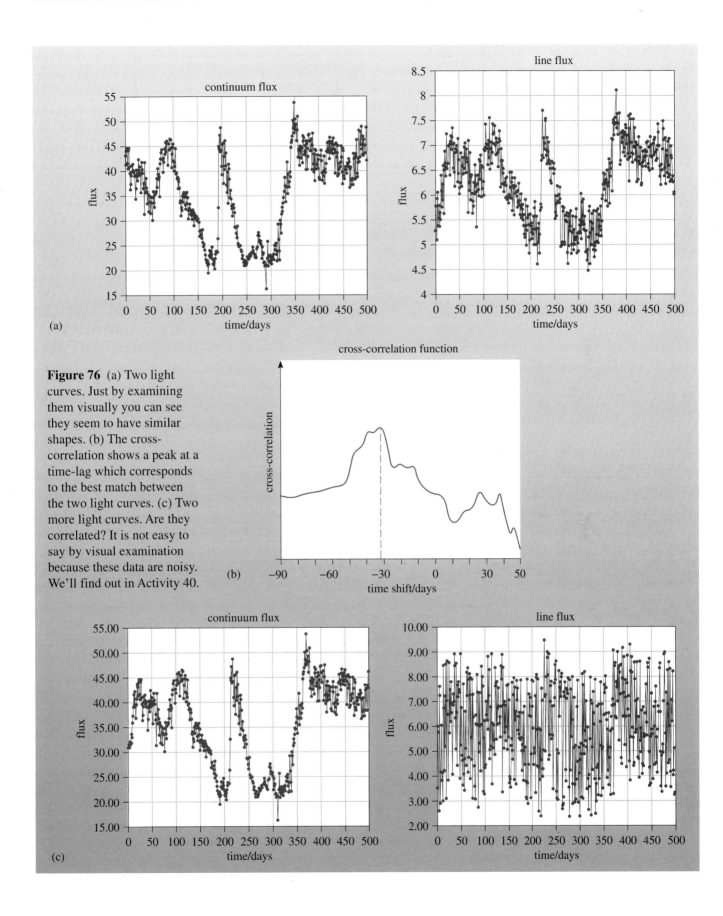

Figure 76 (a) Two light curves. Just by examining them visually you can see they seem to have similar shapes. (b) The cross-correlation shows a peak at a time-lag which corresponds to the best match between the two light curves. (c) Two more light curves. Are they correlated? It is not easy to say by visual examination because these data are noisy. We'll find out in Activity 40.

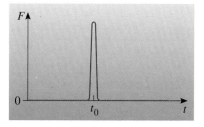

Figure 77 A sharp pulse of light which would provide the ideal illuminating signal for reverberation mapping.

Peterson considers light echoes arising from a thin spherical shell at a distance r from the central source. Figure 78 shows the geometry which leads to Peterson Equation 5.34: the light travel time delay is $\tau = d/c$, where the distance d is the sum of the two paths XY and YZ shown in the figure

$$d = XY + YZ = r + r\cos\theta = (1 + \cos\theta)r$$

consequently

$$\tau = \frac{d}{c} = \frac{(1+\cos\theta)r}{c}$$

Peterson Equation 5.44 may at first seem a surprising dependence on r, however it arises directly from applying the definition of the ionization parameter, U, (Equation 69) and setting U constant.

Keywords: **recombination time**, **isodelay surface** ■

Question 43

What are the basic assumptions made in using reverberation mapping to learn about the geometry of the broad-line region? ■

■   How is the light travel time lag measured for a particular emission line?

❑   Continuum and line light curves are measured, and the shift τ which best matches up the features in the two light curves indicates the light travel time lag. ■

Question 44

Describe the results from reverberation mapping, and the conclusions which have been drawn from them. ■

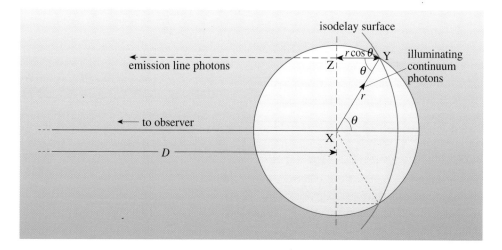

Figure 78 Peterson's Fig. 5.5 is reproduced here with annotations showing the paths travelled by the illuminating continuum and the resulting observed emission line photons. By summing the lengths of these two paths, the light travel time delay between the direct continuum and the reprocessed emission line signals can be calculated.

Cross-correlations

In this activity you will use a spreadsheet to calculate the cross-correlation function between a sample continuum light curve and a corresponding emission line light curve in order to determine the relative shift between the two. This will be the biggest spreadsheet that you work with in this course! The cross-correlation technique multiplies the two light curves together, first shifting one of them in time by an amount τ, and sums over all the points in the light curve. When the features in two functions coincide for a particular shift, τ, this will maximize the sum because big numbers will be multiplied by big numbers and small numbers will be multiplied by small numbers.

Using StarOffice, open the initial spreadsheet for this activity `/S381/spreadsheets/B4_Ac40_initial.sdc`, which is installed on your hard disk by the MM guide installer. You should find it by clicking on the **Spreadsheet** tab in the MM guide.

At first sight you may think this initial spreadsheet looks almost empty. Along the top in row 2 are the headings 'time/days', 'continuum flux' and 'emission line flux' (in columns A, B and C respectively), then a series of numbers labelled as 'shift' which run from −50 in cell D2 to +50 in cell BB2 away off to the right-hand side of the spreadsheet. The data for this exercise are in columns A, B and C but are listed further down beginning on row 53, and run all the way down to row 552. So there are 500 sets of data points, each set comprising a time (in days), a continuum flux and an emission line flux. These are the data that are plotted in Figure 76c.

1   To prepare the data for cross-correlation, begin by selecting (highlighting) the emission line flux data from cell C53 to cell C552, then click on the **Copy** button (or right-click the mouse, then select copy).

2   Now **Paste** these data into column D beginning in cell D3. This is 50 cells higher up the spreadsheet than the original data appeared and corresponds therefore to a timeshift of −50, as indicated by the label at the top of column D.

3   Move to cell E5 (one column across, two rows down) and click **Paste** again. The data in this column is shifted up by 48 cells with respect to that in column C, again as indicated by the label at the top of its column.

4   Repeat this process in columns F to BB, each time you move across one column, move down two rows. At the end of this process you will have 51 columns (D to BB) each filled with a copy of the data in column C and each shifted by a different amount as indicated by the column headings.

To do the cross-correlation we need to multiply the emission line flux data in each of the columns D to BB by the continuum flux data in column B. Fortunately the StarOffice spreadsheet has a facility to do this operation.

5   Scroll down to row 603, where you will find a label **TOTALS** in column A. Move to cell D603 and click on **Insert** then **Function**. From the list of functions offered, select **Sumproduct**. Click on **Next** then in the **Array 1** box type `$B103:$B502` and in the **Array 2** box type `D103:D502`, then click on **OK**.

The number that appears in the cell is then the sum of all the products, i.e. B103×D103 + B104×D104 + … etc. Notice we only use rows 103 to 502 because the higher and lower rows are not filled with data for *all* the shifts we have calculated. It is only for these rows that we have data in all columns. Notice also that we use the $ for column B because we want to multiply the emission line flux in each of columns D to BB by the continuum flux (column B).

6   Now simply copy the formula from cell D603 into each of the other cells in row 603 from column E to column BB. These will fill with the cross-correlation totals corresponding to each shift.

7   The cross-correlation function is now simply a graph of the correlation totals in row 603 against the corresponding time shifts in row 2. So, select the data in these two rows, then click on Insert then Chart. Be sure to check the box **Data series in rows** and produce an XY graph of the result.

If you have difficulties consult the completed spreadsheet for this activity.

Keywords: **cross-correlation** ■

Question 45

(a) Using the spreadsheet from Activity 40, what shift does the peak in the cross-correlation function correspond to? (b) Does the sign of this shift indicate that the emission line flux lags or leads the continuum flux in this case? (c) What might be an interpretation of this shift? ■

5.6 Broad-line region properties

Activity 41   (1 hour)

The nature of the broad-line clouds

Read Sections 5.7 and 5.8 (including its subsections) of Peterson (pages 88 to 92).

The geometry assumed to produce Peterson Equation 5.48 is illustrated in Figure 79.

Note, though he does not explicitly say so, Peterson assumes that l is measured in cm in the intermediate expression in his Equation 5.48.

Peterson Equation 5.50 is analogous to Equation 5.3, the difference being that in this case the volume considered in the $\int dV$ is simply the volume of a single cloud, V, while in Peterson Equation 5.3 the integral is over all the clouds in the broad-line region, i.e. $4\pi r^3 \epsilon/3$.

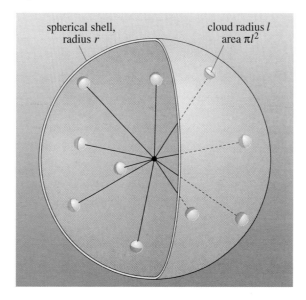

Figure 79 N_c clouds of radius l cover a total area of $N_c \pi l^2$. The surface area of a sphere of radius r is $4\pi r^2$.

By **statistical fluctuations** on page 89, Peterson is referring to the fact that when we count the results of a random process we always find some variation. For example, if during a steady rain you measure on average N raindrops hitting a single tile on your roof each minute, you would not expect every tile to accumulate exactly N raindrops each minute. Some tiles will collect more than the average number, some will collect less. Random events, like raindrops falling on tiles, cars passing a particular point, or the number, N, of broad-line clouds moving with velocity between v and $v + dv$, are described by **Poisson statistics**. Statisticians can show that for Poisson statistics the expected average deviation in the count, N, is equal to $\sqrt{N}$. If a series of measurements are made, about 2/3 of the values obtained should fall within the range $N - \sqrt{N}$ to $N + \sqrt{N}$.

The **Jeans mass** is defined and discussed in Block 2. **Ablation** is defined in Collins.

Note that Peterson Figs. 5.7 and 5.8 are both log–log graphs. In both cases the observed points fall on a straight line, which in general denotes a power-law relationship between the quantities whose logarithms have been plotted. Peterson Fig. 5.7 shows an increase of six decades in the values on both the ordinate (horizontal axis) and abscissa (vertical axis), so in this case the power-law index is 1, and the relationship is a simple linear relationship (Peterson Equation 5.53). In Peterson Fig. 5.8 the overall relationship is a power law (Peterson Equation 5.55) with index $\gamma = 0.83$.

Keywords: **pressure equilibrium**, **two-phase model**, **confinement mechanism**, **replenishment mechanism**, **Baldwin effect** ▇

■ Why does Peterson say (at the bottom of page 87) that it is 'probably safe' to use the CIV results in the virial theorem?

❏ Because the virial theorem only applies if gravity is the dominant force and the system is in equilibrium. If the CIV emitting clouds were moving radially outwards this could not be the case, and in fact some researchers think that the virial theorem is not applicable to the CIV broad line emission. ▇

Question 46

Show that the expression $f \approx \dfrac{N_c l^2}{1.6 \times 10^{33}}$ (Peterson Equation 5.48) corresponds to setting $r \approx 8$ light-days, with l expressed in cm. ▇

■ Cars pass a census taker at an average rate of 25 per minute. How much range would you expect in the measured counts over a series of successive minutes?

❏ Poisson statistics tells us that the deviations are expected to be $\sqrt{N}$, so we would expect most answers to range from $\approx N - \sqrt{N}$ to $\approx N + \sqrt{N}$. In this case we would expect a range with about 2/3 of measured counts falling between 20 and 30 cars passing per minute. ▇

5.7 Summary of Section 5

1   The width of a spectral line can indicate the temperature of the gas in which the line arises. The thermal velocity of the atoms depends on the temperature according to

$$\tfrac{1}{2}mv_{th}^2 \approx \tfrac{3}{2}kT$$

and atoms with a range of speeds between $-v_{th}$ and $+v_{th}$ will give rise to a range of Doppler shifts which broaden the spectral line. Line widths are thus often expressed in velocity units.

2   In thermodynamic equilibrium the kinetic energies, atomic level populations, ionization equilibrium, and radiation field are all as prescribed by a single value of temperature.

3   The principle of detailed balance asserts that in thermodynamic equilibrium each individual process and its inverse balance to maintain the equilibrium populations. This can be used to deduce relationships between the rates of various processes.

4   Collisional processes have rates which are proportional to the number density of each of the colliding particles and proportional to the cross-section (usually given symbol σ) for the process. Cross-sections for collisional processes involving charged particles are dependent on velocity. The collisional transition rate (usually given the symbol q) is defined by integrating (velocity $\times$ cross-section $\times$ velocity distribution function) from the velocity corresponding to the kinetic energy threshold for the process to infinity. Mathematically:

$$q_{i,j} = \int_{\frac{1}{2}mv^2=\chi}^{\infty} v\sigma_{i,j}(v)f(v)\,\mathrm{d}v$$

5   The cross-section for electron–electron collisions is high, so in astrophysical settings the electrons generally establish a Maxwell–Boltzmann kinetic energy distribution with temperature T_e even though full thermodynamic equilibrium may not apply.

6   Optical depth is related to the cross-section for absorption: $\tau = \int_{\substack{\text{along light} \\ \text{path}}} n\sigma\,\mathrm{d}s$

7   Absorption lines in stars arise because the cross-section for absorption for line photons is higher than that for continuum photons, hence the line photons emerge on average from higher, cooler layers in the stellar atmosphere.

8   The broad-line regions and narrow-line regions in AGN are photoionized by energetic continuum radiation. The radiation is more energetic than a blackbody spectrum of the same temperature as the kinetic energy distribution of the particles of the gases in the region. Consequently the populations of ionized and excited states exceed those which would prevail in thermodynamic equilibrium, and emission line radiation is emitted as a consequence of recombinations occurring in these nebulae.

9   The number of recombinations is proportional to the density of the ions recombining, and to the density of electrons. The constant of proportionality is the recombination coefficient. The effective recombination coefficient for a particular recombination line (e.g. emitted in the transition from state i to state j) is indicated with the notation $\alpha_{ij}^{\mathrm{eff}}$. The number of line photons emitted per unit volume per unit time is given by $n_{\mathrm{e}} n_i \alpha_{ij}^{\mathrm{eff}}$, where n_i is the number density of ions.

10 The emissivity of a recombination line is given by

$$j_{ij} = n_{\mathrm{e}} n_i \alpha_{ij}^{\mathrm{eff}} \frac{h\nu_{ij}}{4\pi}$$

11 The total recombination coefficient including recombinations to *all* levels is known as α_{A}. However, recombinations to the ground state emit ionizing photons which are promptly re-absorbed. The effective total recombination coefficient is therefore found by summing over recombinations to all levels

    except the ground state: $\alpha_{\mathrm{B}} = \sum_{i>1} \alpha_i = \alpha_{\mathrm{A}} - \alpha_1$.

12 Case A recombination describes a nebula which is *optically thin* to all line photons, so that all line photons escape from the nebula; case A recombination is generally *not* applicable to astrophysical nebulae. Conversely, case B recombination describes a nebula which is *optically thick* in the Lyman lines of hydrogen (i.e. those spectral lines which have the ground state of hydrogen as their lower level.) Case B recombination is more likely to apply to photoionized nebulae in astrophysics, in particular to the broad-line and narrow-line regions of AGN.

13 The critical density for de-excitation is when radiative and collisional de-excitations are equally probable.

14 Carefully chosen metastable multiplet lines can be used as diagnostics of temperature and density in photoionized nebulae. For example the $\lambda\lambda 6716$, 6731Å doublet of singly ionized sulphur can be used to indicate the electron density, while the doubly ionized oxygen lines at $\lambda\lambda 4363$, 4959 and 5007Å can be used to indicate the electron temperature.

15 Broad emission lines are prominent in many AGN spectra, but their widths show substantial differences from one object to another. Broad lines typically have full width at half maximum of around $5000\,\mathrm{km\,s^{-1}}$, but even in a single spectrum, different lines can have different widths.

16 Broad line profiles often follow a logarithmic dependence of flux on radial velocity shift from the line centre: $F_\lambda \propto -\log_{\mathrm{e}} \Delta v$, but the profiles can also be variable and complex.

17 Many broad lines in AGN spectra can be blended together, such as Lyα $\lambda 1216$ and NV $\lambda\lambda 1239$, 1243, or the small blue bump comprising the Balmer continuum and many FeII lines.

18 The fluxes of broad emission lines vary with time and are correlated with flux variations of the continuum. This indicates that the lines arise in clouds that are optically thick to the ionizing continuum.

19 In AGN broad line spectra, virtually all forbidden lines are collisionally suppressed. This indicates that the electron densities of the broad-line region (BLR) are high. The absence of the [OIII] $\lambda\lambda 4363$, 4959, 5007 lines in AGN broad line spectra indicates a lower limit to the electron density of around $10^8\,\mathrm{cm^{-3}}$, whilst the only strong semiforbidden line seen is CIII] $\lambda 1909$ implying an upper limit of order $10^{11}\,\mathrm{cm^{-3}}$.

20 The intensities of the broad lines indicate gas temperatures of order 10^4 K which implies a thermal velocity of only around $10 \, \text{km s}^{-1}$ for the atoms. This is too low to account for the broad line widths which must instead be due to bulk motions of individual clouds.

21 The total luminosity in the CIV line is

$$L(\text{CIV}) \approx 4.6 \times 10^{-23} \epsilon r^3 n_e^2 \, \text{cm}^3 \, \text{erg s}^{-1}$$

where the filling factor of the BLR is $\epsilon = N_c l^3 / r^3$ and the radius of the BLR, r, can be measured by reverberation mapping as a few light-days (a few $\times 10^{16}$ cm). N_c is the number of clouds in the BLR and l is their typical radius. The filling factor is extremely small ($\epsilon \sim$ a few $\times 10^{-7}$). The number of clouds in the BLR is of order 10^{10}.

22 The fraction of the ionizing continuum emission which is absorbed by BLR clouds is given by the covering factor, f, which is the fraction of sky covered by BLR clouds as seen from the central source. From the relationship between the Lyα flux and the flux of the continuum, f is estimated as being of order 0.1.

23 The number density of photons which can ionize hydrogen ($Q(\text{H})$) is the integral of $L_\nu / h\nu$ over all frequencies from 3.3×10^{15} Hz (corresponding to 13.6 eV) to infinity. The ionization parameter at a distance r from the central source is then this value divided by the particle density:

$$U = Q(\text{H})/4\pi r^2 c n_\text{H}$$

where n_H is the column density of hydrogen.

24 The predicted intensities of the lines from the BLR vary greatly with U, and hence with ionizing flux. The ionization parameter in the BLR is typically around 0.04 although it probably has a radial variation within the region.

25 Assuming photoionization equilibrium (i.e. the photoionization rate equals the recombination rate), the Strömgren depth of a cloud may be estimated. This is the depth to which complete ionization is maintained by the incident photon flux, and is therefore the minimum radius for line emitting clouds. For the clouds in the BLR this distance is estimated as $l \sim 0.7 R_\odot$.

26 A large partially ionized zone (PIZ), beyond the Strömgren depth, gives rise to enhanced Balmer emission and can help to explain the departures from standard case B recombination line ratios.

27 The broad line profiles seen in the spectra contain a lot of information but there is no simple model which explains it all. Asymmetric line profiles can be formed by clouds flowing towards the centre, with more distant ones obscured by intervening material, or by clouds flowing outwards and radiating predominantly from the inwards-facing illuminated surfaces.

28 The peaks of various emission lines occur at different radial velocities, such that higher ionization lines are blueshifted relative to lower ionization lines by as much as $10^3 \, \text{km s}^{-1}$. This implies that the BLR structure is stratified rather than homogeneous.

29 Reverberation mapping uses light echoes to probe the reprocessing structures surrounding the central source in an AGN. This is achieved by observing the response of emission lines to continuum variations.

30 The reverberation mapping technique assumes that: the continuum flux originates in a single compact source; the BLR filling factor is small; the observed optical/UV continuum flux is related in a simple way to the ionizing continuum flux; and the light travel time across the BLR is the only important timescale in the process.

31 Different emission lines are seen to have different time lags such that lines from highly ionized species (such as HeII, NV and CIV) have shorter time lags than lines from lower ionization levels (such as the Balmer lines). This is further indication for a radially stratified ionization structure in the BLR.

32 Cross-correlation of continuum and line fluxes for a range of AGN indicate that a typical size for the BLR is around 10 light-days.

33 The BLR line profiles do not characterize a unique velocity field for the BLR clouds, but for the CIV emitting clouds predominantly radial motion can be ruled out.

34 Assuming a BLR size of 10 light-days and a velocity range of up to $4500 \, \text{km s}^{-1}$ implies a mass for the central object of $M \sim rv^2/G \sim$ a few $\times \, 10^7 \text{M}_\odot$.

35 The BLR clouds are unlikely to be dense condensations in pressure equilibrium with a hotter, low-density medium because this would imply too high a temperature for the intercloud medium. Instead, the BLR clouds may be extended envelopes or material ablated off giant stars.

36 The Baldwin effect expresses the fact that the equivalent width of the CIV emission line is inversely correlated with the continuum luminosity. It is parameterized as

$$L(\text{CIV}) \propto L_\lambda^\gamma$$

where $\gamma \sim 0.8$. The Baldwin effect is also seen in Lyα with $\gamma \sim 0.9$. Suggested explanations for the effect include: a decrease in ionization parameter with luminosity; a decrease in f with luminosity; or disc inclination effects, assuming the continuum arises in an accretion disc. The effect has potential as a standard candle for cosmological investigations.

6 NARROW EMISSION LINES

6.1 Emission lines from low-density gases

We have already covered the atomic physics relevant to the analysis of emission lines in Activity 33. We learned that lines formed in the forbidden transitions can reveal the physical conditions, i.e. the electron densities, n_e, and temperatures, T, of the gas. Now we will apply this to the narrow-line region (NLR). While we found that forbidden transitions do not arise in the BLR, in the NLR they provide an important diagnostic tool which can reveal the physical conditions in this environment.

■ What is a 'BPT' diagram?

❑ It is a diagnostic graph which shows the value of one line ratio on the horizontal axis and another line ratio on the vertical axis. (See Peterson Fig. 2.3.) ■

Activity 42

Narrow-line spectra

Read the beginning of Chapter 6 of Peterson, up to the end of Section 6.1 (pages 93 and 94).

Non-isotropic (which is the same as 'anisotropic') means not the same in all directions, in this case it means that the narrow-line region is more irradiated at some angles that others, as illustrated in Figure 80.

Point (b) in the second paragraph of Peterson Section 6.1 relies first on knowing that, in general, atoms or ions have no preferred orientation. Consequently any photon emitted in a radiative transition will also be randomly directed. When a large number of atoms or ions (an **ensemble**) are considered, therefore, the number of photons emitted is the same in all directions, i.e. the radiation is isotropic. Clearly, as the opening paragraph of Peterson's Chapter 6 states, radiation is not always isotropic, this is because the chances of a photon escaping a source may not be the same in all directions. The second argument Peterson makes in point (b) is that the narrow lines are optically thin, so that the chances of an emitted photon being reabsorbed before escaping the narrow-line region are very small. Consequently the narrow-line emission is isotropic. The radiation which escapes can, however, be anisotropic if emission in some directions is blocked by dust.

In Peterson Table 6.1, the critical density (as defined in Activity 33) is tabulated for the collisionally excited lines.

Keywords: **collisionally excited lines, recombination lines** ■

■ Give three reasons why the narrow-line region (NLR) is interesting to astrophysicists.

❑ (i) It is the largest region in which irradiation from the central AGN dominates over other sources. (ii) It is the only part of AGN to be spatially resolved in optical images. (iii) NLR dynamics might offer clues to the mechanism of AGN fuelling. ■

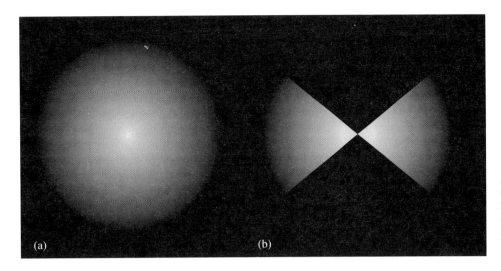

Figure 80 (a) A region which is isotropically illuminated by a central source, (b) a region which is non-isotropically illuminated by a central source.

■ Suggest one possible physical property which might provide the boundary between the broad-line region and the narrow-line region.

❑ The boundary might occur at the dust sublimation radius. ■

■ Why, for recombination lines, is the relevant ionization potential that of the next highest ionization state?

❑ Because recombination line radiation is emitted after an ion and an electron recombine to form an excited ion (or atom) of the next lowest ionization state. ■

As you learned in Activity 33, for collisionally excited lines it is possible to measure the electron density in a plasma by comparing the fluxes in two lines from the same multiplet if one of the lines is in the low-density limit, while the other is collisionally suppressed. When this happens the ratio of the emissivities, and hence of the observed intensities, is dependent on the electron density as shown in Peterson Fig. 6.2 and Figure 81.

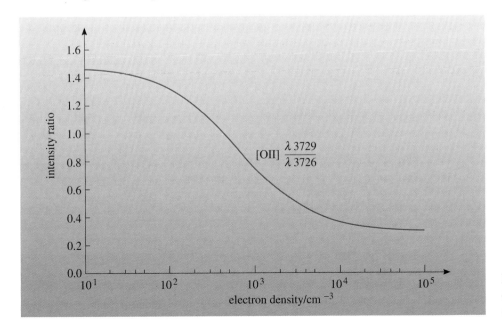

Figure 81 The dependence on electron density of the [OII] doublet $\lambda\lambda3729$, 3726.

Similarly the temperature can be deduced by measuring the line ratios for multiplets in which the excitation potentials for the various upper levels differ enough to produce a measurable temperature dependence in their populations. The emitted line intensity for transitions from any of the upper levels is proportional to the population of that level, which leads to an empirical indication of temperature as shown in Peterson Fig. 6.4.

Activity 43

Using lines to deduce NLR physical conditions

Read the last paragraphs of each of Peterson Sections 6.2.1 and 6.2.2.

The material covered in the omitted parts of these sections of Peterson has already been covered in Section 6 of Activity 33.

Keywords: **electron temperature, T_e, electron density, n_e** ■

■ Why is the range of electron densities measurable with the [SII] $\lambda\lambda 6717, 6731$ doublet confined to $10^2 \, \text{cm}^{-3} \lesssim n_e \lesssim 10^4 \, \text{cm}^{-3}$?

❑ Because at $n_e \lesssim 10^2 \, \text{cm}^{-3}$ both lines are in the low-density limit and at $n_e \gtrsim 10^4 \, \text{cm}^{-3}$ both lines are in the high-density limit. In each of these regimes the emitted line ratio does not depend on n_e, as Peterson Fig. 6.2 shows. ■

6.2 Properties of the narrow-line region

The variables in physical equations are usually expressed as purely algebraic quantities, for example n_e, the electron density, is an algebraic quantity, with the symbol containing both the numerical value and the dimensions of the quantity. It is often convenient to express equations in terms of normalized variables. For example in Question 17(b) the mass M_{BH} was rewritten in units of $10^8 M_\odot$ as $M_{BH} = M_8 \times 10^8 M_\odot$, with M_8 being a dimensionless number, and there were also examples of normalized variables in Block 3. Equations using normalized variables are convenient because they allow researchers to quickly substitute in measured or assumed values for the variables, and immediately show the expected magnitude of the result. As you may have discovered with Question 17 (the Course Team did!), there is a great danger of becoming confused and losing track of units when introducing normalized variables. The next reading in Peterson illustrates this. There are (at least) two errors in the equations given in Peterson Section 6.3. Both arise where numerical values or normalized variables have been introduced. We point out the corrections in the text of Activity 44.

Activity 44   **(45 minutes)**

Basic parameters of the narrow-line region (NLR)

Read Peterson Section 6.3 (pages 101–103). Note that the correct version of the equation following Peterson Equation 6.13 is:

$$j_{H\beta} = \frac{n_e^2}{4\pi}\left(1.24 \times 10^{-25} \, \text{erg} \, \text{s}^{-1} \, \text{cm}^3\right) \text{ster}^{-1}$$

i.e. the units contain cm^3 rather than cm^{-3}. This sort of mixture of algebraic and dimensional numerical quantities is particularly difficult to check, so we advise you to generally keep to purely algebraic equations in your working as far as is possible. Note also that Peterson Equation 6.14 should have units $\text{erg s}^{-1}\,\text{cm}^3$. Further note that the expression for N_c in the penultimate paragraph of page 102 should read

$$N_c \lesssim 10^5 n_3 L_{41}(\text{H}\beta)$$

i.e. n_3 is not squared.

Recall that in *case B recombination* the Balmer series lines are assumed to be optically thin and are produced when: firstly upper levels are populated by recombination of H^+ (i.e. protons) and free electrons, then subsequently transitions are made to the $n = 2$ level. If some of the population of the upper levels (i.e. $n > 2$) is produced by collisional excitation, then the relative populations of these levels will be modified. Hence the observed Balmer series line fluxes are modified accordingly. This is the process considered by Gaskell and Ferland, and mentioned by Peterson in the first paragraph.

Peterson Equation 6.13 may look intimidating at first sight, but as usual all the difficulties are lumped together in the coefficient $\alpha^{\text{eff}}_{\text{H}\beta}$, as explained in the footnote on Peterson page 101. The number of recombinations is proportional to the density of electrons and the density of protons, and $\alpha^{\text{eff}}_{\text{H}\beta}$ is the constant of proportionality which converts this into the number of transitions from $n = 4$ to $n = 2$ which consequently occur, producing a $\text{H}\beta$ photon. The final term in the equation:

$$\frac{h\nu_{\text{H}\beta}}{4\pi}$$

converts the number of recombinations into the energy by multiplying by the energy of a $\text{H}\beta$ photon, and divides by the 4π steradians in a full sphere to give the emissivity. The working to obtain Peterson Equation 6.15 is given in the example following this activity.

The **filling factor**, ϵ, gives the fraction of the total narrow-line region which is occupied by narrow-line emitting clouds. Since the observed line fluxes coupled with direct information on the size of the narrow-line region imply that the filling factor is $\leq 10^{-2}$, the narrow-line region must be clumpy. **Profile structure** refers to the shape of the emission line profile, i.e. how the line flux depends on velocity. Individual clouds will have distinct velocities, consequently if spectra are taken of different parts of the NLR, the profiles obtained will each contain emission at the velocities of all the clouds located within that particular part. Hence the profile structure will change if the velocities vary from place to place, as would be expected if the number of clouds is small or there is a large-scale velocity structure within the NLR.

Keywords: **narrow-line clouds, narrow-line region mass, M_{NLR}**

Example 8

Derive Peterson Equation 6.15 from Peterson Equations 6.13 and 6.14.

Solution

The starting point is Peterson Equation 6.14, i.e.

$$L(\text{H}\beta) = \iint j_{\text{H}\beta}\,d\Omega\,dV$$

and an expression for the integrand is given in Peterson Equation 6.13:

$$j_{H\beta} = n_e^2 \alpha_{H\beta}^{eff} \frac{h\nu_{H\beta}}{4\pi} \tag{72}$$

We will assume that the emitting gas has uniform physical conditions, emits isotropically, and consists of clouds which occupy the total volume, V, with filling factor ϵ. With these assumptions both the integrals are trivial. There is no dependence on direction so the integral over solid angle gives a multiplicative factor of 4π steradians. The integral over volume gives the total volume occupied by emitting gas, which is ϵV or $\epsilon(4/3)\pi r^3$, where r is the radius of the narrow-line region, which is assumed to be spherical.

Following the advice dispensed in Activity 44, we will keep the algebraic expression for $j_{H\beta}$ given in Equation 72, rather than substituting in numerical values. Hence, after performing the two integrals we have:

$$L(H\beta) = \frac{n_e^2}{4\pi} \alpha_{H\beta}^{eff} h\nu_{H\beta} \times 4\pi \, \text{ster} \times \epsilon \frac{4}{3}\pi r^3$$

which simplifies to

$$L(H\beta) = \frac{4\pi}{3} n_e^2 \alpha_{H\beta}^{eff} h\nu_{H\beta} \epsilon r^3$$

This is the purely algebraic form of Peterson Equation 6.14.

Next we make r the subject of the equation, obtaining

$$r = \left(\frac{3}{4\pi} \frac{L(H\beta)}{n_e^2 \alpha_{H\beta}^{eff} h\nu_{H\beta}\epsilon} \right)^{1/3} \tag{73}$$

which is the purely algebraic form of Peterson Equation 6.15. Now all we need to do is to substitute in values for the constants and introduce the normalized units Peterson adopts

$$n_e = n_3 \times 10^3 \, \text{cm}^{-3}$$

$$L(H\beta) = L_{41}(H\beta) \times 10^{41} \, \text{erg s}^{-1}$$

$$h\nu_{H\beta} = 2.55 \, \text{eV} = 2.55 \times 1.602 \times 10^{-12} \, \text{erg} = 4.09 \times 10^{-12} \, \text{erg}$$

where we have used the energy for the $H\beta$ transition given in the solution to Block 1 Question 91, and then converted into ergs using the conversion factor given in the Appendix. Finally,

$$\alpha_{H\beta}^{eff} \approx 3 \times 10^{-14} \, \text{cm}^3 \, \text{s}^{-1}$$

as given in the footnote on page 101 of Peterson. Substituting all this into Equation 73 we have

$$r \approx \left(\frac{3}{4\pi\epsilon} \frac{L_{41}(H\beta) \times 10^{41} \, \text{erg s}^{-1}}{(n_3 \times 10^3 \, \text{cm}^{-3})^2 \times 3 \times 10^{-14} \, \text{cm}^3 \, \text{s}^{-1} \times 4.09 \times 10^{-12} \, \text{erg}} \right)^{1/3}$$

and collecting all the numerical terms and units this is

$$r \approx \left(\frac{3}{4\pi} \frac{10^{41}}{10^6 \times 3 \times 10^{-14} \times 4.09 \times 10^{-12}} \right)^{1/3} \left(\frac{L_{41}(H\beta)}{\epsilon n_3^2} \right)^{1/3} \left(\frac{\text{erg s}^{-1}}{\text{cm}^{-6} \, \text{cm}^3 \, \text{s}^{-1} \, \text{erg}} \right)^{1/3}$$

which simplifies to

$$r \approx (1.95 \times 10^{59})^{1/3} \left(\frac{L_{41}(H\beta)}{\epsilon n_3^2} \right)^{1/3} \text{cm}$$

$$r \approx 5.79 \times 10^{19} \left(\frac{L_{41}(H\beta)}{\epsilon n_3^2} \right)^{1/3} \text{cm}$$

and finally converting from cm to pc we have

$$r \approx \frac{5.79 \times 10^{19}}{3.086 \times 10^{18}} \left(\frac{L_{41}(H\beta)}{\epsilon n_3^2} \right)^{1/3} \text{pc}$$

$$r \approx 19 \left(\frac{L_{41}(H\beta)}{\epsilon n_3^2} \right)^{1/3} \text{pc}$$

which is Peterson Equation 6.15 as required. Phew! ▪

■ Assuming the cloud velocities are random, why is the line profile structure expected to depend on position for partially resolved narrow-line regions if there is a *small* numbers of clouds contributing to the light in a particular spectral exposure?

❏ If the velocities are random, Poisson statistics will hold. Consequently, if the average number of clouds with velocity between v and $v + dv$ in the volume sampled by a single spectrum is N, the expected scatter when different regions are sampled, is $\sqrt{N}$. This will be observable as position-dependent structure in the line profile if N is small. If N is large, $\sqrt{N} \ll N$, the line profile is expected to appear roughly the same at all positions. ▪

Question 47

(a) How do the masses of the broad-line region and narrow-line region gas compare?

(b) How does the amount of line flux produced in each of these two regions compare?

(c) Which is the more efficient emitter of line flux per unit mass?

(d) What is the physical reason for the vastly different emission efficiencies? ▪

Question 48

By taking the Strömgren depth, $r_1 \approx 10^{18} n_3^{-1} \text{cm}$, as a lower limit on the size of narrow-line clouds, show that the number of narrow-line clouds, N_c obeys

$$N_c \lesssim 10^5 n_3 L_{41}(H\beta)$$

Note: This is the *correct* form for the limit on N_c; the expression in Peterson is incorrect. ▪

■ What happens to most Lyα photons produced in the narrow-line region?

❏ Most of them are absorbed by dust and do not escape from the narrow-line region. ▪

141

■ Under what circumstances might a covering factor greater than one be deduced from the Lyα equivalent width?

❏ If the continuum observed on Earth is diminished (by attenuation or anisotropic emission) relative to the continuum incident on the narrow-line clouds, it is possible to deduce a covering factor greater than one. ■

■ Why is the narrow-line emission not, in general, suitable for reverberation-mapping studies?

❏ Because the light travel time across the NLR is ~100 years and the recombination time is ~100 years. ■

Activity 45   **(45 minutes)**

Narrow-line profiles

Read Peterson Section 6.4, including the footnote on the **Faber–Jackson relationship** (pages 103–106).

In Block 1 Section 4.7 ideal gases were discussed. The ideal gas model prescribes what proportion of the particles in a gas have any particular velocity. If a spectral line is formed by an ideal gas it is expected to have a roughly **Gaussian** line profile. Similarly, if clouds are moving randomly, a roughly Gaussian distribution of radial velocities leading to a Gaussian line profile (see Figure 63) might be expected. The first paragraph of this reading discusses possible reasons for the non-Gaussian shape of the narrow-line profiles.

At the end of the second paragraph on page 104, Peterson argues that the opacity leading to the line profile asymmetries must have $\tau \gg 1$. For optical depths $\tau \sim 1$, red photons would be more likely to emerge through dust than blue ones (this is **reddening**), so the effect on Hα photons from a given cloud would be less than that on Hβ photons from the same cloud. Consequently the Hα lines would have relatively more flux at the velocities corresponding to the highest optical depths, and the **Hα/Hβ flux ratio would vary with radial velocity**. It is perhaps worth noting that it is highly plausible that the radial velocity and optical depth will be correlated, for example consider the situation illustrated in Figure 70a.

Peterson's statement '**the narrow-line widths are primarily virial in origin**' means that the velocities of the narrow-line emitting clouds are determined primarily by motion under gravity, hence the Doppler broadening of the lines is determined by the gravitational potential. Because the NLR is extended, the mass encompassed within it consists mostly of stars in the host galaxy, rather than by the supermassive black hole at the centre of the AGN.

Keywords: **emission profiles, profile asymmetries, Faber–Jackson relationship** ▨

■ Why can't self-absorption be important in forbidden lines?

❏ Because by definition forbidden lines correspond to radiative transitions with relatively low probability of occurrence, consequently the cross-section for absorbing a forbidden line photon is low, and self-absorption within the narrow-line region is negligible for them. ■

Question 49

(a) What is the Faber–Jackson relationship?

(b) Give an argument justifying why the Faber–Jackson relationship might be expected, making clear any assumptions required. ■

■ Why do FR II galaxies deviate from the general correlation between bulge luminosity and [OIII] line width?

❏ The correlation is a manifestation of the virial relationship between motions under self-gravity and total mass. If there is a strong radio jet, as in FR II galaxies, this can affect the motion of the NLR gas (e.g. by shocks), so that its dynamics is not determined solely by gravity. ■

Activity 46   (30 minutes)

Narrow-line region morphology

Read Peterson Section 6.5 (pages 106–109).

Shock fronts are discontinuous changes in the properties of a fluid. In Block 3 Section 1.2 we learned that a shock forms when a supersonic accretion flow impacts the surface of a star. In general a shock will form whenever a supersonic flow encounters an obstacle. In the context of this reading, shocks are created by the supersonic radio-emitting plasma emerging from the active nucleus when it encounters the interstellar medium of the host galaxy. At a shock the bulk kinetic energy of the flow is generally abruptly converted into heat. The **post-shock cooling region** is the region downstream from a shock where the heated material cools by radiating away some of the thermal energy gained at the shock.

A **bowshock** is formed by motion through a medium, and the name comes from the disturbance which is formed by a ship moving through water. We cannot spatially resolve the bowshocks inferred in the NLR. We can, however, see astrophysical examples of bowshocks in our own Galaxy, as Figure 82 and the cover of Block 1 show.

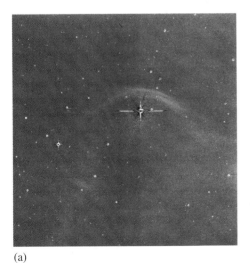
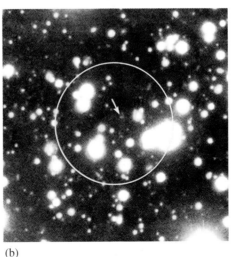

(a)   (b)

Figure 82 Two examples of bowshocks in astrophysics. (a) The bowshock around the high-mass X-ray binary Vela X-1. (b) The bowshock around the neutron star RX J1856.5-3754. These two objects are moving through our Galaxy at velocities of $90 \, \text{km s}^{-1}$ and $100 \, \text{km s}^{-1}$ respectively.

Towards the end of the second paragraph on page 107, where Peterson refers to the **midplane**, he means the midplane of the host galaxy. For a spiral galaxy this would be the imaginary plane which divides the disc and bulge into two halves, each resembling the shape of a fried egg.

After reading the last paragraph you might want to take a quick look ahead to Peterson Fig. 7.1.

Keywords: **on-band image**, **off-band image**, **ionization cones**, **extended narrow-line region**, **classical narrow-line region** ■

■ What is an off-band image and what is it used for?

❑ On-band and off-band images are used to construct a picture of pure emission-line light from an extended source. The on-band image is taken through a narrow filter centred on the wavelength of the emission line, while the off-band image is centred at a nearby wavelength where there is no emission line contribution to the flux. The emission line image is made by subtraction of the off-band image to correct for continuum light in the on-band image. ■

6.3 Summary of Section 6

1 The narrow-line region (NLR) of AGN can be spatially resolved in optical observations and is the largest region of the AGN in which radiation from the central source dominates. Some of the NLR emission may be absorbed by dust since the NLR lies outside the dust sublimation radius.

2 Electron densities in the NLR are low enough that forbidden transitions are not collisionally suppressed, so line ratios of certain forbidden lines allow densities and temperatures of the NLR to be determined. An average NLR electron density is found to be about $2000 \, \text{cm}^{-3}$ and a typical value for the temperature is around $16\,000 \, \text{K}$.

3 A wide range of ionization states are present in spectral lines from the NLR. Some of the strongest lines seen are Lyα $\lambda1216$, CIV $\lambda1549$, CIII] $\lambda1909$, [OII] $\lambda3727$, Hβ $\lambda4861$, [OIII] $\lambda\lambda4959, 5007$ and Hα $\lambda6563$.

4 The [OIII] $\lambda5007$/Hβ line ratio of ≥3 locates AGN on the BPT diagram and indicates that the NLR gas is ionized by the AGN continuum rather than by stars.

5 The FWHM of narrow lines is between about $200 \, \text{km s}^{-1}$ and $900 \, \text{km s}^{-1}$, with the majority lying around 350–$400 \, \text{km s}^{-1}$.

6 To deduce the properties of the NLR, the luminosity of the Hβ line is used. This is a recombination line, and so insensitive to temperature. It is also optically thin and less sensitive to collisional effects than Hα.

7 The emissivity of the gas in the Hβ line is

$$j_{H\beta} = n_e^2 \alpha_{H\beta}^{\text{eff}} \frac{h\nu_{H\beta}}{4\pi} = \frac{n_e^2}{4\pi} 1.24 \times 10^{-25} \, \text{erg s}^{-1} \, \text{cm}^3 \, \text{ster}^{-1}$$

where n_e is the electron density and $\alpha_{H\beta}^{\text{eff}}$ is the effective recombination coefficient for Hβ ($\sim3 \times 10^{-14} \, \text{cm}^3 \, \text{s}^{-1}$). Integrating this over all directions and the entire volume of the NLR gives a luminosity for the Hβ line of

$$L(H\beta) = \frac{4\pi \epsilon n_e^2}{3} 1.24 \times 10^{-25} r^3 \, \text{erg s}^{-1} \, \text{cm}^3$$

where ϵ is the filling factor of the NLR, defined as $N_c l^3 = \epsilon r^3$. The number of narrow-line clouds is N_c, the radius of each cloud is l and the radius of the NLR is r.

8   The size of the NLR is inferred to be $r \gtrsim 100$ pc with a filling factor of $\epsilon \lesssim 10^{-2}$. So, the NLR, like the BLR, is clumpy. The total mass of the NLR is estimated to be of order $10^6 M_\odot$.

9   Models for the photoionization properties of the NLR predict an ionization parameter $U \sim 0.01$, so the Strömgren depth is around 10^{18} cm. Assuming this is a lower limit for the size of an individual cloud, it implies the number of clouds in the NLR is $\lesssim 10^5$.

10   The equivalent width of the Lyα line cannot be used to estimate the covering factor of the NLR because most Lyα photons are absorbed by dust before they can emerge.

11   Since the NLR is relatively large, with a light travel time of order ~ 100 years, variability of narrow lines is not expected to be observed. Since the recombination timescale for the NLR is of order 100 years, emission line variations will also be damped out.

12   The profiles of the narrow emission lines are non-Gaussian, with wider bases and usually with more flux on the blue side of the line than the red side. The phenomenon is due to either net outflow of the NLR clouds through a dusty region, or net infall of the clouds which are filled with dust.

13   The centroids of narrow lines are often slightly blueshifted (by 50–100 km s^{-1}) relative to the motion of the AGN as a whole, but the peaks of the lines are close to the redshifts of the host galaxies. This indicates that most of the emission arises in a region which is symmetrical around the centre of the AGN, but another component arises in outflowing material on the near side of the AGN.

14   The Faber–Jackson relationship links the luminosity, L, of a galaxy to its velocity dispersion, σ, via $L \propto \sigma^4$. Thus the luminosity of the central bulge of a galaxy is an indicator of the gravitational potential of this bulge. The correlation between the bulge luminosity and the [OIII] $\lambda 5007$ line width for Seyfert galaxies therefore indicates that the velocities of the narrow-line emitting clouds are determined primarily by motion under the influence of gravity. The line widths indicate the gravitational field resulting from all the stars contained within the extended NLR.

15   The profiles of the various forbidden lines in a particular AGN have different widths. This indicates that there is a radial stratification of the NLR with density and/or ionization level increasing towards the centre.

16   There is some evidence for a gradual merging of the NLR into the BLR.

17   The NLR is generally found not to be spherically symmetric, but rather is symmetric along an axis which coincides with the axis of extended radio structures (where seen). The outflowing plasma which creates the radio emission is thought to cause bowshocks as it propagates through the NLR; collisional ionization in the post-shock gas enhances NLR emission along the radio axis.

18   Ionization cones are wedge shaped structures with opening angles of $30°–100°$ within which the [OIII] $\lambda 5007$/Hα flux ratio is >1. This indicates a region of low-density gas ionized by the AGN continuum radiation. The structures range in size from ~ 50 pc to ~ 15 kpc and are sometimes referred to as the extended narrow-line region (ENLR).

19   The ENLR indicates that the ionizing continuum is emitted anisotropically, perhaps collimated by an obscuring torus close to the centre of the AGN.

7 UNIFIED MODELS OF AGN

The last paragraph of Peterson Section 6.5, which you read at the end of Activity 46, foreshadowed the topic of this section. We are now going to attempt to fit everything (!) we have learned about AGN into a simple picture of their structure. This simple picture is known as a **unified model**.

7.1 Light travelling through dust

Before embarking on a study of unification, however, we must first examine another effect that matter can have on the photons travelling through it: the interaction of radiation with matter can cause the radiation to become polarized. In the box on 'Polarization of electromagnetic radiation' (in Section 1.7) we introduced the topic of polarization, and as you will see, it provides some important clues about the appropriate unification schemes for AGN. To introduce the topic, recall what you know about electron scattering.

■ What happens to the energy and direction of travel of photons when they scatter from electrons?

❑ As discussed in Section 1.7.4, if the photons have low energy, such that $h\nu \ll m_{e}c^2$, the process is known as Thomson scattering, and in this case the photons do not gain or lose energy, but merely change their direction (i.e. the scattering is *elastic*). When high-energy photons scatter from electrons, they can either lose energy (this is Compton scattering) or gain energy (this is inverse Compton scattering), as well as undergoing a change in direction. ■

There is one other effect of electron scattering that we have not yet mentioned. *The scattered radiation is polarized*. Even if the incident radiation has completely random orientations of its electric and magnetic fields, the scattered radiation is polarized such that the electric field vectors of the radiation all lie perpendicular to the direction the radiation was travelling prior to the scattering event (like the reflected ray shown in Figure 11). It is also important to note that the effect is independent of the initial energy of the photons (or equivalently, independent of the wavelength or frequency used to characterize the wave-like behaviour of the radiation). An unpolarized beam of radiation in which each photon undergoes electron scattering will emerge polarized.

■ Can you recall another way of producing polarized radiation?

❑ Synchrotron radiation, produced by electrons travelling through a magnetic field, is polarized. ■

If the radiation travels through a large column density of electrons, then radiation will typically undergo multiple scatterings before emerging. The effect of multiple scatterings will be to *depolarize* the radiation, since each scattering will result from radiation travelling in a different direction, and so give rise to radiation which is polarized in a different direction. Adding together the net result of countless electron scattering events will give rise to radiation which has no overall polarization.

Electromagnetic radiation can also be scattered by dust grains. Radiation scattered by dust also emerges polarized. Dust grains are believed to be elongated and they preferentially take up an orientation parallel to the local magnetic field. The scattering of radiation then depends on the orientation of the electric field vectors of the incident radiation relative to the long axes of the grains, and as a result the scattered radiation is polarized. The major difference between scattering by electrons and scattering by dust is that in the latter case the degree of polarization depends on the energy of the incident photon (or equivalently on the wavelength or frequency used to characterize its wave-like propagation). For the visible and near infrared regions of the electromagnetic spectrum, experimentally it is found that the percentage polarization at a particular wavelength, P_λ, relative to the maximum percentage polarization observed, P_{max}, is:

$$\frac{P_\lambda}{P_{max}} = \exp\left(-1.66\lambda_{max}\log_e^2\left(\frac{\lambda_{max}}{\lambda}\right)\right) \tag{74}$$

where λ_{max} is the wavelength at which maximum polarization is observed in a particular case. For longer wavelengths, into the far infrared, the relationship is the simpler:

$$P_\lambda = P_1\lambda^{-1.8} \tag{75}$$

where P_1 is a constant for the particular line-of-sight in question.

- According to Equation 75, which wavelength radiation will exhibit the larger polarization as a result of scattering by dust: radiation with a wavelength of $10\,\mu m$ or radiation with a wavelength of $25\,\mu m$?

- ❏ Since the percentage polarization varies as $\lambda^{-1.8}$, the shorter wavelength radiation will exhibit the greater amount of polarization. ■

Finally, when electromagnetic radiation passes through dust, it will also be absorbed by varying amounts, again as a function of wavelength. As you saw in Block 1 Section 2.8, the amount of absorption is less for longer wavelengths, so the partially absorbed radiation will undergo more absorption in the blue part of the spectrum than in the red.

- What will be the effect on a power-law spectral energy distribution (SED) if it undergoes reddening?

- ❏ Since the amount of absorption varies with wavelength, the resulting SED will no longer (in general) have a power-law shape. ■

Radiation emerging from a dusty environment will be reddened, as well as polarized, and will not have the power-law shape of the original spectral energy distribution.

7.2 Occam's razor

In Chapter 7 of Peterson we embark on an ambitious attempt to pull together many of the plethora of facts you have encountered in earlier sections of this block. The urge to simplify is embodied by the famous maxim known as Occam's razor:

'A plurality must not be asserted without necessity'

William of Occam, Quodlibeta Septem *c*.1320

Occam urges us to attempt to explain the wealth of phenomena we observe in AGN with as few underlying 'free parameters' as possible.

Activity 47   **(30 minutes)**

Introduction to unification

Read the beginning of Chapter 7 of Peterson, up to the end of Section 7.1 (pages 110–112).

UV through IR spectrum is American English for 'the spectrum from UV to IR'.

Morphological is used in the first sentence of Section 7.1 in a different sense to the definition of morphology (≈ shape) given in Activity 5, as is clear from the explanation Peterson gives. In the last paragraph of Section 7.1, morphology is used to simply mean shape.

Peterson Fig. 7.1 is important. This simple cartoon should give you a context within which to place many of the detailed observational findings you have learned about in this block.

Keywords: **weak unification models**, **strong unification models** ■

Question 50

Sketch a copy of Peterson Fig.7.1, and include arrows indicating the viewing angles corresponding to seeing

(i) a BL Lac object

(ii) a broad-lined radio galaxy

(iii) a narrow-lined radio galaxy. ■

7.3 Unification in Seyferts

Activity 48   **(1 hour)**

Only one type of Seyfert?

Read Peterson Section 7.2 (pages 112–118).

By **nuclear components** in the last sentence on page 114, Peterson means the broad-line region and the AGN continuum emission, both of which are emitted by the spatially unresolved nucleus of the active galaxy.

Peterson Equation 7.1 assumes that all of the Hβ flux arises from the upper level being populated by case B recombination, as discussed in his Section 6.3. Equation 7.2 arises straightforwardly from the previous work in Section 5.3, with the only difference being Peterson Equation 5.17 implicitly assumes uniform physical conditions throughout the emission region, while Peterson Equation 7.2 performs an integral over the volume, so would produce the correct result if n_e varied appreciably. This dependence on $\int n_e^2 \, dV$ appears in both Peterson Equation 7.1 and Peterson Equation 7.2, and therefore cancels when they are combined to give Peterson Equation 7.3.

Keywords: **obscuring torus**, **scattering medium** ▧

■ Why is it very unlikely that Seyfert 2 galaxies are simply Seyfert 1 galaxies in a low state?

❏ Because in Seyfert 1 galaxies the broad lines never completely disappear. ■

Question 51

How does the number of Seyfert 1 galaxies and Seyfert 2 galaxies found per unit volume give an estimate of the solid angle subtended by the torus at the centre of an AGN? ■

Question 52

Make an addition to the sketch you drew for Question 50 showing the scattering medium invoked to explain the observations of NGC 1068, and show the path of an observed NGC 1068 broad-line photon. ■

Example 9

(a) Define 'isotropic'.

(b) Summarize a method which can be used to assess whether or not the radiation field from the central source in Seyfert 2 galaxies is isotropic, giving details of the assumptions made, the key equations, the results it yields, and the caveats to which the results are subject.

Solution

(a) Isotropic means the same in all directions, i.e. with no dependence on angle.

(b) We can use the ionizing flux (i.e. flux with $v > v_1$, where v_1 is the frequency at the Lyman edge) to assess whether or not the radiation emerging from the central regions is isotropic. We can infer the number of ionizing photons produced by the nucleus of the Seyfert 2 galaxy straightforwardly from the measured nuclear emission and the distance, d:

$$Q_{\text{obs}}(\text{H}) = 4\pi d^2 \int_{v_1}^{\infty} \frac{f_v}{hv} \, dv \tag{76}$$

This implicitly assumes that the emission is isotropic, so that the received flux (per unit area) can be multiplied by the surface area of the sphere ($4\pi d^2$) over which the emission has been spread. The integral is from the frequency corresponding to the ionization energy of hydrogen, and the factor of hv in the denominator converts from energy to number of ionizing photons.

We can also infer the number of ionizing photons by measuring the emission in recombination lines from the ionization cones. This estimate of the nuclear emission assumes that the ionization cones are photoionized by the nucleus and that there is no additional source of excitation for the upper level of the emission line being measured. For example, following Peterson, we can use the Hβ line emission to indicate the photoionizing flux from the nucleus. The measured line flux is proportional to the number of recombinations:

$$L(H\beta) = \alpha_{H\beta}^{eff} h\nu_{H\beta} \int n_e^2 \, dV \qquad (77)$$

Assuming an ionization cone which is optically thick to ionizing photons:

$$\text{the net number of recombinations per unit time} = \alpha_B \int n_e^2 \, dV \qquad (78)$$

If the ionization cones are in a state of photoionization equilibrium then this is equal to the number of ionizing photons from the central source:

$$Q(H) = \int_{\nu_1}^{\infty} \frac{L_\nu}{h\nu} \, d\nu \qquad (79)$$

Substituting for the integral $\int n_e^2 \, dV$ from Equation 77 into Equation 78, and then equating the right-hand side of Equation 79 to the number of recombinations leads to the equation

$$Q(H) = \frac{L(H\beta)}{h\nu_{H\beta}} \frac{\alpha_B}{\alpha_{H\beta}^{eff}} \qquad (80)$$

Equation 80 allows the number of ionizing photons to be calculated from the observed Hβ luminosity. Equation 80 measures the number of ionizing photons 'detected' by the ionization cones. This can be compared with Equation 76 to see if the number of ionizing photons 'detected' by the ionization cones is consistent with the number detected by us. The results from applying this analysis to observations of Seyfert 2 galaxies generally imply that the ionization cones 'detect' a higher ionizing flux than we do.

There is an inconsistency in this analysis, however, because we have implicitly assumed that *all* the ionizing photons cause photoionizations within the ionization cones: if this were literally true, of course, no ionizing photons would remain to be detected by us. In the unification picture illustrated in Peterson Fig. 7.1, this inconsistency would be resolved by multiplying Equation 79 by the fraction of the sky subtended by the ionization cones (as seen by the central source). If this fraction of $Q(H)$ remains greater than $Q_{obs}(H)$ then the ionization cones see an apparently more luminous central source than we do, supporting the hypothesis that we observe the central source through an obscuring torus.

There are further caveats: the ionization cones may be clumpy, and if this is the case then Equation 80 must be modified to depend on the filling factor and Strömgren depth of an individual cloud, as well as on the area subtended by the ionization cones. With all these factors to consider, a clear-cut test of the unification hypothesis is not really provided. ■

The penultimate paragraph of Peterson Section 7.2, which discusses the IR emission from the heated dust in the torus, foreshadows one of the areas of research where much effort is currently being directed. As well as providing empirical data to assess the unification models, IR observations of AGN can be used to assess the idea that the supermassive black holes grew in dust-enshrouded galactic nuclei in the early Universe. For these and many other reasons, at the beginning of the 21st century, many sensitive high spatial resolution IR facilities are being planned and commissioned. The IR region is invaluable for studying dust enshrouded objects, because IR photons suffer from much less extinction than higher energy photons.

In the time between Peterson writing his book, and this Study Guide being produced for S381, much work has been done on testing the ideas for unification in Seyferts which we examined in Activity 48. In the next activity we will catch up on one aspect of this recent work, which uses the (at the time of writing) largest telescope dedicated solely to IR observations (United Kingdom Infrared Telescope, UKIRT), to probe through the dusty torus in Seyfert 2 galaxies.

Activity 49   (1 hour)

Observing through the torus

This activity enables you to practise accessing the journal archives on the World Wide Web to search for work which follows up a particular research line. By following the instructions you will learn how to find all articles which **cite** a particular prior article. When a paper gives a **citation** to a previous work, generally this means it is reporting new results which are relevant to the previous work. Key **seminal** papers tend to have the most citations, as they open up a new area and stimulate many other workers to explore it.

Connect to the S381 home page, select Block 4, Activity 49 and follow the instructions on screen.

Having obtained a copy of the paper, first read the first three paragraphs of the abstract. **J-band** and **K-band** were defined in Block 1, Section 2.7; the **L-band** is the next IR photometric passband longward of K. **Paschen (Pa)** and **Brackett (Br)** are the hydrogen line series with lower levels $n = 3$ and $n = 4$ respectively. **Column depth** is a measure of how much obscuring material the observed light has travelled through. This can be measured in various ways, which is what is referred to when 'infrared [column densities]' and 'X-ray column densities' are referred to in the second paragraph of the abstract. Have a quick look through Figures 1 and 2 in the paper, and then read the first five paragraphs of the 'discussion' and the first three paragraphs of the 'summary'. Do not worry if you do not understand everything you read. With luck you should find enough that is familiar to allow you to piece together the gist of the paper.

Keywords: **broad infrared lines**, **obscured broad-line region**

Question 53

(a) What proportion of the Seyfert 2 galaxies observed by Veilleux, Goodrich, and Hill were found likely to harbour obscured broad-line regions?

(b) How do the widths of the Paschen and Brackett lines in these proposed obscured Seyfert 1 galaxies compare with the line widths in Seyfert 1 galaxies.

(c) How do the predicted Hβ fluxes for these objects compare with those for Seyfert 1 galaxies?

(d) How does the broad-line region luminosity inferred from these infrared observations compare with that inferred from optical spectropolarimetry?

(e) Are these observations encouraging for the scenario for the unification of Seyferts outlined in Peterson Section 7.2? Are there any other models which have been considered? What do the authors of this paper conclude about them?

7.4 Unification and grand unification

Activity 50   **(90 minutes)**

The big picture

Read Peterson Sections 7.3 and 7.4, including all subsections (pages 118–125).

Faraday depolarization and the **Poynting vector** were introduced in the box entitled 'Polarization of electromagnetic radiation' in Section 1.7 of this Study Guide.

By **de-project** in the paragraph following that containing Peterson Equation 7.7, Peterson is describing the geometry illustrated in Figure 83. The measured linear size ($=D\theta$) is an underestimate because a long structure is being observed almost edge-on, and consequently is seen foreshortened. By estimating the angle at which the observer is placed, the true linear size can be calculated using trigonometry, i.e. the measured linear size can be 'de-projected'.

Cosmological evolution in the last paragraph of Section 7.4.2 refers to possible evolutionary changes in the characteristics of a particular type of object over the age of the Universe, and will be discussed in the last section of this Study Guide.

Bimodal is a statistical term. The mode of a distribution is the value which occurs most frequently, but in some cases a sample is drawn up of two distinct subsamples, and the distribution might appear like that shown in Figure 84. If a statistician tabulated the weekly leisure time of a randomly selected sample of British 60-year-olds, the results might give a bimodal distribution. Some 60-year-olds have retired, while others remain in full-time occupations. The former group will clearly have more hours of leisure time. A distribution like that shown in Figure 84, which has two modes, corresponding to two different underlying distributions, is bimodal. Peterson refers to the radio luminosity distribution, which is bimodal: the lower-valued subsample are the radio-quiet AGN, the higher-valued subsample are the radio-loud AGN.

Keywords: **parent population, distance-limited sample** ■

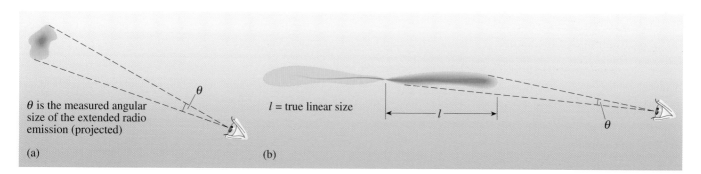

θ is the measured angular size of the extended radio emission (projected)

(a)

l = true linear size

(b)

Figure 83 The geometry of projection and de-projection. (a) A superluminal radio source is observed from a direction close to the velocity of the approaching jet. The angular size of the extended radio emission is θ, corresponding to a projected linear size of $D\theta$, where D is the distance between the source and the observer. (b) The (un-projected) linear size of the radio source is l, which is much bigger than $D\theta$ because the observer's view is foreshortened.

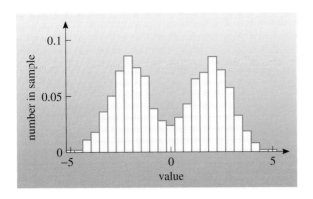

Figure 84 Histogram showing a bimodal distribution.

The luminous IRAS sources Peterson mentions in point (3) in his Section 7.4.1 will be the subject of your next Web-based activity. These luminous extragalactic infrared sources have been the subject of much recent research activity. They have become known by the acronyms ULIG, or ULIRG, standing for 'ultraluminous IR galaxy'.

■   Is the spectrum of the compact radio cores flat or steep? Is the spectrum of the extended radio lobes flat or steep?

❏   The compact radio cores are have flat spectra. The extended component has a steep spectrum. ■

Are there any components of the AGN emission which can reasonably be assumed to emit isotropically, and can therefore be used to indicate the intrinsic AGN luminosity, free of viewing-angle inclination-dependence? Discuss each of the following in your answer:

- core radio emission
- broad-line region emission
- extended radio emission
- hard X-ray emission
- far-infrared emission
- extended narrow-line emission ■

■   What evidence from polarization studies supports the inference that the jet side of a double-lobed radio source is closer to us?

❏   The lobe containing the jet is generally found to be more highly polarized. This is consistent with a greater Faraday depolarization of the radiation from the other lobe. This arises from a longer path length through the circum-galactic diffuse ionized medium. A higher degree of polarization is expected from the lobe which is closer to us. ■

■   What is meant by grand unification?

❏   The attempt to explain all observed AGN phenomena within a single conceptual framework. ■

■   What three fundamental physical parameters were considered by Blandford in his attempt to build a phenomenological 'grand unification' scheme?

❑   The mass of the central engine, M, the accretion rate, $\dot{M}$, and the angular momentum of the central source. ■

■   What, in 1995, did Wilson and Colbert suggest might be responsible for the bimodal radio-luminosity distribution?

❑   They suggested a bimodal distribution in the spin rates of the central black holes is a result of mergers of galaxies. They hypothesized that only when two comparable-mass black holes merge, is a rapidly spinning black hole formed. ■

Activity 51

ULIRGS as obscured quasars

Connect to the S381 home page, select Block 4, Activity 51 and follow the instructions on screen.

Keywords: **obscured quasar** ■

Question 55

Write a brief summary of the findings reported in the journal paper you downloaded in Activity 51. ■

7.5 Summary of Section 7

1   Electromagnetic radiation scattered by an electron is polarized, and this effect is independent of the wavelength of the incident radiation. If radiation undergoes multiple electron scattering events, the net polarization of the emergent radiation will be close to zero. Radiation scattered by dust grains is also polarized, but in this case, the degree of polarization depends on the wavelength of the incident radiation. Radiation emerging through dust is also selectively reddened.

2   The wide variety of AGN phenomena is assumed to be due to a combination of real differences (due to parameters such as luminosity) and apparent differences (due to parameters such as orientation). Unified models of active galaxies are based on the assumption that the classification of the system depends upon the inclination angle between the observer and the axis of symmetry close to the centre of the AGN, defined by an obscuring gas and dust torus.

3   Weak unified models of AGN allow more diversity and more intrinsic parameters (such as both optical and radio luminosity). A strong unified model of AGN assumes there is only a single intrinsic parameter (such as total luminosity) and all other differences are due to variations in viewing angle.

4   A possible weak unification scheme is shown in Table 3.

Table 3   A possible weak unification scheme for AGN.

Radio properties	Face-on	Edge-on
radio-quiet	Seyfert 1, QSO	Seyfert 2, ULIRG/FIR galaxy?
radio-loud	BL Lac, BLRG, Quasar/OVV	FR I, NLRG, FR II

Amongst the radio-loud objects, there is probably *not* a direct link between each of the three types of face-on objects and any one of the three types of edge-on objects.

5   The approximate current space densities of the various classes of AGN are shown in Table 4 assuming a Hubble constant of $100 \, \text{km s}^{-1} \, \text{Mpc}^{-1}$.

Table 4 The current space densities of different types of AGN.

Radio properties	Type of object	Space density/Gpc^{-3}
radio-quiet	Seyfert 2	800 000
	Seyfert 1	300 000
	QSO	800
radio-loud	FR I	20 000
	BL Lac	600
	FR II	80
	Quasar	20

6   The simple idea that Seyfert 2 galaxies are the same as Seyfert 1 galaxies, but with their central regions viewed through an attenuating medium, poses the problem that Seyfert 2 spectral continua are power laws, whereas a reddened Seyfert 1 continuum should not be a power law (due to reddening). Furthermore, their UV spectra are very similar and Seyfert 2 galaxies are only about 1 magnitude fainter than Seyfert 1 galaxies, yet their broad lines are completely extinguished.

7   A better solution is to suppose the existence of a dusty torus around the central regions of the AGN, such that in Seyfert 2 galaxies the BLR is completely hidden from view. The relative space density of the two types of object indicates that the torus must block out about three-quarters of the sky as seen from the centre, which is consistent with the opening angles of the observed ionization cones.

8   To explain the presence of continuum radiation in Seyfert 2 galaxies, a scattering medium is invoked. This lies above the hole in the torus, and scatters light from the central source back into the observer's line of sight. The idea is supported by the presence of polarized continuum light in Seyfert 2 galaxies.

9   Infrared spectral observations confirm that many Seyfert 2 galaxies have hidden BLRs, with the BLR having a higher extinction that the NLR, implying that the obscuring dust is located between the BLR and the NLR.

10   Carrying out statistical tests for unification is difficult because the populations of different objects may change with time (and hence because of light travel time, with distance) and because intrinsic luminosities are difficult to ascertain with certainty.

11   The only emission components which may be assumed to be emitted isotropically are the extended radio emission and the extended narrow-line emission. However, the former indicates the nuclear luminosity at an earlier epoch and the latter is often obscured by dust, so both have limited usefulness as independent indicators of luminosity.

12   Amongst radio-quiet objects, there is good evidence that *some* Seyfert 2 galaxies are the same as Seyfert 1 galaxies, but viewed at a different inclination angle. However, all QSOs (high-luminosity objects) have Seyfert 1 type spectra, so there is a puzzle as to where the QSOs corresponding to Seyfert 2 galaxies are. One possible solution is that these 'missing obscured QSOs' are the far-infrared (FIR) galaxies seen by the InfraRed Astronomy Satellite (IRAS), now commonly known as ULIGs or ULIRGS (ultraluminous infrared galaxies).

13   In radio-loud objects, jet structures often appear one-sided. This is attributed to relativistic beaming of the approaching jet. The extended emission on the jet side tends to be more polarized than the extended emission on the non-jet side. The approaching jet is closer to us, so emission from its lobe suffers less Faraday depolarization.

14   It is possible that radio-loud objects whose axes lie close to the plane of the sky are not detected as quasars, but are instead seen as FR II radio galaxies. Consequently if quasars are face-on objects, FR II galaxies are the same thing seen edge-on. The edge-on equivalent of BLRGs may also appear as FR II galaxies.

15   Low-luminosity radio galaxies (FR I type) may be related to BL Lac objects; whereas the higher luminosity radio galaxies (FR II type) may be related to OVVs.

16   Unification schemes between radio-loud and radio-quiet objects have been proposed but none successfully match the observed source properties and statistics.

17   Three fundamental parameters may be required to account for observed properties of AGN: the mass of the black hole, the accretion rate, and the angular momentum of the black hole; plus the inclination angle at which the system is seen.

8 COSMOLOGY AND EVOLUTION OF AGN

For any distant object we observe, we are looking back in time by an interval which corresponds to the light travel time between us and the object. This can be illustrated by the **light cone** shown in Figure 85. We are at the apex of the cone, and the vertical axis corresponds to time, which increases downwards. What we can directly measure is redshift, z, so we have labelled the vertical axis with z. r denotes distance from us, and we are ignoring the third spatial direction in the diagram, because we can't draw a four-dimensional shape. If we denote the present time as $t = t_0$, then the objects we can see all fall on the surface of the light cone, which is mathematically described by

$$r = c(t_0 - t)$$

Our view of the Universe is limited only to events which fall on the surface of this light cone.

Hubble's law (Equation 7) states that the redshift of a distant object is dependent on its distance from us. This is a consequence of the overall expansion of the Universe. More distant objects are receding from us more rapidly. Consequently we can use the measured redshifts of quasars to indicate their distance, and hence their **lookback time**. This means we could use a conversion between the redshift we measure and lookback time to re-label the vertical axis in Figure 85 in terms of time, t. We observe nearby objects at small lookback times, and the lookback time increases with distance from us.

■ What is the value of redshift, z, at the apex of the light cone?

❑ At the apex of the light cone we are at the present time and $z = 0$. ■

As we learned in Activity 10, only the most luminous objects are detectable at large distances. It is only because quasars are so very luminous that we are able to observe them at high redshift. These most distant quasars emitted the light we currently

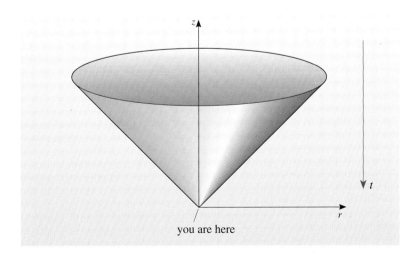

you are here

Figure 85 Our light cone. As we look at more and more distant objects (r increasing) we see light that has been travelling towards us for an increasing time. For the most distant observed objects, the Universe was only a fraction of its current age when the light was emitted.

observe when the Universe was only a fraction of its current age. Hence quasars are vital to the field of observational cosmology. The light from distant quasars allows us to look back in time to the era when the Universe was young.

As mentioned in Section 1.5, the Hubble 'constant' has probably actually changed over time as the Universe's rate of expansion has changed. In fact in the year or so before writing, there have been widely publicized findings that the Universe's expansion is accelerating. This remains subject to considerable debate. The change in the Universe's expansion rate can be described by the deceleration parameter, q_0.

THE SCALE FACTOR AND THE DECELERATION PARAMETER, q_0

The most basic result in observational cosmology is that the Universe is expanding, as described by Hubble's law. One key concept which cosmologists generally adopt is a coordinate system which expands as the Universe expands. A **scale factor** describes the overall change in the size of the Universe, and the scale of the coordinate system. These coordinates, which expand with the Universe, are known as **comoving coordinates**, and a volume which is specified by a set of comoving coordinates is known as a **comoving volume**. Any particular comoving volume will grow at a rate described by the scale factor. Figure 86a shows four possible time dependences of the scale factor. The differences between these four curves are that they correspond to differing amounts of deceleration.

It is logical to expect that the rate of expansion of the Universe has decelerated as a consequence of the mutual gravitational attraction of all the mass in the Universe. Hence cosmologists describe the changing expansion rate in terms of the **deceleration parameter**, q_0. Figure 86a is, accordingly, labelled with four possible values of q_0 corresponding to the four curves. Whatever the value of q_0, we know the rate of expansion at the current epoch must match our measurements of the recessional velocities of (cosmologically) nearby galaxies (Figure 86b). The age of the Universe, and its ultimate fate depend on the value of q_0.

If the Universe has always expanded at the same rate, the deceleration parameter, $q_0 = 0$. Because this implies no self-gravitational deceleration, this is known as an **empty Universe**. Another significant value is $q_0 = 1/2$, which separates **open Universes** ($q_0 < 1/2$), which expand forever, and **closed Universes** ($q_0 > 1/2$), in which the deceleration halts expansion and the Universe eventually contracts to a **big crunch**. $q_0 = 1/2$ corresponds to a Universe which expands forever but decelerates so that it reaches a state of rest at infinite time. The recent suggestions of an accelerating Universe correspond to $q_0 < 0$.

The conversion between redshift and lookback time (or distance) depends how fast the Universe has expanded throughout the time the redshifted light has been travelling. Figure 87 shows the relationship between redshift and lookback time for four possible values of q_0. One of the goals of contemporary observational cosmology is to obtain a robust empirical determination of q_0, hence learning the correct relationship between lookback time and redshift.

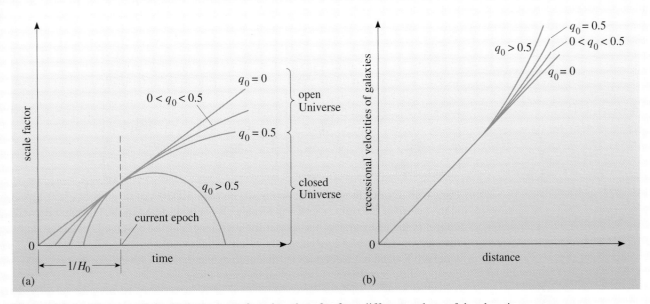

Figure 86 (a) The size of the Universe as a function time for four different values of deceleration parameter, q_0. (b) The deviation from a straight-line relationship between distance and recessional velocity (i.e. Hubble's law) is not obvious for (cosmologically) nearby objects. Hence it is not easy to directly determine the value of the deceleration parameter.

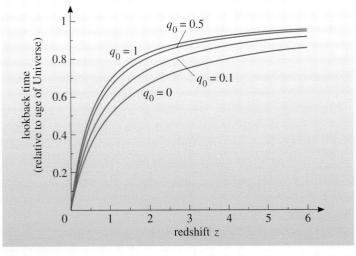

Figure 87 Lookback time as a function of redshift for four possible values of the deceleration parameter, q_0.

(a) Which of the values of q_0 shown in Figure 86a suggests the highest value for the current age of the Universe?

(b) If the Universe's expansion is accelerating, how would its age compare to the age corresponding to your answer in part (a)? ■

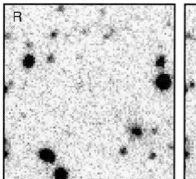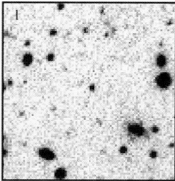

Figure 88 One of the most distant known quasars, RD300, at redshift $z = 5.50$ appears in the centre of the right-hand I band image. It is not detected in the left-hand R band image. In the rest frame of the quasar the wavelength of the observed R band is shorter than the wavelength of Lyman α, so photons which would have appeared in the observed R band have energies sufficient to excite the $n = 1$ level in hydrogen, and consequently are efficiently absorbed by intervening gas.

The most distant observed quasars and radio galaxies have redshifts $z \geq 5$. The light from objects at these distances has taken a large fraction of the age of the Universe to reach us, as Figure 87 shows. Figure 88 shows one of the most distant known quasars, an object called RD300, which has redshift $z = 5.50$.

Question 57

How old was the Universe (as a fraction of its current age) when the I band photons from RD300 shown in Figure 88 were emitted? ■

You might expect that studying the evolution of AGN throughout the age of the Universe would be reasonably straightforward, since there is a simple (albeit unknown!) relationship between the observed redshift of a particular object and the age of the Universe at the time the photons we collect were emitted. Hence distant objects like RD300 (Figure 88) show us how AGN appeared while the Universe was young, and increasingly nearby objects might show us how they change as the age of the Universe increased to the present day. Unfortunately, in practice this is not particularly easy, partly because it becomes increasingly difficult to identify and study AGN as distance increases.

Peterson covers a lot of material on host galaxies, the geometry of the expanding Universe, and observational surveys of quasars before addressing the subject of evolution of AGN. While you are, of course, welcome to read these chapters in Peterson, the material will not be examined in this course. In particular, Chapter 9 of Peterson contains 111 equations (!), summarizing the geometry of the expanding Universe. At the distances quasars are found, the general relativistic curvature of spacetime must be considered. General relativity is beyond the scope of this course, though the 'Course resources' section of the S381 website can direct you to alternative sources of information. We will simply state the results we need from these omitted sections of Peterson, as we proceed to summarize what is known about quasar evolution.

8.1 Number counts and what they reveal

The Malmquist bias studied in Activity 10 can be turned to our advantage. In the following readings an ingenious method is described in which the number of sources detected with fluxes above a limiting value (S) is used.

CUMULATIVE DISTRIBUTION

A **cumulative distribution** is an accumulated count. We will consider $N(S)$, the number of sources with observed flux exceeding the value S. If a histogram was made of number of sources versus detected flux, F, then $N(S)$ would correspond to the number of sources in the histogram between $F = \infty$ (or in reality, F equal to the flux of the brightest source detected) down to $F = S$.

8.1.1 Standard candles in Euclidean space

In the next reading, space is assumed to be **Euclidean**, i.e. general relativistic effects are ignored. In this case distances, areas and volumes can all be calculated using our everyday geometrical equations. For example, the volume of a thin spherical shell with radius r and thickness dr would be given by the surface area of the sphere multiplied by the thickness dr, i.e.

$$V_{shell} = 4\pi r^2 dr$$

and a portion of this shell which subtends a solid angle $d\Omega$ at the centre of the sphere would have a volume dV given by

$$dV = 4\pi r^2\, dr \times \frac{d\Omega}{4\pi} = r^2\, dr\, d\Omega$$

$\log_{10} N$–$\log_{10} S$ for standard candles of uniform space density

Read from the beginning of Peterson Section 10.1.1 (page 159) down to the bottom of page 160.

In this reading, all of the observed sources are assumed to have the same luminosity, L. The astronomical jargon for a source belonging to such a population is '**standard candle**'. For a flux-limited survey of standard candles, whether or not a particular source is detected depends *only* on its distance from us. The sources are assumed to have density, $n(r)$, throughout space, so the number in volume element dV is simply $n(r)dV$.

Pedantically we might also specify that the source must lie within the portion (described by the solid angle, Ω) of the sky which is being observed.

Some notes on the derivation of Peterson Equations 10.6, 10.7 and 10.8 follow this activity.

Keywords: **standard candle, cumulative distribution, space density** ◼

In Peterson Equation 10.4 all that is done is to relabel the sources by their distance rather than their observed flux. The resulting integral is straightforward for uniform density sources:

$$N(S) = \int_0^{r_{max}} n(r) r^2\, dr = n_0 \int_0^{r_{max}} r^2\, dr = n_0 \left[\frac{r^3}{3} \right]_0^{r_{max}} = n_0\, \frac{r_{max}^3}{3}$$

Substituting from Peterson Equation 10.3 then leads to the result

$$N(S) = \frac{n_0}{3}\left(\frac{L}{4\pi S}\right)^{3/2} \tag{81}$$

Before following the rest of Peterson's method, consider the following:

■ Which of the quantities on the right-hand side of Equation 81 are variable?

❑ n_0 is the constant density and L is the constant luminosity. The other quantities are numerical constants except for S which is the limiting flux. Since $N(S)$, which we are working out, is the number of sources which would be detected for any value of S, S is the independent variable. ■

We are interested in how $N(S)$ depends on S, so it would be sensible to try to separate S from the constants. Doing this shows that, in fact, in Equation 81 we have a simple power-law relationship:

$$N(S) = \text{constant} \times S^{-3/2}$$

Peterson arrives at this conclusion by taking logarithms of both sides, leading to

$$\log_{10} N(S) = \log_{10}\left(\frac{n_0}{3}\left(\frac{L}{4\pi S}\right)^{3/2}\right)$$

which we can manipulate using the laws of logarithms. In general

$$\log_{10}(x/y) = \log_{10} x - \log_{10} y$$

and $\quad \log_{10}(x)^n = n \log_{10} x$

Applying these rules in succession:

$$\log_{10}\left(\frac{n_0}{3}\left(\frac{L}{4\pi S}\right)^{3/2}\right) = \log_{10}\left(\frac{n_0}{3}\left(\frac{L}{4\pi}\right)^{3/2}\right) - \log_{10}(S)^{3/2}$$

$$= \log_{10}\left(\frac{n_0}{3}\left(\frac{L}{4\pi}\right)^{3/2}\right) - \frac{3}{2}\log_{10} S$$

i.e. $\quad \log_{10} N(S) = \text{constant} - \dfrac{3}{2}\log_{10} S \tag{82}$

You should recognize this as a power-law relationship, expressed in a form which lends itself to determination of the power-law index by plotting a graph of $\log_{10} N(S)$ versus $\log_{10} S$.

The last part of the reading uses the relationship between apparent magnitude and flux from Block 1 Equation 51a. You may be mystified by Peterson only having one flux and one magnitude in his relationship

$$m \propto -2.5 \log_{10} S \tag{83}$$

while Block 1 Equation 51a states:

$$m_1 - m_2 = -2.5 \log_{10}\left(\frac{S_1}{S_2}\right)$$

where we have used S rather than F for flux to be consistent with the notation used in Peterson. Any astronomical magnitude scale is a relative scale, i.e. it is ultimately defined relative to the flux observed from some standard star, whose magnitude is defined as being zero. If we denote this standard star's apparent magnitude and flux as being m_2 and S_2, then Block 1 Equation 51a becomes

$$m_1 = -2.5 \log_{10}\left(\frac{S_1}{S_2}\right) + m_2 = -2.5 \log_{10} S_1 + (2.5 \log_{10} S_2 + m_2)$$

$$= -2.5 \log_{10} S + A$$

where A is a constant determined by the choice of the standard star. Strictly speaking, there is actually a constant to be added on to Equation 83, but this doesn't change any of the conclusions drawn in the last paragraph on Peterson page 160.

8.1.2 Sources with a luminosity distribution

The **luminosity function** for any class of object gives the number of objects found at each value of luminosity within a fixed volume of space. For example, Figure 89 shows the luminosity function of galaxies and the luminosity function of quasars in the local Universe (i.e. close to $z = 0$).

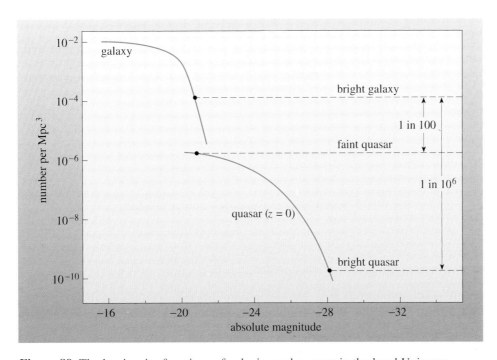

Figure 89 The luminosity functions of galaxies and quasars in the local Universe.

$\log_{10} N$–$\log_{10} S$ for a distance-independent luminosity function

Read the remainder of Peterson Section 10.1.1 from the top of page 161.

In this reading, sources are assumed to have a distance-independent **luminosity function**, $\phi(L)$. The luminosity function is defined such that the number of sources per unit volume with luminosity between L and $L + dL$ is $\phi(L)dL$.

The resulting prediction is that again $N(S) \propto S^{-3/2}$, with the constant of proportionality now including a factor involving an integral over the luminosity function.

Keywords: **luminosity function** ■

8.1.3 General relativistic modifications

A full discussion of the modifications to the expected relationship between $\log_{10} N(S)$ and $\log_{10} S$ for realistic cosmologies is beyond the scope of this course. It requires the working presented in Peterson Chapter 9, which discusses the geometry of the expanding Universe. This geometry is generally discussed in terms of comoving volumes which were introduced in the box on the scale factor and the deceleration parameter. Any particular comoving volume will grow at a rate described by the scale factor.

One of the most mathematically simple general relativistic cosmologies is the Einstein–de Sitter Universe. In the Einstein–de Sitter Universe the kinetic energy of the Universe at the Big Bang is exactly equal to the gravitational energy of the Universe. In this case the expansion of the Universe gradually slows down under self-gravity, so that the acceleration becomes zero at infinite time. This is the cosmological analogue of a projectile in a gravitational field having exactly the escape velocity and corresponds to $q_0 = 1/2$. The Einstein–de Sitter Universe is particularly simple in that it corresponds to 'flat' spacetime in which Euclidean geometry holds, i.e. parallel straight lines never intersect, the angles in a triangle add up to 180°, and the circumference of a circle is 2π times its radius. You may think that in this case, no modifications to the results of Section 8.1.1 would be required, however the Universe expands significantly during the light travel time between high redshift objects emitting photons and us detecting them. This means that the distance between us and the source must be carefully defined, and this leads to a new variable, the **luminosity distance** which is needed for the conversion between luminosity and detected flux. The overall expansion of the Universe means we need to consider comoving volumes, and this requires the scale factor (which depends on H_0 and q_0) to be used. Hence the working leading to Equation 81 is dependent on the cosmological parameters H_0 and q_0 even in the simplest realistic case.

For other possible cosmologies, spacetime is warped so that parallel lines can diverge or intersect. Clearly this introduces serious modifications to the geometry needed to calculate the expected relationship between $\log_{10} N(S)$ and $\log_{10} S$.

For the Einstein–de Sitter Universe and the other possible cosmologies considered by Peterson, the power-law relationship between $N(S)$ and S for constant density standard candles is expected to be shallower than predicted by Equation 81, i.e.

$$N(S) \sim S^{-\alpha} \quad \text{where} \quad \alpha < \tfrac{3}{2}$$

or equivalently, $\dfrac{\mathrm{d} \log_{10} N(S)}{\mathrm{d} \log_{10} S} > -1.5$, the form Peterson uses in a reading in Activity 54.

8.1.4 What can we learn from source counts?

Observational cosmologists would like to use measurements of the relationship between $\log_{10} N(S)$ and $\log_{10} S$ to determine cosmological parameters such as q_0, and hence learn about the evolution of the Universe as a whole. In principle this can be done, but even in an ideal Universe it is technically challenging for several reasons.

Firstly the K-correction (see Activity 29) must be properly and consistently applied. The sample of objects should have their fluxes compared at the same rest wavelength. Generally observations of a sample will be made at a given observed wavelength, and hence a correction must be applied which depends on both the redshift of the source, and on its spectral energy distribution. One of the great strengths of the $\log_{10} N(S)$ versus $\log_{10} S$ method is that it does not require the distances to individual sources to be known, however this advantage is lost in practice because the redshift is required to apply the correct K-correction.

Secondly, the selection of the sample should not be biased. Most quasars are discovered on the basis of their colours, and hence the efficiency of detection is highly dependent on the redshift. We encountered a specific example of this in Activity 8 where the Lyman α selection effect was discussed. Clearly if the sample of quasars being counted has an unsuspected redshift dependence in the detection efficiency this would lead to erroneous conclusions about the geometry of the Universe (i.e. an incorrect value of q_0, would be inferred).

Most importantly, the luminosities of cosmological sources in the real Universe do not obey the assumptions made in either Activity 52 or Activity 53. That is to say the sources themselves evolve, and this evolution must be properly understood before we can proceed to the goals of observational cosmology, and examine the evolution of the Universe as a whole.

Activity 54

$\log_{10} N - \log_{10} S$ and evolution

Read Peterson Section 11.1 (page 175) to the end of the first paragraph of Section 11.1.1 ('… to measure their redshifts'). Then read the first paragraph of Peterson Section 11.1.2 (page 178) including the caption for Peterson Fig. 11.1.

Note that S in Peterson Fig. 11.1 is calibrated in units of mJy. Thus a value of 1 on the horizontal axis corresponds to $S = 10^1$ mJy $= 10 \times 10^{-3}$ Jy $= 10^{-2}$ Jy. Similarly, $S = 1$ Jy corresponds to $S = 10^3$ mJy, i.e. a value of 3 on the horizontal axis.

The dotted line shows $N(S) \propto S^{-3/2}$, while the solid line shows the actual observed cumulative distribution for radio galaxies. At the faint (left) end of the graph, the observations produce a shallower slope than $N(S) \propto S^{-3/2}$ predicts. This can be understood in terms of the general relativistic corrections discussed in Section 8.1.3. At the brighter (right) end of the graph, the observations produce a steeper slope than $N(S) \propto S^{-3/2}$ predicts. This is not consistent with general relativistic corrections for any of the expected cosmologies, and is probably due to evolution of the radio galaxy population, i.e. the excess of sources at fainter fluxes between $S = 1$ Jy (a value of 3 on the horizontal axis) and $S = 10$ Jy (a value of 4 on the horizontal axis) is because the density $n(r, L)$ is not constant. Rather, the observations suggest that the local Universe has a lower space density of luminous radio galaxies than does the Universe at higher distances.

Since higher distances correspond to higher lookback times, this in turn suggests the density of luminous radio galaxies was higher in the past than it is at the current epoch.

Keywords: **radio galaxy evolution** ▪

8.2 Overview of quasar evolution

The source counts method discussed in Section 8.1 leads to the conclusion that the quasar luminosity function is not constant. In order to examine in what way the population of quasars has evolved with time, we need to compare the luminosity functions at various redshifts by using surveys in which the individual sources in the sample have known (measured) redshifts. The subject of how these surveys are performed, and how biases in the sample selection are evaluated and ameliorated is enormous. Peterson devotes an entire chapter to it. In S381 we will skip almost all the details, and focus instead on summarizing the principal conclusions.

Activity 55

The quasar luminosity function at low redshifts

Read the first paragraph of Peterson Section 11.2 (on page 183), then read the second paragraph on page 184 of Peterson (i.e. from 'As suitable samples …') down to Peterson Equation 11.30 and look at Peterson Fig. 11.2.

The function described by Peterson Equation 11.30 has two contributing power laws. The luminosity at which the function changes slope from one power law to the other is determined by the parameter L^*. The parameter ϕ^* determines the overall density.

Peterson Fig. 11.2 (solid lines) shows the function described by Peterson Equation 11.30 for three different redshifts, with the values of L^* and ϕ^* determined by matching observations of over 700 sources.

Keywords: **quasar luminosity function** ▪

Question 58

(a) Describe the QSO luminosity function for redshift $z = 2$.

(b) Describe how the QSO luminosity function changed from redshift $z = 2$ to redshift $z = 0.5$. ■

Activity 56

Density evolution and luminosity evolution

Read the first paragraph of Peterson Section 11.3 (on page 186) which describes the two possibilities illustrated in Figure 90, then read the first part of Peterson Section 11.3.2 (page 189), down to '… appear to us as normal' (page 190). Then read the second paragraph of Peterson page 191, from 'Examination of Fig. 11.2 …' to '… alone to be viable'.

The unit **dex** used in the discussion of the shift required to match the redshift $z = 2$ QSO luminosity function to the $z = 0$ Seyfert 1 luminosity function, is one which was historically widely used by astronomers. 1 dex is a factor of 10, or a change of 1 when the quantity being discussed is expressed as a logarithm to the base 10. The 1.7 dex shift Peterson mentions corresponds to a factor of 50, or a change in the value of the logarithm of 1.7. Since the horizontal axis of Peterson Fig. 11.2 is a magnitude scale (i.e. $\propto 2.5 \log_{10} L$) a shift of 1.7 dex in luminosity is a shift of $(1.7 \times 2.5) = 4.25$ in magnitude. If you imagine sliding the redshift $z = 2$ QSO luminosity function along to the left by 4.25 units on the horizontal axis, you will see it would then match the plotted Seyfert measurements.

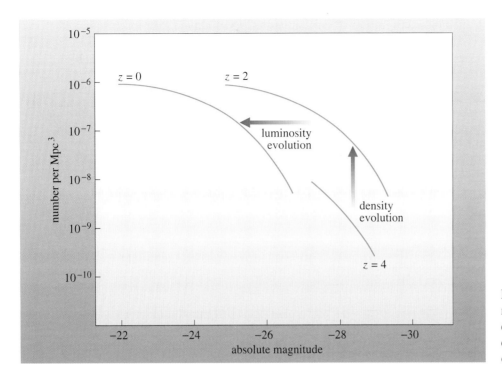

Figure 90 A schematic representation of how pure density evolution and pure luminosity evolution would change the observed QSO luminosity function.

Don't worry too much about deciphering all the numbers in the middle of the paragraph on page 191, just extract the conclusions reached from the quantitative analysis of the luminosity functions.

Keywords: **density evolution**, **luminosity evolution**

Question 59

(a) How is the change in the QSO luminosity function between redshift $z = 2$ and redshift $z = 0.5$ explained in the 'pure density evolution' scenario?

(b) How is it explained in the 'pure luminosity evolution' scenario?

(c) What observational fact rules out the pure density evolution scenario for the changes between redshift $z = 2$ and redshift $z = 0.5$?

A problem prevents us from explaining the changes in the Universe's population of quasars as due to pure luminosity evolution. This explanation would mean that the Universe's population of quasars has accreted continuously, with their luminosities changing in such a way as to create the dependence of the QSO luminosity function on redshift which is observed. This would require the objects which are apparent at redshift $z = 2$ as QSOs of luminosity $L \sim 10^{48}\,\mathrm{erg\,s^{-1}}$ to have accreted roughly the entire mass of the Milky Way Galaxy between redshift $z = 2$ and redshift $z = 0$. This seems unlikely, and difficult to reconcile with observations of galaxies in the local Universe.

Hence, both pure luminosity evolution, and pure density evolution seem unsatisfactory. It is far more likely that the Universe's population of AGN has evolved in a more complex way, with a hybrid **luminosity-dependent density evolution**. In this scenario, individual AGN have both active and dormant states, and the likelihood of a particular AGN becoming dormant is dependent on its luminosity. These active and dormant states may be analogous to the outbursts in dwarf novae and soft X-ray transient binary star systems discussed in Block 3, but in the case of

AGN the timescales for individual sources to evolve are too long for us to directly observe their luminosity evolution. This complicates the use of AGN for cosmological purposes, as we shall see in the case study with which we complete this block.

8.3 Radio galaxies: an evolutionary case study

To give you a feeling for contemporary research, we will now focus on one recent comprehensive study which considers an aspect of AGN evolution. This study, by Blundell, Rawlings and Willott, focuses on radio galaxies and illustrates some basic principles in studying AGN evolution. In the discussion we will highlight, and hope to avoid, some of the pitfalls which can befall extragalactic astronomers. As you read this you should bear in mind that this is a developing research area, and new findings may alter some of the conclusions we present in our case study.

As we learned in the introductory sections, one of the reasons that astronomers have been so interested in AGN is that their prodigious luminosity allows us to see them at large distances, and consequently large lookback times. Therefore astronomers might be able to use AGN to place constraints on cosmological theories. Understandably, there is enormous enthusiasm to do this, but as we will learn in this section, it is absolutely vital to thoroughly understand the AGN themselves before we begin to draw conclusions about parameters like the rate of deceleration (or acceleration) of the Universe.

8.3.1 Brief encounters

Total energy arguments, akin to the mass accretion requirement which ruled out pure luminosity evolution in Section 8.2, imply that the active lifetime of a radio galaxy is much less than the Hubble time. Consequently if we return to the light cone shown in Figure 85 and indicate the timelines of individual radio galaxies with arrows, we obtain Figure 91. Each arrow represents the radio-emitting timeline of an individual radio galaxy and is much shorter than the height of the cone in Figure 91. We are only able to detect a radio galaxy if its timeline intersects our light cone. It is possible for the timeline to intersect the light cone at any stage in the active phase of a radio galaxy's life. Consequently we might, in principle, observe a recently turned on radio galaxy at any epoch in the history of the Universe. There is no correspondence between the time since an observed radio galaxy turned on (i.e. the length of the timeline before it intersected the light cone) and its redshift. The interception of a radio source with our light cone is random and brief.

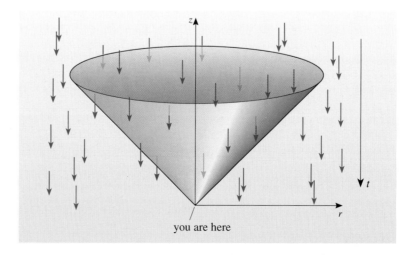

Figure 91 Each arrow represents the radio-loud lifetime of a particular radio galaxy.

8.3.2 Setting the scene

The total bolometric luminosity of a classic double-lobed radio source like those shown in Figure 22 is dominated by the radio emission from the lobes. It is the huge luminosity of these lobes which renders radio galaxies visible at large redshifts, and also leads to the argument that the individual observed sources must have lifetimes far shorter than the age of the Universe.

Observational cosmologists seek to use the observed properties of distant objects to probe the evolutionary changes in the Universe as a whole.

One of the fascinating consequences of the non-Euclidean geometry of the expanding Universe is shown in Figure 92. For objects at cosmological distances, the relationship between the observed angular size, $\delta\theta$, and actual linear size, D, is dependent on the value of the deceleration parameter, q_0. Double-lobed radio sources, such as those shown in Figure 22, can be detected out to cosmological redshifts. If these sources can be regarded as 'standard rods', i.e. having the same linear size, D, irrespective of their redshift, then it might be possible to determine q_0 from them. Comparison of the observed angular sizes of standard rods as a function of redshift with the results shown in Figure 92 would determine which value of q_0 is required.

This is potentially extremely revealing, so of course it has been attempted. Astronomers have used the observed angular size of a sample of double-lobed radio sources to compare with the theoretical expectations shown in Figure 92, and the results tend to favour a low value of q_0, implying that the Universe is open.

Before attempting to draw such conclusions, however, we must be sure that we understand any selection effects which might bias the sample being used, and that we understand the mechanisms by which double-lobed radio sources evolve.

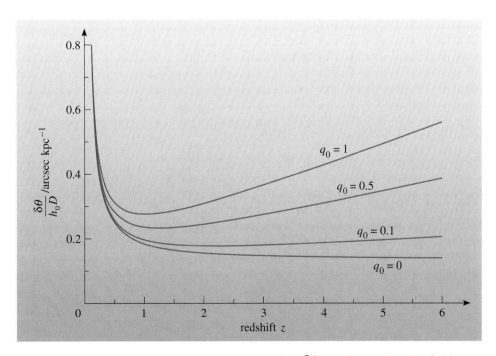

Figure 92 The relationship between the angular size ($\delta\theta$) and linear size, D, of objects as a function of redshift, z, for four different values of the deceleration parameter, q_0. Adapted from Peterson Fig. 9.3.

8.3.3 The basic astrophysics of a classical double-lobed radio source

Here we briefly describe the processes which power the radio emission in a radio galaxy. This is the picture developed into a numerical model by Katherine Blundell and her collaborators, building on the body of prior work, and it has been used in a thorough interpretation of the observed properties of radio galaxies. The most fundamental underlying physical parameters in the model are the jet power, Q, and the age of the source (i.e. the time since it commenced radio-jet emission). This model seems to be successful in providing straightforward self-consistent explanations for the observations, and hence is a useful basis for our discussion. You should, however, bear in mind that this is work at the cutting edge of research, and consequently these ideas are likely to be refined, modified, or possibly even refuted by new developments.

Figure 93 shows a cartoon of one half of a double-lobed radio galaxy. The energy powering the radio emission comes ultimately from the bulk kinetic energy which is transported out along the jet. The bulk kinetic energy of the jet causes a thrust to be applied at the hotspot, where the jet encounters the ambient medium. Momentum must be conserved at the hotspot, and because the relativistic jet has low density, the hotspot advances away from the central engine at a speed much less than the speed of light.

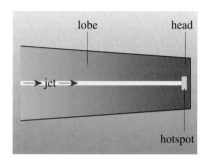

Figure 93 A schematic illustration of the basic features of a radio source.

The hotspot is where the jet's bulk kinetic energy is thermalized at the shock interface between the relativistic jet and the surrounding medium. In this region the magnetic fields are high because the shock processes may amplify the magnetic field so that the magnetic energy density may well approach the thermal energy density. Particle acceleration may therefore occur in the hotspot shock region, and consequently the hotspot and its magnetic field affect the energy spectrum of electrons injected into the head of the radio lobe.

After they leave the hotspot the electrons lose energy by a number of processes, but predominantly by radiating synchrotron radiation, and are consequently gradually degraded to lower and lower energies (a process known as **synchrotron cooling**). This means the lowest frequency radiation is predominantly from the radio lobes, and is relatively uncontaminated by emission from the hotspot. In the lobes the net plasma flow is back towards the central engine because the pressure is highest at the head and decreases steadily back towards the centre. This pressure gradient is illustrated by the red shading in Figure 93.

As the source evolves, the hotspots are pushed further and further away from the core by the jets. The radio lobes expand, and the magnetic field in the lobes is diminished as a consequence of the expansion. Because the magnetic field declines, the Lorentz factor of the electrons contributing to synchrotron emission at a given frequency must increase (see Equations 15 and 24). The electron energy distribution generally gets steeper at higher energies (or equivalently higher Lorentz factors) and consequently the spectrum of the emitted synchrotron radiation gets steeper as the magnetic field decreases.

This means that even if the power of the jet remains constant, the radio emission changes as the radio source evolves.

8.3.4 The luminosity function, the birth function and cosmic evolution

An important issue in considering the cosmic evolution of radio sources is how their properties and numbers change over the history of the Universe. We cannot address this issue by simply comparing the observed luminosity functions at various redshifts because we know that the high redshift observations will miss the lower luminosity sources. We really want to know about the **birth function**, and all we can directly observe is the (high-luminosity part of the) luminosity function.

There is a wide and ill-defined gulf between the luminosity function and the birth function. In Activity 57 you will see how the colourfully named Monte-Carlo simulation technique can be used to give astrophysicists information about objects they can't see. A Monte-Carlo simulation generates a sample of objects via computer by using distribution functions to define the relative numbers of objects with various characteristics. For example, a simulated sample of observed galaxies could be generated from a luminosity function (like that shown in the upper left curve in Figure 89). The luminosity function gives the relative numbers of galaxies observed at each absolute magnitude. The 'Monte Carlo' aspect of this is that a random number generator within the computer is used to select each galaxy in the sample from a distribution defined by the luminosity function. The sample will, therefore, be statistically consistent with the population as defined by the luminosity function. Each time a sample is drawn it will be different, and selected by chance.

The work in this case study uses Monte-Carlo simulations to draw samples of radio galaxies based on the model described in Section 8.3.3. The distribution functions fed into the simulation are of the underlying physical parameters of radio galaxies, such as jet power Q, which govern the (unobservable) birth function. The computer modelling is then used to deduce what the characteristics of the observed population would be. This is a more sophisticated application of the sort of work you did in Activity 10, where the observed flux limits are imposed on the sample in the computer to generate a simulated observed luminosity function corresponding to each assumed birth function.

8.3.5 The key observables

In studying these radio sources there are four key observable quantities:

- the luminosity, L
- the linear size, D
- the redshift, z
- the spectral index, α

We will consider the four quantities listed above and how the observed relationships between them might arise from the physics of the radio galaxies themselves and observational selection effects. Our treatment follows the work of Blundell, Rawlings and Willott, and will allow us to see why some earlier conclusions were flawed.

Clearly any study which examines how the properties of sources change with redshift z needs to consider a large sample of sources, with a range of redshift. The selection of the sample to be studied is a crucial initial issue which needs to be carefully thought out. Unless selection effects are understood, erroneous conclusions will be drawn.

Luminosity and redshift: the Malmquist bias

Activity 10 introduced us to the Malmquist bias, which is the obvious fact that we can always see more luminous objects at greater distances than we can see less luminous objects. The simplest sort of survey astronomers can perform finds a **flux-limited** sample: objects whose flux density at the detector exceeds the sensitivity threshold are detected. Only relatively rare high-luminosity objects can be detected at large redshifts. Because these luminous objects *are* rare they tend to only be found once a large volume of space has been sampled, i.e. they are much more likely to be found at high redshift. Consequently in a flux-limited sample, there is generally a tight *but completely artificial* correlation between L and z, like that shown in Figure 94. This figure shows results for sources from the 3C radio catalogue (the pioneering radio astronomy survey which was discussed in Section 1). While there is a lot of scatter amongst the points, there is also a trend: higher redshift sources tend to be more luminous. This sort of trend is what astronomers mean by a *correlation*. The top-left part of Figure 94 is not populated with objects because high-luminosity objects are rare, and the volume of space sampled at low redshifts is not sufficient to find them. The bottom-right part of Figure 94 (overleaf) is unpopulated because the objects which lie there are too faint to be detected at these redshifts.

In order to circumvent the Malmquist bias's overwhelming influence on the 3C sample, the sensitivity limit must be improved. This was done in subsequent radio surveys, and Figure 95 shows the results. The improved sensitivity means the lower right part of the diagram is populated with intermediate luminosity objects at high redshifts.

■ Why don't the higher sensitivity surveys fill in the top-left region of Figure 94?

❑ Because this gap is due to lack of rare high-luminosity objects in the small volume sampled out to low redshifts. No survey will find objects which are not there (we hope!) ■

Astronomers now have a large sample of radio galaxies. At redshift $z = 2$ the sample shown in Figure 95 spans two orders of magnitude in luminosity, and the sample allows comparison of radio galaxies of a given luminosity over a wide range of redshifts. Of course the Malmquist bias still plays a role at the sensitivity limit of the most sensitive survey, but if we are careful we can understand the way it biases the sample, and hence avoid erroneous conclusions.

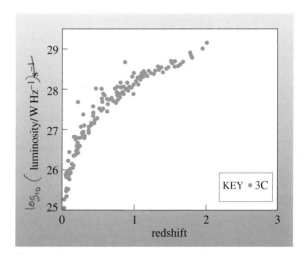

Figure 94 Luminosity versus redshift for objects found in the 3C radio survey. Looking at these data, it would be tempting to conclude that there is a general relationship between redshift and luminosity.

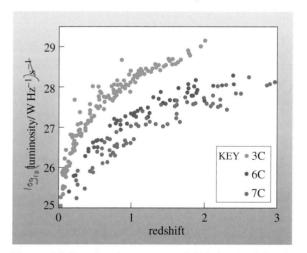

Figure 95 Luminosity versus redshift for the 3C, 6C and 7C radio surveys. The gap between the 3C points and the 6C points arises because the 3C survey covers a larger area of sky, and consequently discovers more of the rare high-luminosity sources than do the 6C and 7C surveys.

The spectral index, α

In our earlier readings about radio galaxies, we learned the conventional wisdom that the radio spectra are power laws which can be described by the spectral index, α. In fact this is an over-simplification.

As Figure 96 shows, when comparing the spectral index of various sources, it is essential that the same part of the spectrum *in the rest frame of the source* is used for all the sources being considered.

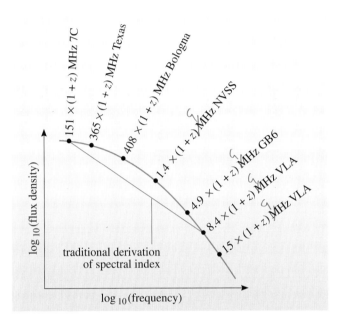

Figure 96 (Blue line) The spectrum of a typical radio galaxy actually looks something like this. The frequencies marked with the bullet points are the frequencies observed by the various radio telescopes indicated, and the $(1 + z)$ factor corrects the observed frequency (constant for any given telescope) to the rest-frame frequency of the emitting radio source (dependent on the redshift, z). (Red line) The traditional derivation of the spectral index α clearly falls short of a complete description of the spectrum.

The linear size, D

We have already mentioned attempts to use the observed angular sizes of radio galaxies to deduce the corresponding linear sizes, and by assuming the radio galaxies can be treated as 'standard rods', learn about the cosmic deceleration parameter q_0. Clearly before conclusions such as these can be made secure, we need to understand what determines the linear size, D, of a particular source. This will allow us to assess whether it is reasonable to make the assumption that extended radio galaxies are good 'standard rods'.

Once an AGN begins to eject jets, lobes will begin to form and gradually expand outwards into the surrounding medium. Consequently the source will grow. The rate of growth will depend on the jet power, Q, and on the density of the ambient medium the head of the lobe is expanding into. Radio galaxies are generally found in groups of galaxies. An approximation to the gas density, ρ, in such groups is given by

$$\rho(r) = \rho_0 \left(\frac{r}{a_0} \right)^{-\beta} \qquad \text{for } r > a_0 \qquad (84)$$

where ρ_0 and a_0 are constants, and the index β determines the variation of the density with distance from the centre of the group.

■ What are the dimensions of the constants ρ_0 and a_0?

❏ ρ_0 has dimensions of mass divided by volume, i.e. it is a density, and a_0 has dimensions of length. ■

The index β is empirically found to be generally ≈ 1.5. Note that Equation 84 is implicitly assuming all radio sources have similar environments. It is known that, in at least some cases, ρ_0 can vary by a factor of about 100.

Ambient gas (assumed to have density determined by Equation 84) is swept up by the bowshock (cf. Figure 82) of the radio source. This leads to a dependence of the linear size, D, on time, t, of the form:

$$D(t) \propto \left(\frac{t^3 Q}{\rho_0}\right)^{1/(5-\beta)} \tag{85}$$

This formula for the evolution of the size of a radio source was published by Falle in 1991; you don't need to know the details of its derivation.

8.3.6 Correlations between observables

Luminosity and spectral index

It has been known since 1960 that the spectral index, α, and the luminosity for observed radio galaxies are correlated, with the more luminous sources having steeper spectral indices. Debate ensued in the subsequent decades about whether the dominant dependence was genuinely on luminosity, or whether in fact the correlation was with redshift. Since objects identified in individual surveys have an artificial correlation between redshift and luminosity (see Figure 94) this issue was not easy to settle. Furthermore, the radio spectrum typically steepens at higher frequencies (see Figures 96 and 97), so sources observed at higher redshifts will have the steeper part of the spectrum redshifted into the frequencies typically used to determine the spectral index as Figure 97 shows. This effect alone will lead to a correlation between redshift and spectral index, and consequently a correlation between luminosity and spectral index for sources found in an individual survey.

Our case study combines samples from the surveys with three different flux limits, consequently overcoming the artificial correlation between redshift and luminosity. The work shows that the luminosity and spectral index *are* genuinely correlated. The model outlined in Section 8.3.3 reveals this is because both quantities are ultimately

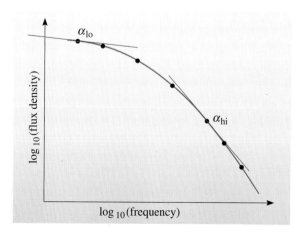

Figure 97 (Blue line) The spectrum of a typical radio galaxy. The red lines schematically indicate how the spectral indices α_{lo}, for low redshift objects, and α_{hi}, for high redshift objects, differ from each other.

dependent on the power of the jets. Higher Q objects are more luminous, and they have higher magnetic fields in their hotspots, which leads to steeper electron energy distributions being injected into the lobes. The steeper electron energy distribution in turn leads to a steeper spectral index.

Linear size, D, and spectral index, α_{lo}

Figure 98 is a graph showing the linear size, D, against the low-frequency radio spectral index, α_{lo}, for objects discovered in the 3C, 6C and 7C surveys. While there is a lot of scatter amongst the points, there is also a trend: bigger sources tend have larger values of α_{lo}.

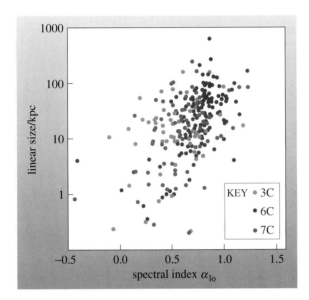

Figure 98 The linear size, D, plotted against spectral index, α_{lo}, for sources from the 3C, 6C and 7C catalogues. Sources with lower spectral indices tend to be smaller.

The correlation between D and α_{lo} can be understood as arising from the underlying physics of synchrotron emission and the expanding radio lobe.

*   As a given radio galaxy ages, its lobes expand and the jet pushes the hotspot ever further from the central engine. The magnetic field in the lobes will decrease as this occurs.

*   Equation 13 tells us that for a given frequency of emission, ν, the electrons contributing synchrotron radiation have a Lorentz factor $\gamma \propto B^{-1/2}$.

Putting these two pieces together, as the source expands, B decreases, so ever more energetic electrons contribute the emitted synchrotron radiation at a particular frequency, ν. Because electrons become increasingly rare at higher values of γ, the emitted spectrum of radiation becomes steeper.

The linear size, D, and the luminosity, L

From the discussion given in Section 8.3.3, it should be clear that we should not expect the luminosity, L, of a particular radio galaxy to remain constant, even if the kinetic power delivered by the jets, Q, remains constant throughout the lifetime of the source. Using the physical model for the radio source outlined in Section 8.3.3 it is possible to calculate the luminosity of the source as it ages.

Clearly there are a number of ingredients which go into this calculation, and we will not attempt to explain and justify them all here. Two of the principal assumptions are that Q is constant throughout the lifetime of each source, and all sources are in environments where the density is described by Equation 84, with index $\beta = 1.5$.

In the next activity we will see the results from the calculations.

8.3.7 Simulating radio galaxies

The physics sketched in Section 8.3.3 was used to build a computer program which calculates the characteristics and evolution of radio sources. In this section we will see some of the output from this work. Numerical simulations have become increasingly important in astrophysical research, and this particular piece of work illustrates two ways that simulations can be used.

1   Firstly, and most straightforwardly, the program calculates the evolution of a single radio galaxy, for input parameters given by the researcher running the program. That is if the researcher specifies the jet power, Q, (which is assumed constant for the lifetime of the source) and the properties of the ambient medium (for instance using Equation 84), the program will output the size, luminosity and emitted spectrum, as a function of time.

2   The program was run many times to simulate entire populations of radio galaxies with different ranges of the input parameters. These populations can then be compared with observational surveys. By matching the key observables in the simulated radio galaxies to the observed surveys it is possible to learn about the range of parameters manifest in the radio galaxies in the real Universe.

Activity 57   **(30 minutes)**

Virtual radio galaxies

From *The Energetic Universe* MM guide, start up the multimedia activity 'Virtual radio galaxies'.

Keywords: **jet power, linear size, flux limit** ■

As we saw in Activity 57 the simulations reveal that the maximum age (since the start of radio emission) at which we can see a source depends on its redshift. As Figure 99 shows, nearby radio galaxies can be detected at all ages, the highest approaching 10^9 years, while at redshift $z = 2$ the oldest sources which are detected switched on less than 10^7 years ago. Consequently if all the objects found in a particular flux-limited survey were examined, the average age of the objects would steadily decrease as redshift increases. This systematic trend is a result of the Malmquist bias selection effect, combined with the declining luminosity of individual sources as they age.

If the physics underlying the radio emission had been left unexamined, there would be no reason to suspect the Malmquist bias would preferentially exclude old radio galaxies at high redshifts. As you might expect, a number of conclusions regarding the changes in radio galaxies as the Universe aged have been drawn by researchers. We will now examine some of these conclusions.

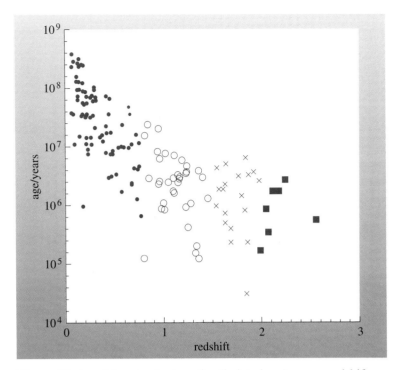

Figure 99 Age (since beginning of radio jet phase) versus redshift from the simulated population of detected radio galaxies.

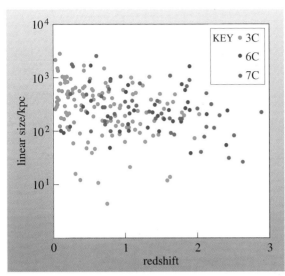

Figure 100 Linear sizes plotted as a function of redshift for objects from the 3C, 6C and 7C surveys. Note that the vertical axis is logarithmic. While there is a lot of scatter, the high redshift sources tend to be smaller.

8.3.8 Observed properties as a function of redshift

In recent decades, trends in radio galaxy properties with redshift have been found and studied. These trends have inspired explanations in which fundamental parameters such as the matter density in the Universe are determined, or which require dramatic evolution in the properties of the intergalactic medium to have occurred. We will examine these trends one by one.

Linear size

Figure 100 shows the linear sizes of classical double-lobed radio sources found in the 3C, 6C and 7C surveys. While there is a lot of scatter, there is a clear correlation in this graph: on average the nearby sources have larger sizes. Note that the vertical axis is logarithmic, so there is a huge spread in sizes plotted. In the 1980s and 1990s there were several studies of this, and no clear-cut conclusions were made about whether the linear size, D, was more strongly correlated with luminosity, L, or redshift, z. This ambiguity was inevitable as the samples being studied contained sources in which the Malmquist bias had introduced a strong artificial correlation between luminosity, L, and redshift, z.

■ What is the difference in linear size between the largest and smallest sources shown in Figure 100?

❑ The smallest is $\approx 10^{0.5}$ kpc, while the largest is $\approx 10^{3.5}$ kpc, so the difference is $(10^{3.5} - 10^{0.5})$ kpc, i.e. $\approx (3000 - 3)$ kpc ≈ 3000 kpc. ■

The work examined in Activity 57 makes it clear what is going on. The linear size, D, of any particular source grows as it ages. Simultaneously the luminosity, L, decreases.

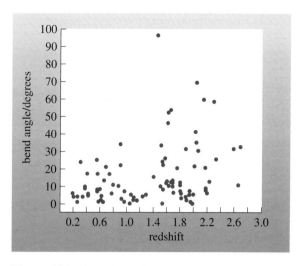

Figure 101 The values of the bend angle plotted as a function of redshift.

The Malmquist bias means that at high redshifts we only detect the luminous sources, which are consequently young. Because these sources are young, they have not expanded as far, and D is on average smaller for them. Hence the correlation in Figure 100.

Any attempt to use the linear size of these radio sources to calibrate the expansion history of the Universe, i.e. determine q_0, must ensure that all systematic effects introduced by observational biases have been understood, calibrated, and removed. These biases introduce effects which are bigger than the differences caused by varying q_0. Consequently Blundell and Rawlings conclude 'the use of classical double-lobed radio sources as 'standardizable rods' is beyond reach'.

Bend angle

While the figures we have seen so far show nice tidy classical double-lobed radio sources, not all of them are aligned in a simple linear shape. Sometimes there is an appreciable bend, with the two jets not being in a single straight line. This distorted geometry can be simply characterized by measuring the bend angle.

In 1988 Barthel and Miley noticed that these distortions increased with increasing redshift, as shown in Figure 101. We see the higher redshift sources as they were in a younger, and on average denser Universe. Barthel and Miley's suggested interpretation of the bend-angle trend was that the higher redshift sources were expanding into an ambient medium which was systematically more likely to induce bending distortions. The trend of bend angle with redshift can alternatively be understood in the context of the younger average age for the high redshift sources: we view them relatively shortly after a jet-inducing event. If, for example, jets are induced by galaxy–galaxy interactions, one might expect a distinctly non-spherical geometry for the intergalactic medium shortly afterwards.

Asymmetric depolarization

As we learned in Activity 50, the polarization of extended radio emission is stronger in the radio lobe on the closer side of a double-lobed radio source. This is attributed to greater Faraday depolarization on the far side, because this radio emission must travel a longer path through the halo of depolarizing gas surrounding the source.

In addition to this asymmetry in the polarization from a single source, it is found that depolarization is greater for sources at higher redshifts. We now know that these higher redshift radio sources are, on the whole, younger. The younger sources are smaller and hence deeper within the gravitational well of the galaxy cluster, where the density will be higher. Consequently the Faraday depolarization will be higher.

Without the realization that the higher redshift radio galaxies are systematically younger, it would be logical to conclude that the properties of the gas haloes around the groups of galaxies which generally harbour radio galaxies had systematically changed as the Universe evolved.

8.3.9 Evolution of radio galaxies: conclusions

In the case study presented here, we have learned that the evolution of radio sources during their individual lifetimes has far-reaching effects on their observed characteristics as a function of redshift. Before attempting to make deductions about cosmological evolution, it is important to thoroughly understand the astrophysics of the sources being used as probes of cosmological evolution. In Section 8.3.8 we saw several examples where individual source evolution produced apparent trends with redshift as a consequence of the Malmquist bias.

We chose this particular study as an example because it shows how unsuspected factors can lead to logical but erroneous conclusions. The true population of radio galaxies in the Universe is greater than that sampled by current surveys. In particular there are many radio galaxies at high redshifts with large values of the jet bulk kinetic power, Q, which have fallen below the detection limit of the surveys because their luminosity diminishes as they age. While we may never detect all these objects, the Monte-Carlo simulation technique may allow us to learn something about them. By including as much of the underlying physics as possible, and seeking a detailed match with all the characteristics of the observed radio source population, the simulations may reveal the underlying birth function, i.e. the history of radio galaxy formation throughout the time since the Big Bang. Learning this has considerable importance for astronomy.

We conclude by saying that the study of optically selected quasars is probably far less vulnerable to the pernicious selection effects we have discussed for classic double-lobed radio galaxies.

8.4 Summary of Section 8

1   The enormous luminosity of AGN means that they can be observed at large distances, and consequently at large lookback times. Therefore observations of AGN have the potential to place constraints on cosmological theories. In practice this is not easy to do correctly because of selection effects and because AGN evolve with time.

2   The conversion between redshift and lookback time (or distance) depends on the deceleration parameter of the Universe. A parameter of $q_0 = 0.5$ separates a closed Universe from an open Universe, whilst $q_0 < 0$ indicates an acceleration.

3   In Euclidean space, the $\log_{10} N$–$\log_{10} S$ relationship between cumulative number count and flux, for standard candles of uniform space density, is $\log_{10} N = \text{constant} - (3/2) \log_{10} S$ or equivalently $\log_{10} N(m) \propto 0.6m$ where m is the apparent magnitude.

4   When realistic space geometries are considered, such as the Einstein–de Sitter Universe, the power-law relationship between N and S for constant density standard candles is shallower, i.e. $N(S) \propto S^{-\alpha}$ where $\alpha < 3/2$.

5   The observed $\log_{10} N$–$\log_{10} S$ relationship for quasars is steeper than the 3/2 power-law prediction at large fluxes. This is opposite to the predictions of an Einstein–de Sitter Universe model. The observations imply there were more radio sources per unit comoving volume in the past (i.e. at large lookback times) than there are now.

6   The luminosity function gives the number of objects found at each value of luminosity within a fixed comoving volume of space. The observed $\log_{10} N$–$\log_{10} S$ dependence indicates that the luminosity function of quasars must be a function of redshift. A useful parameterization of the luminosity function describes it as a combination of two power laws of different slope, with a smooth break point between them.

7   Two possibilities for the evolution of the quasar luminosity function are (i) a small fraction of galaxies contain AGN and the luminosities of these sources changes with time (luminosity evolution) or (ii) virtually all galaxies contain AGN but at any given time most are dormant and the fraction of galaxies with AGN in an active state changes with time (density evolution) with the relative numbers of bright and faint AGN remaining fixed.

8   Pure density evolution is not consistent with the observation that very bright AGN were a higher proportion of the entire population at redshift $z = 2$ compared with redshift $z = 0.5$. Pure luminosity evolution would require that AGN accrete roughly the entire mass of a typical galaxy between redshift $z = 2$ and $z = 0.5$, which is difficult to reconcile with observations of nearby galaxies. A hybrid luminosity-dependent density evolution is likely to have occurred.

9   The active lifetime of a radio galaxy is much less than the age of the Universe (or the Hubble time, $t_0 = 1/H_0$), so we cannot observe all AGN at all redshifts. Recently turned on radio galaxies may (in principle) be observed at any epoch in the history of the Universe. An AGN is observed only if its active time line intersects with our light curve.

10 The total bolometric luminosity of a double-lobed radio galaxy is dominated by the radio emission from the lobes. The energy powering this emission ultimately comes from the bulk kinetic energy which is transported along the jet.

11 The hotspot in the lobe is where the jet's bulk kinetic energy is thermalized. After leaving the hotspot, electrons lose energy by synchrotron cooling.

12 The four key observable quantities in studying the evolution of radio galaxies are their luminosity (L), linear size (D), redshift (z) and spectral index (α).

13 In a flux-limited sample of galaxies (such as the 3C radio survey), only relatively rare, high-luminosity sources can be detected at large redshifts, so there is generally a tight correlation between L and z. This is known as the Malmquist bias. Improving the sensitivity limit of a survey (such as in the 6C and 7C radio surveys) means that more low-luminosity objects are found at high redshift.

14 The spectra of radio galaxies cannot be completely described by simple power laws across a large range of frequency. Hence, when comparing the spectral slopes of different galaxies, it is vital that the same part of the spectrum in the rest frame of the source is used in each case.

15   Radio spectra typically steepen at higher frequencies, so sources observed at large redshift will have the steeper parts of the spectrum shifted into the region usually used to measure spectral indices. This correlation between z and α leads to an observed correlation between L and α.

16   As a radio galaxy ages, its lobes expand and the magnetic field in the lobes decreases. So the energy of the electrons contributing to the synchrotron radiation at a particular frequency must increase. Because the electron energy distribution is steeper at higher energies, the emitted spectrum of radiation becomes steeper. Hence there is a correlation between D and α in the sense that bigger sources tend to have larger values of spectral index.

17   Computer simulations of expanding radio galaxies reveal that for a constant jet power, luminosity decreases with age. The Malmquist bias then means that the maximum age at which we can see a source depends on its redshift. Nearby radio galaxies can be detected at all ages (up to $\sim 10^9$ years old) whilst at redshift $z = 2$, the oldest detected sources switched on less than $\sim 10^7$ years ago. Consequently, in a flux-limited sample, the average age of the objects will decrease with increasing redshift.

18   Observational studies of radio galaxies reveal that in general, nearby radio galaxies have larger sizes than more distant ones. At high redshift we only detect luminous sources (the Malmquist bias), which are consequently young and which have therefore not expanded as much.

19   Observational studies also reveal that the bend angle of double-lobed radio sources increase with redshift. Since the detected high redshift radio galaxies are younger, their jets have only recently formed (perhaps as a result of galaxy–galaxy interactions), and so the local intergalactic medium is likely to be inhomogeneous and more likely to induce bends in jets.

20   Depolarization is seen to be greater for sources at larger redshifts. Since these sources are on average younger, and in dense environments which recently triggered jet formation (i.e. by galaxy mergers), the disordered intergalactic medium is particularly suitable for giving a large Faraday depolarization.

9 CONSOLIDATION AND REVISION

You have now reached the final week of the final block of *The Energetic Universe*. Your study of AGN over the last eight weeks has explored many aspects of their behaviour, however, there remains much more we could have covered, had time allowed. The last few chapters of Peterson for instance cover many interesting aspects of AGN and cosmology. There is simply not the space or time in this course to pursue that topic comprehensively, but we hope Section 8 gave you a taste. Other Open University courses offer you opportunities to study space, time and cosmology and to explore these links further. An indication of the breadth of topics in astrophysics related to AGN, as noted by Peterson, is that *one-fifth* of all research astronomers study AGN! One consequence of this, as remarked earlier, is that the subject is one which is evolving rapidly and where theories are continuously being modified and developed. The material you have studied in Section 8 covers one such area at the forefront of current research. However, you should certainly not feel disheartened that there is so much more to learn – that is one of the joys of astrophysics – it really is impossible to know it all. Having reached this point in the course, you now have an extremely thorough grounding in the astrophysics of active galaxies. Should you choose to pursue your study of this topic further, at postgraduate level for instance, this block provides an excellent preparation. And if this course represents the culmination of your astrophysics study, you can rest assured that you are up-to-date with the current knowledge concerning the most distant and energetic phenomena in the Universe.

9.1 Reviewing the properties of AGN

At this point, however, you should sit back to revise and consolidate what you have learnt in Block 4 of this course. The main theme of the block has been an exploration of the various components of electromagnetic radiation that are emitted by AGN and how their locations and emission mechanisms can be explained in terms of a 'unified model' of the various subclasses of AGN. The questions and activities below will help you to consolidate your understanding of this topic.

As a first step in your revision week you may wish to reread the summaries of the preceding eight main sections. Reflect on each item in the summary lists. Repeat the statements in your own words, and expand on them as if you had to explain the underlying concepts, ideas and implications to somebody who has a general background in astrophysics, but who is not an expert in active galaxies. It is quite likely that you will have difficulties recalling the context and importance of quite a few of these summary items. There is no reason to be afraid if this is the case. Rather, go back to the relevant individual subsections and find the corresponding discussion in the Study Guide or Peterson.

The following few questions allow you to revise some of the key topics in this block. First, to help you appreciate the differences between two important regions that are recognized in AGN, in Question 60 you are asked to compare quantitatively the physical properties of the broad- and narrow-line regions. Then, in Question 61 you will revise the simple model for explaining the difference between Seyfert 1 and Seyfert 2 galaxies in terms of an orientation effect and the visibility of the BLR and

NLR. Question 62 looks at the role of special relativity in explaining the observed properties of blazars and radio galaxies, and Question 63 asks you to compare the properties and behaviour of AGN and interacting binaries. Question 64 looks at the mechanisms for the emission of continuum electromagnetic radiation that you have read about in this block, whilst Question 65 focuses on the diagnostic properties of forbidden emission lines.

Question 60

Refer back to the data in Peterson Chapters 5 and 6 (or the summaries for Sections 5 and 6 in this Study Guide) to complete Table 5 comparing the various properties of the broad-line region and the narrow-line region in AGN. Comment on the differences and similarities between their properties. ■

Table 5 For use in Question 60.

Property	Broad-line region	Narrow-line region
line widths, Δv		
cloud temperature, T		
cloud electron density, n_e		
overall size of region, r		
total mass of region		
total number of clouds, N_c		
filling factor, ϵ		
size of a typical cloud, l		
covering factor, f		

Question 61

(a) Explain how different inclination angles between the line of sight and the plane of symmetry in an AGN produce different views of the BLR and NLR and so lead to a classification of Seyfert galaxies into two main types. (b) Comment on what the relative numbers of galaxies in these two subclasses imply about the geometry of the central regions of these AGN. ■

Question 62

Summarize the role of the constant speed of light and special relativistic effects in giving rise to (a) the emission from blazars and (b) the observed motion of components seen in the compact cores of radio galaxies. ■

Question 63

Write a paragraph (less than about 300 words) comparing the physical properties and accretion processes that occur in the central engines of AGN and in interacting binary stars. ■

Question 64

Several different mechanisms for the production of continuum electromagnetic radiation are seen to operate in AGN. Write a summary (less than about 500 words) comparing and contrasting the three main continuum emission mechanisms you have read about in this block. Pay particular attention to the type of spectral energy distribution produced by each mechanism, and whether each process is thermal or non-thermal in origin. ■

Question 65

Explain how the presence or absence of forbidden emission lines in the spectra of AGN gives an indication of the physical conditions of the regions within which the lines arise. ■

Activity 58 and Activity 59 direct you to two review articles on AGN topics. These articles are not written for a popular audience, but aimed at astrophysicists who wish to update their knowledge in fields where they are not necessarily experts. Therefore you should *not* expect that the articles will be *easy* to read. What is more, they will contain some new concepts and ideas, and may use a slightly different notation from what you are used to. You are *not* expected to remember – or in fact completely understand – these new concepts. The review articles should give you a slightly different perspective on the issues that we have discussed in the block. When you read the reviews, compare them with the material in the corresponding sections of the Study Guide.

Activity 58   (90 minutes)

The BLR revisited

For an extensive discussion of the BLR, and a revision of the material you read in Section 5, go to the S381 home page and follow the instructions there to download a journal article on the topic of AGN broad-line regions.

Keywords: none ■

Activity 59   (90 minutes)

Unification revisited

For an extensive discussion of AGN unification, and a revision of the material you read in Section 7, go to the S381 home page and follow the instructions there to download a journal article on the topic of AGN unification.

Keywords: none ■

The concluding activity of the course provides you with a final look at the Image Archive. Active galaxies exhibit some of the most stunning astronomical visions of the Universe and represent a suitably inspiring note on which to end the block.

Images of AGN

Use the Image Archive (from *The Energetic Universe* MM guide) to search for and display all images of active galaxies that are available and read their captions. In particular you may wish to concentrate on:

1   Images of quasar host galaxies revealing the environments in which luminous AGN are located.

2   Images of so called 'type 2 quasars' or 'obscured quasars' which are predicted to exist by unification models and which are now beginning to be found.

Keywords: none ■

9.2 The end of the course

Congratulations! You have now reached the end of *The Energetic Universe*. We hope you have enjoyed learning about the life and death of stars, about interacting binary stars and about active galaxies. Throughout the course we have tried to demonstrate how physical processes which have been discovered in laboratories here on Earth can be applied to these vastly more distant astrophysical phenomena. In doing so we have drawn on a huge range of physics from Newtonian mechanics and gravitation to special and general relativity, from the classical physics of gases to the quantum physics of degenerate matter, and from atomic and nuclear physics to the physics behind the production of electromagnetic radiation and its interaction with matter. The treatment of these topics has been quite mathematical in places: this was necessary to obtain a *quantitative* understanding of the phenomena in question. As we noted right at the beginning of the course, we hope you did not get bogged down in the mathematics and instead were able to see the underlying physics that described the astrophysical processes in each case.

The fact that you embarked on this course in the first place probably means that you share our enthusiasm and excitement about the Universe and the remarkable things it contains. We hope that, having learnt something about the astrophysics involved with the three topics which form the basis of Blocks 2, 3 and 4 of the course, you will be inspired to continue your exploration of, and your interest in, the Energetic Universe.

ACHIEVEMENTS

Now that you have completed this block, you should be able to:

A1   Explain the meaning of the newly defined (emboldened) terms introduced in this block, and understand these when they are used in scientific articles not specifically written for students.

A2   Use specialized vocabulary relevant to AGN appropriately and accurately.

A3   Convert between SI, cgs, and other units used by astronomers.

A4   Use on-line research archives effectively, including using citation lists to find research which follows-up the work reported in any given paper.

A5   Understand the meaning and importance of unbiased samples, selection effects, and observational biases, such as the Malmquist bias.

A6   Explain how aberration arises as a result of the Earth's motion through space.

A7   Describe how relativistic beaming arises in an AGN and explain why the luminosity of an approaching jet is enhanced.

A8   Describe the observations which lead to the detection of apparent superluminal motion in AGN and explain how this arises.

A9   Explain how gravitational (macro-) lensing arises and describe the observational consequences, and describe what information might be learned from gravitational microlensing of AGN.

A10 Understand how flux variation timescales can be used to place limits on the size of an emitting region, as a result of light travel time arguments.

A11 Describe how time delays between different emission components can be used to determine distance scales within an active galaxy, including an understanding of the concept of reverberation mapping.

A12 Appreciate what is implied by a cross-correlation and what information may be obtained by performing such an operation on two light curves.

A13 Describe how cyclotron, synchrotron, thermal bremsstrahlung and blackbody radiation are produced and calculate the synchrotron spectrum using a spreadsheet.

A14 Understand what is implied by Thomson scattering and Compton scattering of radiation and describe how the processes of synchrotron self absorption and synchrotron self Comptonization arise.

A15 Distinguish between those radiation mechanisms which are thermal and non-thermal, those which are optically thin and optically thick, and those which gives rise to polarized emission and those which do not.

A16 Understand how radiation may become polarized or depolarized and what is meant by Faraday depolarization.

A17 Recognize a power-law relationship and determine the power-law index from a log–log plot.

A18 Recognize the atomic transitions that are responsible for Lyman and Balmer lines, and understand how features such as absorption edges arise.

A19 Distinguish between permitted and forbidden transitions and lines and recognize under what circumstances each of these arise.

A20 Describe the typical broad-band SED of an AGN including the major spectral features such as the big blue bump, small blue bump, IR bump and submillimetre break, and how each of these features is thought to arise.

A21 Describe how IR emission from AGN is thought to arise and the importance of sublimation of dust grains in determining the form of the SED.

A22 Understand how X-ray spectra are characterized and appreciate the relationship between the photon index and energy index of a SED.

A23 Appreciate under what circumstances electron–positron pair production can occur in AGN.

A24 Recognize what is meant by K-shell and L-shell absorption edges and spectral lines in X-ray spectra.

A25 Describe the role of reflection components in explaining the X-ray SEDs of AGN.

A26 Appreciate how the width of a spectral line can indicate either the temperature of the gas or the bulk motion of the material in which it arises.

A27 Describe the difference between case A and case B recombination, and know why case B is more applicable to astrophysical nebulae.

A28 Use the concept of a recombination coefficient to determine the emissivity of a recombination line.

A29 Have familiarity with fine structure sublevels in atomic energy levels and how these lead to multiplet spectral lines.

A30 Know how to describe the relative probabilities of various processes in terms of Einstein probability coefficients, cross-sections, and collision rates.

A31 Appreciate the interplay between radiative and collisional excitation, de-excitation, ionization, and recombination mechanisms in astrophysical nebulae.

A32 Understand how ratios of multiplet spectral lines can be used to measure the electron temperature and electron density of the narrow-line region, and other low-density nebulae.

A33 Understand how photospheric absorption lines in stars arise as a consequence of the temperature gradient and wavelength-dependent absorption cross-sections.

A34 Appreciate what is meant by an ionization parameter and what it implies about conditions in different parts of an AGN, and explain the concept of ionization equilibrium and Strömgren depth.

A35 Demonstrate knowledge of the most important historical developments in the study of AGN.

A36 Understand the cosmological interpretation of redshifts, and some of the evidence supporting this for quasars.

A37 State the accepted explanation for the power source of active galaxies.

A38 Apply the virial argument to observed quantities and consequently deduce masses of relevance to AGN.

A39 Appreciate under what circumstances accretion of material gives rise to emission of radiation and when it does not, and describe the importance of the Eddington luminosity and Eddington accretion rate.

A40 Use the concept of the Roche limit to determine how close to a black hole an object may approach without being tidally disrupted.

A41 Appreciate how the angular momentum of accreting material influences the accretion process and the consequent emission of radiation, and why luminous AGN cannot be predominantly fed by undisrupted stars.

A42 Appreciate how the temperature of an accretion disc around a black hole may be determined and describe the theoretical form of the emission spectrum and luminosity of a multicolour blackbody accretion disc.

A43 Recognize what modifications to the theoretical picture of an accretion disc may be required at very low and at very high accretion rates.

A44 Explain the distinctions between Seyfert galaxies and quasars, between type 1 and type 2 Seyfert galaxies and between broad- and narrow-line radio galaxies. Explain what blazars, BL Lacs and OVVs are believed to be and classify radio galaxies according to type (FR I or FR II).

A45 Understand what LINERs are and describe how a BPT diagram may be used to distinguish them from narrow line AGN.

A46 Describe the nature of broad emission lines observed in AGN spectra and how the parameters of these lines may be used to infer the physical properties of the region in which they arise.

A47 Describe the nature of narrow emission lines observed in AGN spectra and how the parameters of these lines may be used to infer the physical properties of the region in which they arise.

A48 Compare, quantitatively, the physical properties of the broad-line region and narrow-line region in AGN.

A49 Understand the concepts of filling factor and covering factor generally, and in relation to the broad-line region and narrow-line region in AGN.

A50 Describe what ionization cones are, where they occur in AGN, and what measurements of them imply about the structure of AGN.

A51 Describe models which attempt to explain the broad-line profiles and narrow-line profiles in AGN spectra and the limitations of these models.

A52 Describe what is meant by the Baldwin effect and what it implies.

A53 Describe what is meant by the Faber–Jackson relationship and give an argument explaining how it might arise.

A54 Describe schemes for the unification of AGN and explain how differences in observed characteristics may arise as a result of a combination of real differences (due to parameters such as luminosity, black hole mass, accretion rate, black hole angular momentum) and apparent differences (due to parameters such as orientation).

A55 Describe the difference between weak and strong unified models of AGN.

A56 Describe the limitations and successes of different unification schemes, and how different schemes may be tested.

A57 Appreciate what is implied by the phrase 'obscured QSOs' or 'type 2 quasars' and how these may be related to ULIRGs (ULIGS).

A58 Explain the importance of AGN for cosmological studies and appreciate the limitations arising from selection effects and an incomplete understanding of the evolution of individual sources.

A59 Understand the role of the scale factor and deceleration parameter in describing the history of the Universe, and explain how these parameters are related to the Hubble 'constant'.

A60 Understand how conversions may be made between redshift and lookback time, and how this depends on the deceleration parameter.

A61 Explain how the $\log_{10} N$–$\log_{10} S$ relationship appropriate to Euclidean space arises. Describe the departures from this relationship which arise from realistic general relativistic geometries. Know how the observed $\log_{10} N$–$\log_{10} S$ relationship behaves, and what this implies.

A62 Explain what is meant by the luminosity function of AGN, and describe the various possibilities for how it might have evolved with time.

A63 Describe how apparent correlations between observable quantities in AGN, for example luminosity, linear size, redshift and spectral index in radio galaxies, may arise as a result of selection effects.

A64 Appreciate that the finite lifetime of a radio galaxy and the fact that they fade as they age imply that the maximum age at which we can see a radio galaxy depends on its redshift, and consequently that, in a flux-limited sample, the average age of objects will decrease with increasing redshift.

A65 Explain how observations such as the bend angle of double-lobed radio sources increasing with redshift, and depolarization of radio sources increasing with redshift, may be understood in terms of a radio galaxy evolution model.

A66 Appreciate the potential importance of infrared observations for studying the early phases of AGN evolution.

A67 Appreciate the evidence that normal galaxies may be quiescent AGN.

ANSWERS TO QUESTIONS

Question 1

It is thought that accretion onto supermassive black holes powers the emission from active galactic nuclei. In basic physics terms, the electromagnetic radiation is powered by the liberation of gravitational potential energy as matter falls in the gravitational field.

You may also have included some discussion of how the viscosity of the accreting material plays a role in converting kinetic energy into thermal energy and consequently radiation, drawing on your knowledge from Block 3.

Question 2

The virial theorem is derived from the equation of *hydrostatic equilibrium*: therefore the assumption behind the use of Peterson Equation 1.1 is that a state of equilibrium under self-gravity holds.

If the Seyfert galaxy was far from equilibrium, it would be unlikely that the emission would last for as long as 10^8 years (cf. Peterson page 4). So, while it is clear that some material must be falling under the gravitational influence of the supermassive black hole, it is probably safe to assume a near-equilibrium configuration for our first estimate of the mass of the central black hole.

Question 3

Redshift refers to the shifting of the wavelength of a spectral line. Cosmological redshift indicates that this shifting in wavelength in the light emitted by a distant source occurs as a consequence of the overall expansion of the Universe. If a redshift is cosmological, Hubble's law can be used to infer the distance of the emitting object.

Question 4

Choosing two convenient points on the straight line, for example $(x = 9.0, y = 1.75)$ and $(x = 10.0, y = 1.25)$, we can calculate the slope of the line. The slope is

$$\frac{\Delta y}{\Delta x} = \frac{1.75 - 1.25}{9.0 - 10.0}$$

Putting in the values we get

$$\frac{\Delta y}{\Delta x} = -0.5$$

Comparing this with the information in Section 1.7.3, we see that in this case, the power-law index, α, is $\alpha = 0.5$. But we must note that the question asked instead for the particle exponent, s, so we need to determine s using the relationship $\alpha = (s - 1)/2$.

Rearranging, we have $s = 2\alpha + 1$, i.e. $s = 2(0.5) + 1$,

Our final answer is that the graph shows synchrotron emission from a distribution of electrons with a particle exponent $s = 2$.

Question 5

There are three ways you might have approached this question. A method which the material in this chapter might have suggested is to use Figure 9, noting that it has logarithmic axes. The Rayleigh–Jeans tail is the part of the Planck function which appears as a positive gradient straight line in this graph. A power-law relationship will always appear as a straight line in a log–log plot. Since the line has a positive gradient, p must be positive: both facts imply that $B_{v,\text{Rayleigh–Jeans}}$ increases as v increases. We can use this to check that our answer makes sense.

Clearly, the Rayleigh–Jeans tail is easiest to measure for the uppermost curve plotted on Figure 9 because it is (a) longer, and (b) less cluttered by other lines which might confuse the issue. To measure the gradient of the straight line, we need to:

(i) choose two points which are widely separated, and read off the $(\log_{10} v, \log_{10} B_v)$ values for each;

(ii) subtract them to work out the values of $\Delta \log_{10} v$ and $\Delta \log_{10} B_v$ for each; and

(iii) divide to evaluate

$$\frac{\Delta \log_{10} v}{\Delta \log_{10} B_v}$$

which is the gradient of the line in the graph.

Applying this method, the points marked on Figure 102 illustrate one sensible choice. Reading off the $(\log_{10} v, \log_{10} B_v)$ values, we have the lower point at $(\log_{10} v = 5, \log_{10} B_v = -19.5)$ and the upper point at $(\log_{10} v = 16, \log_{10} B_v = 2.5)$.

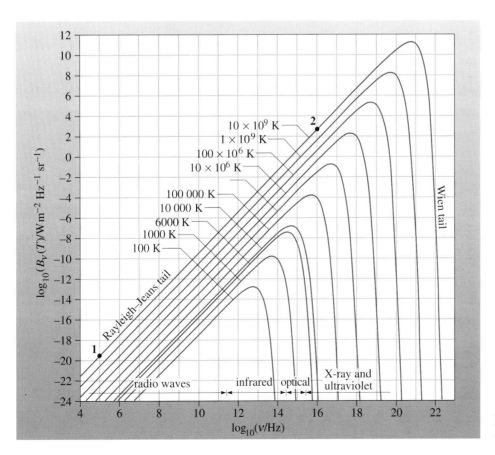

Figure 102 A copy of Figure 9 with two example points chosen.

Therefore $\Delta\log_{10} v = 16 - 5 = 11$ and $\Delta\log_{10} B_v = 2.5 - (-19.5) = 22$

Hence $\quad \dfrac{\Delta\log_{10} v}{\Delta\log_{10} B_v} = \dfrac{22}{11} = 2$

The question asked us 'if we write $B_{v,\text{Rayleigh–Jeans}} \propto v^p$, what is the value of p?'. Taking logarithms of both sides of the expression we have

$$\log_{10} B_v = \log_{10} v^p = p\log_{10} v$$

where we used the properties of logarithms in the second step. Hence if we make the substitutions $y = \log_{10} B_v$ and $x = \log_{10} v$, and recall that a straight-line graph represents the general equation

$$y = mx + \text{constant}$$

we see that a graph of $\log_{10} B_v$ versus $\log_{10} v$ will be a straight line of gradient p. Thus, using the result evaluated in (iii) above, we see that $p = 2$.

Therefore the Rayleigh–Jeans tail of the Planck function is a power law, $B_{v,\text{Rayleigh–Jeans}} \propto v^2$.

Alternatively, if you are mathematically inclined, you might have looked back to Block 1, Equation 154a:

$$B_v(T) = \frac{2hv^3}{c^2}\,\frac{1}{\exp\!\left(\dfrac{hv}{kT}\right) - 1}\ \text{W m}^{-2}\,\text{Hz}^{-1}\,\text{sr}^{-1} \qquad \text{(Block 1, 154a)}$$

Noting that the Rayleigh–Jeans tail occurs at the lowest energies, so $(hv/kt) \ll 1$ we can expand in powers of (hv/kt) using the Maclaurin series expansion, exactly as in Block 1, Example 21. Referring back, we see that the Rayleigh–Jeans tail obeys the equation

$$B_v(T) = \frac{2kTv^2}{c^2}$$

as in Equation 11. From this we see that our deduction, $p = 2$, from the graph was correct, and further that the constant of proportionality in this power law is $2kT/c^2$.

Comparing these two methods, clearly the second is more powerful: it gives additional information, and the answer is exact. Reading values from graphs will always be subject to some uncertainty due to measurement errors. Of course sometimes we only have measurements, and no exact mathematical description explaining the underlying relationship. In these cases, plotting measured quantities on a log–log graph will immediately show (by the presence of a straight-line relationship) if there is a power-law relationship between the quantities plotted.

The third, and most straightforward way to answer the question would have been to use the expression for the Rayleigh–Jeans tail given in Equation 11 to deduce $p = 2$.

Question 6

(a) From the spreadsheet produced in Activity 4, using a magnetic field strength of 10^{-9} T, to produce synchrotron radiation with radio frequencies, i.e. a few $\times\, 10^9$ Hz, requires input electron energies of a few $\times\, 10^9$ eV, i.e. a few GeV. This means that very energetic electrons are needed to produce even radio synchrotron emission which lies at the low-energy end of the electromagnetic spectrum.

(b) If the magnetic field strength is reduced to 10^{-10} T, then even more energetic electrons, with energies of at least 10 GeV (10^{10} eV), are required to produce radio synchrotron emission.

Question 7

With an electron energy power-law index of 2.7, the slope of the synchrotron spectrum is −0.85. This agrees with the relationship in the text: $\alpha = (s-1)/2$.

Question 8

The first paragraph of Peterson Section 1.3 gives

- star-like objects identified with radio sources
- time-variable continuum flux
- large UV flux
- broad emission lines
- large redshifts
- large X-ray flux

as typical common characteristics of quasars.

Question 9

(a) 3C 465 is a FR I galaxy. It is clearly brightest in the centre, with the surface brightness decreasing towards the edges of the lobes. Figure 103 shows an annotated version of the intensity maps in Figure 23.

(b) 3C 105 shows the regions of enhanced emission at the edge of the radio lobes characteristic of the FR II class.

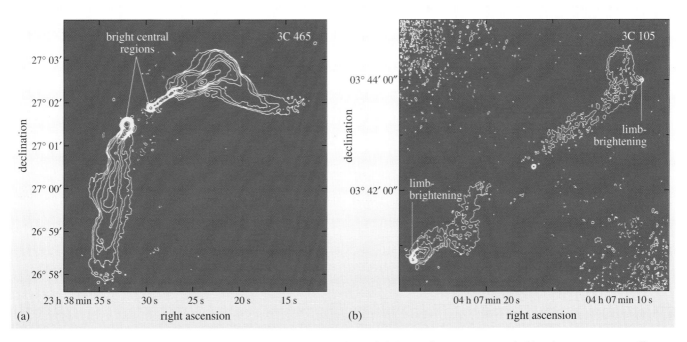

Figure 103 (a) The central regions of this radio galaxy (3C 465) are brightest: they are surrounded by the most contour lines. Hence it can be classified as a member of the FR I class. (b) This radio galaxy (3C 105) shows regions of bright emission at the extreme edges of the lobes, i.e. it exhibits 'limb-brightening'. Hence it can be classified as a member of the FR II class.

Question 10

The permitted lines are: Hδ, Hγ, Hβ, Hα, HeI λ3587, CaK, HeII λ4686, HeI λ5876, NaD, Lyα, NV λ1240, SiIV λλ1394, 1403, CIV λ1549, HeII λ1640, OI λ1304, CII λ1335.

The forbidden lines are: [NeV] λ3425, [OII] λ3727, [FeVII] λ3760, [NeIII] λ3869, [OIII] λ4363, [OIII] λ4959, [OIII] λ5007, [FeVII] λ6087, [NII] λ6583, [OI] λ6300, [NV] λ3346, [NIII] λ3968, [SII] λ4071, [CaV] λ5309, [FeVII] λ5721, [OI] λ6364, [FeX] λ6374, [SII] λλ6717, 6731.

The semiforbidden lines are: OIV] λ1402, OIII] λ1663, SiIII] λ1892, CIII] λ1909, NIV] λ1486, NIII] λ1750

Question 11

The wavelength and frequency are related by the wave equation: $c = \lambda \nu$, where c is the speed of light and λ and ν are the wavelength and frequency respectively (Block 1, Equation 151). Therefore, at wavelength 912 Å, the frequency is

$$\nu = c / \lambda = \frac{2.998 \times 10^{10}}{912 \times 10^{-8}} \frac{\text{cm s}^{-1}}{\text{cm}}$$

where we have been careful to use consistent units of length. Evaluating this we obtain $\nu = 3.29 \times 10^{15}$ Hz.

The energy of the photon is given by $E_{\text{ph}} = h\nu$ (Block 1, Equation 152), so evaluating this with $h = 6.626 \times 10^{-34}$ J s, we obtain $E_{\text{ph}} = 6.626 \times 10^{-34} \times 3.29 \times 10^{15}$ J, i.e. $E_{\text{ph}} = 2.18 \times 10^{-18}$ J. If we instead use the cgs value for h: $h = 6.626 \times 10^{-27}$ erg s, we obtain $E_{\text{ph}} = 6.626 \times 10^{-27} \times 3.29 \times 10^{15}$ erg, i.e. $E_{\text{ph}} = 2.18 \times 10^{-11}$ erg. We could alternatively have arrived at this by multiplying the answer in joules by 10^7, since there are 10^7 erg per joule. To obtain the energy of the photon in electronvolts we need to remember that an electronvolt is the energy gained by accelerating an electron through a potential difference of 1 volt. Since the charge on the electron, $e = 1.602 \times 10^{-19}$ C, and 1 joule is liberated by accelerating a coulomb of charge through a potential difference of 1 volt, the energy in electronvolts is the energy in joules divided by the number of coulombs carried by a single electron. Hence

$$E_{\text{ph}} = 2.18 \times 10^{-18} \text{ J} = (2.18 \times 10^{-18})/(1.602 \times 10^{-19}) \text{ eV} = 13.6 \text{ eV}$$

The natural choice of units here is electronvolts, as the value of E_{ph} is an easily visualized quantity in these units.

If you look back to Block 1 Section 4.9.1, you will see that this value is quoted for the energy required to ionize hydrogen.

Question 12

In the complete sample of galaxies, all distances are represented at all luminosities. In contrast, in the flux-limited samples, we see no intrinsically faint galaxies at large distances – the only galaxies seen at large distances are the intrinsically bright ones, which are actually fewer in number. As the flux limit of the sample is increased (i.e. set to numerically smaller apparent magnitudes), more faint, distance galaxies are excluded and the observed sample becomes even more biased.

Question 13

In Figure 30b there is a pronounced increase in flux on a timescale, Δt, of only about 2 days. In order for this increase in flux not to be blurred out by the difference in the light travel time between the near side and far side of the emitting region, we require $l/c < \Delta t$, where l is the size of the emitting region.

Converting $\Delta t = 2$ days into seconds we have $\Delta t = 2 \times 24 \times 60 \times 60$ s, hence the size of the emitting region must satisfy

$$l < \Delta t \times c = 2 \times 24 \times 60 \times 60 \times 3 \times 10^{10} \text{ cm}$$

i.e. $l < 5 \times 10^{15}$ cm. Converting this into AU, we have

$$l < \frac{5 \times 10^{15} \text{ cm}}{1.5 \times 10^{13} \text{ cm AU}^{-1}} = 330 \text{ AU}$$

The light curve in Figure 30b implies that the extreme UV emitting region in NGC 5548 is less than about 400 AU in size.

Question 14

Assuming $\eta \approx 0.1$, following the working in Peterson Section 3.2, we know that a quasar with $L_{QSO} \approx 10^{46}$ erg s^{-1} consumes $2M_\odot$ per year. The mass of the Earth is $\approx 6 \times 10^{27}$ g, while the mass of the sun is $M_\odot \approx 2 \times 10^{33}$ g. Hence the number of Earth masses consumed each year by a quasar with $L_{QSO} \approx 10^{46}$ erg s^{-1} is given by:

$$n_{Earth} = \text{(mass consumed)/(mass of Earth)} = \frac{2 \times 2 \times 10^{33}}{6 \times 10^{27}}$$

Evaluating this we obtain $n_{Earth} = 6.7 \times 10^5$, i.e. about a *million* Earth masses are consumed each year by a fairly high-luminosity quasar.

Question 15

(a) Our starting point is

$$\left| \frac{M_*}{R_*^2} \right| = \left| -\frac{4M_{BH}R_*}{r^3} \right|$$

and we want to evaluate the distance $r = r_{roche}$ at which the magnitudes of the two accelerations are equal. Since all of the variables are positive we can write this without the modulus signs by dropping the minus sign on the right-hand side, hence we have:

$$\frac{M_*}{R_*^2} = \frac{4M_{BH}R_*}{r^3}$$

collecting alike terms we obtain

$$\frac{M_*}{R_*^3} = \frac{4M_{BH}}{r^3} \tag{86}$$

Looking at the form we require, clearly we need to re-express this in terms of the mean densities

$$\rho_* = \frac{M_*}{\frac{4}{3}\pi R_*^3} \quad \text{and} \quad \rho_{BH} = \frac{M_{BH}}{\frac{4}{3}\pi R_S^3}$$

The left-hand side of Equation 86 is already encouragingly close to ρ_*, and the left-hand side at least has M_{BH} which we can use to introduce ρ_{BH}, though it is important to note $r \neq R_S$. Substituting into Equation 86, we obtain:

$$\frac{4\pi}{3}\rho_* = 4 \times \frac{4\pi}{3}\rho_{BH} \times \left(\frac{R_S}{r}\right)^3$$

and what we actually want is an equation giving the value of the variable r at which the equality holds. Cancelling numerical factors and rewriting to make r the subject of the equation (by putting r^3 alone on the left-hand side, and taking the cube root of both sides of the equation) we find:

$$r = \left(4\frac{\rho_{BH}}{\rho_*}\right)^{1/3} R_S$$

which is of the form required.

(b) The value obtained for the constant is $C = 4^{1/3}$, which evaluates to $C = 1.6$ (2 significant figures). This clearly does not agree with the value given in Peterson. The major reason why the two values do not agree is because in fact the star will be disrupted before it satisfies the condition we used. Disruption occurs at a distance where the differential gravitational force is smaller than the self-gravitational force. (This is because catastrophic oscillations develop. Once these oscillations begin, the approximation that the star is spherically symmetric no longer holds.) A smaller discrepancy arises because we used an approximation (the Taylor expansion) to reach the starting equation for this question.

Question 16

(a) The graph (and table of numbers) produced in Activity 14 shows that the Roche limit for tidal disruption of a solar-mass main-sequence star exceeds the Schwarzschild radius of a black hole until the black hole reaches a mass of about $5 \times 10^8 M_\odot$. At black hole masses less than this, a solar-mass main-sequence star would be tidally disrupted *before* it passes the event horizon. Therefore, a one solar mass main sequence star would be tidally disrupted just as it reaches the event horizon of a black hole of mass about $5 \times 10^8 M_\odot$.

Note: It is also possible to answer this question algebraically by using the equations for the Schwarzschild radius and the Roche limit (Equation 2 and Peterson Equation 3.12) to evaluate the black hole mass at which a solar-mass main-sequence star's Roche limit exactly equals the black hole's Schwarzschild radius. Sometimes an algebraic solution is not possible, however, and a numerical solution is the only way to obtain an answer.

(b) The graph (and table of numbers) produced in Activity 14 shows that the Roche limit for tidal disruption of a solar-mass neutron star exceeds the Schwarzschild radius of a black hole until the black hole reaches a mass of about $25 M_\odot$. At black hole masses less than this, a solar-mass neutron star would be tidally disrupted before it passes the event horizon. Therefore, a one solar mass neutron star would be tidally disrupted just as it reaches the event horizon of a black hole of mass about $25 M_\odot$.

Question 17

(a) The starting point is Peterson Equation 3.18:

$$T(r) = \left(\frac{3GM_{BH}\dot{M}}{8\pi\sigma R_S^3}\right)^{1/4}\left(\frac{r}{R_S}\right)^{-3/4}$$

and the form we are trying to prove expresses the mass accretion rate as a fraction of the Eddington mass accretion rate, which we are told to write as:

$$\dot{M}_E = \frac{4\pi G m_p}{\eta c \sigma_e} M_{BH} \tag{87}$$

Introducing $\dot{M}_E$ in the form suggested, we can re-express the starting equation as

$$T(r) = \left(\frac{3GM_{BH}}{8\pi\sigma R_S^3}\frac{4\pi Gm_p M_{BH}}{\eta c \sigma_e}\right)^{1/4}\left(\frac{\dot{M}}{\dot{M}_E}\right)^{1/4}\left(\frac{r}{R_S}\right)^{-3/4}$$

where we have multiplied the first bracket by the right-hand side of Equation 87 (taken to the power 1/4) and divided the second bracket by the left-hand side of Equation 87 (also taken to the power 1/4), i.e. multiplying by $1^{1/4} = 1$ overall, leaving the value of the starting equation unchanged. Comparing this with what we are asked to prove, we see that the only symbol currently inside the first bracket which we do not ultimately wish to be there is the Schwarzschild radius, R_S. Encouragingly, the second and third brackets are already in the form we want. If we replace R_S with its definition:

$$R_S = \frac{2GM_{BH}}{c^2}$$

we obtain:

$$T(r) = \left(\frac{3GM_{BH}c^6}{8\pi\sigma(2GM_{BH})^3}\frac{4\pi Gm_p M_{BH}}{\eta c \sigma_e}\right)^{1/4}\left(\frac{\dot{M}}{\dot{M}_E}\right)^{1/4}\left(\frac{r}{R_S}\right)^{-3/4}$$

Gathering terms and cancelling where possible this becomes:

$$T(r) = \left(\frac{3c^5}{2^4\sigma GM_{BH}}\frac{m_p}{\eta\sigma_e}\right)^{1/4}\left(\frac{\dot{M}}{\dot{M}_E}\right)^{1/4}\left(\frac{r}{R_S}\right)^{-3/4}$$

which is equivalent to Peterson Equation 3.19.

(b) Writing $M_{BH} = M_8 \times 10^8 M_\odot$, and taking M_8 outside the first bracket we obtain an equation of the form of Peterson 3.20:

$$T(r) = \left(\frac{3c^5}{2^4\times10^8\sigma GM_\odot}\frac{m_p}{\eta\sigma_e}\right)^{1/4}\left(\frac{\dot{M}}{\dot{M}_E}\right)^{1/4}(M_8)^{-1/4}\left(\frac{r}{R_S}\right)^{-3/4}$$

and everything in the first bracket except for η is a constant. We can rewrite this as

$$T(r) = C\eta^{-1/4}\left(\frac{\dot{M}}{\dot{M}_E}\right)^{1/4}(M_8)^{-1/4}\left(\frac{r}{R_S}\right)^{-3/4}$$

with $$C = \left(\frac{3c^5 m_p}{2^4\times10^8\sigma GM_\odot\sigma_e}\right)^{1/4}$$

Substituting in values for all the constants (of course making sure to use a consistent set of units) will allow us to evaluate the constant C. If we choose cgs units for all the constants, and work to 2 significant figures, the values to substitute are

$c = 3.0 \times 10^{10}$ cm s^{-1}, $m_p = 1.7 \times 10^{-24}$ g, $\sigma = 5.7 \times 10^{-5}$ erg cm^{-2} s^{-1} K^{-4}, $G = 6.7 \times 10^{-8}$ dyne cm^2 g^{-2}, $M_\odot = 2.0 \times 10^{33}$ g, $\sigma_e = 6.6 \times 10^{-25}$ cm^2

So working out the expression for C we obtain $C = (1.5 \times 10^{22} \, \mathrm{K}^4)^{1/4} = 3.5 \times 10^5 \, \mathrm{K}$. Comparing the consequent expression

$$T(r) = 3.5 \times 10^5 \eta^{-1/4} \left(\frac{\dot{M}}{\dot{M}_E}\right)^{1/4} (M_8)^{-1/4} \left(\frac{r}{R_S}\right)^{-3/4}$$

with Peterson Equation 3.20 we find they are the same if

$$3.5 \times 10^5 \, \eta^{-1/4} = 6.3 \times 10^5$$

Solving this to find the required value of η, we find $\eta^{-1/4} = 1.8$, i.e. $\eta = (1/1.8)^4 \approx 0.1$. Since Peterson states

$\eta \approx 0.1$ is … suitable for the calculations here

it is reassuring to derive this value after all the manipulation which was required.

Question 18

(i) A photon of energy 6 keV is an X-ray photon, (ii) an electromagnetic wave of frequency 10 GHz is a microwave, and (iii) an electromagnetic wave of wavelength 3 μm is an infrared wave.

By the end of this course you should be able to recognize to roughly what part of the electromagnetic spectrum a given photon energy, frequency, or wavelength corresponds. If you do not yet, refer to the course bookmark when you need this information.

Question 19

(a) To use Peterson Equation 3.21, $\nu_{max} = 2.8kT/h$, we need to convert $\lambda = 5000 \, \text{Å}$ into the corresponding photon frequency, to be identified as ν_{max}. We need to use the wave equation, $\lambda\nu = c$, to do this:

$$\nu_{max} = \frac{c}{\lambda} = \frac{3.0 \times 10^{10} \, \mathrm{cm \, s^{-1}}}{5000 \times 10^{-8} \, \mathrm{cm}} = 6.0 \times 10^{14} \, \mathrm{Hz}$$

where, as always, we have taken care to ensure the units being used are consistent, and we have retained only 2 significant figures since none of our starting information is more precise than that. Rearranging Peterson 3.21 in order to make T the subject of the equation we have

$$T = h\nu_{max}/(2.8\,k)$$

which we evaluate as usual by substituting in the numerical values using a consistent set of units (and retaining only 2 significant figures): $h = 6.6 \times 10^{-27} \, \mathrm{erg \, s}$; $\nu_{max} = 6.0 \times 10^{14} \, \mathrm{Hz}$; $k = 1.4 \times 10^{-16} \, \mathrm{erg \, K^{-1}}$.

$$T = (6.6 \times 10^{-27} \times 6.0 \times 10^{14})/(2.8 \times 1.4 \times 10^{-16}) \, \mathrm{K}$$

which evaluates to $T = 1.01 \times 10^4 \, \mathrm{K}$. Or to 2 significant figures, we have $T \approx 1.0 \times 10^4 \, \mathrm{K}$.

(b) We want to calculate the radius r_{5000} at which $T(r) = 10^4$ K, and we are told that Peterson Equation 3.18 holds, and that $\dot{M} = \dot{M}_E$ and $M_{BH} = 10^8 M_\odot$. The most convenient way to calculate r_{5000} is to use Peterson Equation 3.20, in which the numerical values of all the constants have been entered and evaluated. Hence we have:

$$T(r) \approx 6.3 \times 10^5 \left(\frac{\dot{M}}{\dot{M}_E}\right)^{1/4} (M_8)^{-1/4} \left(\frac{r}{R_S}\right)^{-3/4} \text{ K}$$

and substituting in the values given for $\dot{M}$ and M_8, the terms inside the first two brackets are unity. Hence:

$$T(r) \approx 6.3 \times 10^5 \times 1^{1/4} \times 1^{-1/4} \times \left(\frac{r}{R_S}\right)^{-3/4} \text{ K}$$

so manipulating this to make r the subject we have:

$$\left(\frac{r}{R_S}\right)^{3/4} = \frac{6.3 \times 10^5 \text{ K}}{T(r)} \quad \text{so} \quad \frac{r}{R_S} = \left(\frac{6.3 \times 10^5 \text{ K}}{T(r)}\right)^{4/3}$$

Putting in the temperature we obtained in part (a), we can evaluate r_{5000}:

$$r_{5000} = \left(\frac{6.3 \times 10^5 \text{ K}}{1 \times 10^4 \text{ K}}\right)^{4/3} R_S = 251 R_S$$

Clearly it is ridiculous to give an answer to 3 significant figures when we used an input temperature which was only an order of magnitude estimate. It would be acceptable to give either $r \sim 250 R_S$, or $r \sim 300 R_S$ as our answer.

(c) The Keplerian angular speed, ω_{Kep}, can be derived by equating the centripetal acceleration required to move in a circle of radius r with the gravitational acceleration provided by the central black hole. Hence

$$\omega^2 r = \frac{GM_{BH}}{r^2}$$

so $$\omega = \left(\frac{GM_{BH}}{r^3}\right)^{1/2}$$

and we can use this to determine ω_{5000}, the Keplerian angular speed at radius r_{5000}.

$$R_S = \frac{2GM_{BH}}{c^2}$$

$$\omega_{5000} = \left(\frac{GM_{BH}}{r_{5000}^3}\right)^{1/2} = \left(\frac{GM_{BH}}{(300 R_S)^3}\right)^{1/2} = \left(\frac{GM_{BH}}{\left(300 \times \frac{2GM_{BH}}{c^2}\right)^3}\right)^{1/2}$$

$$= 600^{-3/2}\left(\frac{c^6}{G^2 M_{BH}^2}\right)^{1/2} = 6.8 \times 10^{-5}\left(\frac{c^3}{GM_{BH}}\right)$$

Substituting in values $c = 3 \times 10^{10}$ cm, $G = 6.7 \times 10^{-8}$ dyne cm^2 g^{-2}, $M_{BH} = 10^8 \times 2 \times 10^{33}$ g, we obtain

$$\omega_{5000} = 6.8 \times 10^{-5} \frac{(3 \times 10^{10})^3}{6.7 \times 10^{-8} \times 2 \times 10^{41}} \text{ s}^{-1}$$

where we have used the fact that the cgs unit of force, the dyne = 1 g cm^2 s^{-2} (see Appendix).

Evaluating this, we obtain the Keplerian angular frequency for material which emits radiation at 5000 Å is $\omega_{5000} \sim 1 \times 10^{-7}\,\mathrm{s}^{-1}$. The corresponding Keplerian frequency f_{Kep} is simply given by $f_{\mathrm{Kep}} = \omega_{\mathrm{Kep}}/(2\pi)$ since there are 2π radians in a full circle. Hence

$$f_{\mathrm{Kep}} \sim 2 \times 10^{-8}\,\mathrm{s}^{-1}$$

(d) Thus the orbital period for material emitting at 5000 Å, is

$P_{5000} = f_{\mathrm{Kep}}^{-1} \sim 5 \times 10^{7}\,\mathrm{s}$. This is more conveniently expressed in days:
$P_{5000} \sim 600$ days.

The time-resolution and duration of observations to search for periodic variations at $P_{5000} \sim 600$ days should ideally be a time resolution of better than $P/10$, i.e. data sampled at no less than 60-day intervals, and a duration of several P, i.e. a light curve of ~10 years duration. This is a significant fraction of any astronomer's career!

Question 20

Reddening is caused by preferential scattering of blue light by dust and gas. Consequently, as its name suggests, it causes the light from a distant object to appear redder than the true emitted spectrum. If the diagnostic diagram shown in Peterson Fig. 2.3 was made using lines of very different wavelengths, then the more highly reddened sources would have line ratios in which the fluxes of the bluer lines were artificially depressed. This would cause the position in the diagram to depend strongly on the reddening by intervening material as well as on the intrinsic properties of the source. This would lead to scattering of intrinsically similar sources, so that the division into three distinct classes would be less clear. A mathematical treatment of such effects is given in Block 1, Section 3.8.

Question 21

Selection effects caused the first AGN discovered to come in two apparently distinct classes. On the one hand, Seyfert classified nearby galaxies which had broad high-excitation emission lines in their high-surface brightness cores. Apart from this, these Seyfert galaxies appeared normal: the luminosity from the nuclear activity did not drown out the normal starlight from the surrounding galaxy. These first Seyfert galaxies turned out to be extremely low-luminosity AGN. On the other hand, early radio astronomers generally found the brightest radio galaxies first. These AGN were not only unusual in being radio-loud, but many of them were blazars, boosted in apparent brightness by Doppler favouritism. It was some time before these 'quasi-stellar radio sources' were identified as extremely active nuclei embedded in distant and hence faint galaxies. By selecting nearby galaxies, optical astronomers were looking at relatively common low-luminosity AGN, while radio astronomers could only see the intrinsically rare, high-luminosity and relativistically beamed sources.

Question 22

(a) Using Equation 40 we know that the angle of the aberration, α, is:

$$\alpha = (v/c)\sin\theta$$

where v is the magnitude of the velocity and θ is the angle between the velocity and the direction to the star. Obviously the value of the aberration will be a maximum when $\sin \theta = 1$, therefore we can substitute the value for α given in the question into

$$\alpha = v/c \tag{88}$$

It is very tempting to immediately rearrange the equation to make v the subject, put in the values $\alpha = 21''$ and $c = 2.998 \times 10^{10}\,\text{cm s}^{-1}$ and consequently get a value for v. However, the units of v would then be incorrect. We need to convert the angle α into dimensionless units, radians

$$\alpha = 21'' = 2\pi \times \frac{21}{360 \times 60 \times 60}\,\text{radians}$$

where we have multiplied by 2π, the number of radians in a full circle, and divided by the number of arcsec in a full circle. $21/(360 \times 60 \times 60)$ is the fraction of a full circle represented by 21 arcsc. Evaluating this we have $\alpha = 1.0 \times 10^{-4}$. Therefore, rearranging to make v the subject of the equation, and substituting in values we have:

$$v = \alpha c = 1.0 \times 10^{-4} \times 2.998 \times 10^{10}\,\text{cm s}^{-1} = 3.0 \times 10^6\,\text{cm s}^{-1}$$

Whenever possible, it is a good idea to check that your answer makes sense. In this case, there is a simple way to calculate the approximate orbital speed of the Earth, by assuming the orbit is a perfect circle. The distance of the Earth from the Sun is $1\,\text{AU} = 1.5 \times 10^{13}\,\text{cm}$, therefore the circumference of the orbit is $2\pi \times 1\,\text{AU}$, and the orbital speed is this circumference, divided by the time taken to complete one orbit, i.e. 1 year ($= 365 \times 24 \times 60 \times 60\,\text{s}$). Therefore

$$v = \frac{2\pi \times 1.5 \times 10^{13}}{365 \times 24 \times 60 \times 60} = 2.9 \times 10^6\,\text{cm s}^{-1}$$

which is almost the same answer. The discrepancy between the two answers arises because the Earth's orbit is in fact elliptical, so the maximum velocity, which is what the maximum value of the aberration leads to, is greater than the average value assuming a circular orbit.

(b) In this case the method is exactly the same: we calculate v this time using $\alpha = 0.3''$ as our starting point. Converting α into radians, this time we obtain $\alpha = 1.4 \times 10^{-6}$, a value which we can check against our previous working:

$$\frac{1.4 \times 10^{-6}}{1.0 \times 10^{-4}} = \frac{0.3}{21}$$

substituting our value into Equation 88 above, in this case

$$v = 1.4 \times 10^{-6} \times 2.998 \times 10^{10}\,\text{cm s}^{-1} = 4.4 \times 10^4\,\text{cm s}^{-1}$$

Once again we can check this against the values in part (a) for consistency:

$$\frac{4.4 \times 10^4}{2.9 \times 10^6} = \frac{0.3}{21}$$

Question 23

Applying trigonometry to the triangle in Figure 48 in the case $u = u' = c$, we see that $\cos\theta' = \dfrac{u'_x}{c}$. Substituting from Equation 45a for u'_x we have:

$$\cos\theta' = \frac{1}{c}\frac{u_x + v}{\left(1 + \dfrac{vu_x}{c^2}\right)} = \frac{\cos\theta + \dfrac{v}{c}}{1 + \dfrac{v}{c}\cos\theta}$$

where we have used $\cos\theta = u_x/c$ to substitute for u_x.

Question 24

Using Equation 57 we know that the overall boosting of an approaching source is $\gamma^{3+\alpha}$. This is the factor which tells us how much brighter the approaching jet appears when compared to a stationary isotropically emitting source of the same luminosity and distance. The question tells us that $v = 0.9c$, and that $\alpha = 0.7$. The first step is to calculate the Lorentz factor, γ, corresponding to $v = 0.9c$

$$\gamma \equiv \frac{1}{\sqrt{\left(1 - \frac{v^2}{c^2}\right)}} = (1 - 0.9^2)^{-1/2} = (0.19)^{-1/2} = 2.3$$

where we have retained only 2 significant figures. To calculate the boosting factor, therefore we need to evaluate:

$$(2.3)^{3+0.7} = 2.3^{3.7} = 22$$

where again we have retained only 2 significant figures.

The approaching jet appears more than 20 times brighter than a stationary isotropically emitting source of the same luminosity and distance.

Question 25

First let's deal with $p = \beta \sin \theta$. We need to find the partial derivative with respect to θ, and we know that β does not depend on θ. Hence the expression to differentiate is simply 'constant $\times \sin \theta$'. Referring back to Block 1, Table 8, entry 5, and making the identifications $\omega = 1$, $a = \beta$, we have:

$$\frac{\partial p}{\partial \theta} = \beta \cos \theta$$

The expression for q is more complex and we need to use the chain rule, which we revised in Block 1, Section 3.5, and Equation 81. Following Block 1, we apply the chain rule by identifying the function '$1 - \beta \cos \theta$' as p', where we have introduced the prime to make it clear that this is not the same p as above. With this substitution, we have:

$$q = (1 - \beta \cos \theta)^{-1} = p'^{-1}$$

Hence:

$$\frac{\partial q}{\partial \theta} = \frac{dq}{dp'} \frac{\partial p'}{\partial \theta} = (-1)p'^{-2} \times (0 - (-\beta \sin \theta))$$

and multiplying this out and substituting back for p' we obtain:

$$\frac{\partial q}{\partial \theta} = \frac{dq}{dp'} \frac{\partial p'}{\partial \theta} = -\frac{\beta \sin \theta}{(1 - \beta \cos \theta)^2}$$

Question 26

(a) Of the curves plotted in Activity 25, the minimum value of β for which the curve rises above $\beta_T = 1$ is that corresponding to $\beta = 0.745$ (or $\gamma = 1.500$).

(b) At this value of β, apparent superluminal motion ($\beta_T > 1$) is observed for ejection angles between about $\theta = 27°$ and $\theta = 62°$.

Question 27

The BL Lac objects are blazars, i.e. objects in which the jet velocity is directed almost exactly towards us. In the notation of Peterson Section 4.4.2, this means the angle θ is very small, i.e. $\theta < \cos^{-1}\beta$ is likely to hold. Consequently in BL Lac objects, β_T is most likely to be less than $\beta_T^{\max}$, and they correspond to the lowest θ region in Peterson Fig. 4.7.

Question 28

Your sketch should resemble Figure 104. The SED resembles that shown in Peterson's Fig. 4.1, with the features identified as shown.

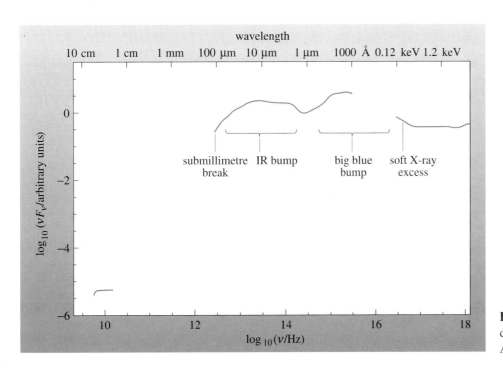

Figure 104 The spectral energy distribution (SED) of a radio-quiet AGN.

Question 29

We set this question to make you aware of how much progress you have made in learning the powerfully concise language of physics. You probably found you needed several sentences to explain the meaning of these six words: 'optically thin thermal radiation is isotropic'. This might partially explain why scientists are often understandably accused of communicating using jargon which excludes others from participating in scientific debate.

The following is our attempt at an answer:

The visible light our eyes detect is electromagnetic radiation. This radiation can be created in a variety of ways, for example the glow from an electric fire or the filament of a light bulb is created as a result of heat energy. When radiation is created from heat energy it is called thermal radiation. There are two main types of thermal radiation: one type (described as optically thick) comes from generally dense emitting material in which light is created and scattered or reabsorbed several times before escaping; the other type (described as optically thin) comes from material in which the light escapes without being reabsorbed or scattered. This second, optically thin, type of thermal radiation is created so that equal amounts flow in all directions. The independence of the amount and type of radiation on direction is called **isotropy**, and radiation of this type is described as being isotropic.

As you work through the readings in Peterson it is a good idea to mentally rehearse these kinds of translations from the technical terms to everyday language. This is an excellent way to identify places where your understanding is weak. A good rule of thumb is that if a person is unable to explain something, they probably do not properly understand it.

Question 30

This is a case of making the appropriate unit conversions, just as was required in Example 1(b). We are given the flux in units of photons $cm^{-2} s^{-1} keV^{-1}$, i.e. photons per unit area per unit time per unit energy interval, and we require the equivalent value expressed in $erg s^{-1} cm^{-2} Hz^{-1}$, i.e. *energy* per unit area per unit time per unit *frequency* interval.

Clearly we have two conversions to make: (i) from photons to the equivalent energy, and (ii) from unit energy interval to unit frequency interval.

(i) to convert from photons to energy we need to multiply the number of photons by the energy carried by each photon. The value on the horizontal axis of the graph is photon energy, and reading off this scale, we see that the peak flux occurs at about $E = 6.4 \, keV$. We want energy in erg, however, not keV:

$$6.4 \, keV = 6.4 \times 10^3 \, eV \times 1.602 \times 10^{-12} \, erg \, eV^{-1} = 1.025 \times 10^{-8} \, erg$$

i.e. each photon carries an energy of 1.025×10^{-8} erg.

(ii) the second conversion is slightly more tricky. The unit energy interval and the equivalent unit frequency interval refer to the electromagnetic spectrum, and the relationship between energy and frequency for electromagnetic radiation is $E = h\nu$.

Consequently the energy interval ΔE and the frequency interval $\Delta \nu$ are related by $\Delta E = h\Delta \nu$.

We must also make sure that the units of the energy interval are appropriate to the units in which we express Planck's constant, h. Adopting cgs units, we must convert ΔE from keV to erg, which is the same numerical conversion we used in part (i):

$$\Delta E = 1 \, keV = 1 \times 10^3 \, eV \times 1.602 \times 10^{-12} \, erg \, eV^{-1}$$

and the corresponding frequency interval is given by

$$\Delta \nu = \frac{\Delta E}{h} = \frac{1.602 \times 10^{-9} \, erg}{6.626 \times 10^{-27} \, erg \, s} = 2.418 \times 10^{17} \, s^{-1} = 2.418 \times 10^{17} \, Hz$$

Thus we see that an interval of 1 keV corresponds to an interval of 2.418×10^{17} Hz. Consequently if a flux is expressed per keV it should be a much bigger number than a flux expressed per Hz, since the unit interval is much bigger (by a factor of 2.418×10^{17}) in the first case than the second.

Putting these two conversions together, we see that

$$1.3 \times 10^{-4} \, photons \, cm^{-2} \, s^{-1} \, keV^{-1}$$

$$= 1.3 \times 10^{-4} \, photons \, cm^{-2} \, s^{-1} \, keV^{-1} \times 1.025 \times 10^{-8} \, erg \, photon^{-1}$$
$$\times (2.418 \times 10^{17} \, Hz \, keV^{-1})^{-1}$$

$$= 5.5 \times 10^{-30} \, erg \, cm^{-2} \, s^{-1} \, Hz^{-1}$$

where we have retained only 2 significant figures in the answer, since we could only read the initial value from the graph at this precision.

Note: It is well worth writing out the units in the form we have given the final answer in, namely $\mathrm{erg\,cm^{-2}\,s^{-1}\,Hz^{-1}}$, rather than yielding to the temptation to cancel s^{-1} with Hz^{-1}. If we did this we would have a flux of $5.5 \times 10^{-30}\,\mathrm{erg\,cm^{-2}}$, the meaning of which is not immediately obvious. Writing out the units as we have helps to make it clear that we are expressing an energy per unit area per unit *time* per unit *frequency interval*.

Question 31

For pair production to be important there needs to be a source of sufficiently high-energy photons, i.e. γ-rays. The density of these γ-rays needs to be high, so that interactions between two photons with energies E_1 and E_2 such that $E_1 E_2 > (m_e c^2)^2$ are likely to occur. These conditions are most likely to be satisfied in a small and luminous γ-ray source. This requirement is expressed in terms of the compactness parameter (Peterson Equation 4.12).

Question 32

One of the fastest changes occurs at around 7730 on the horizontal axis (Julian date $\approx 244\,0000+7730$) where the flux density increases from $\sim 2.3 \times 10^{-15}\,\mathrm{erg\,s^{-1}\,cm^{-2}\,\mathring{A}^{-1}}$ to $\sim 6.5 \times 10^{-15}\,\mathrm{erg\,s^{-1}\,cm^{-2}\,\mathring{A}^{-1}}$ over less than about 20 days. Assuming that the light source cannot more than double its luminosity on a time faster than the light-crossing time, because otherwise the variations at the furthest edge of the region would need to lead those at the nearest edge, this means that the light-crossing time, $l/c \leq 20$ days. Consequently the size of the region emitting the 5100 Å radiation has a size l which is limited by this.

Converting 20 days into seconds we get 20 days $= 20 \times 24 \times 60 \times 60\,\mathrm{s} = 1.7 \times 10^6\,\mathrm{s}$. Here we have kept only 2 significant figures, because we certainly can't read the 20 day time interval from the graph to more than 2 significant figures, in fact we will retain only 1 significant figure in our final answer. Hence, we can say the size l must satisfy
$$l \leq c \times 1.7 \times 10^6\,\mathrm{s}$$

and evaluating this we obtain $l \leq 5.1 \times 10^{16}\,\mathrm{cm}$. Converting this into parsecs we obtain $l \leq (5.1 \times 10^{16})/(3.1 \times 10^{18})\,\mathrm{pc}$, which evaluates to $1.6 \times 10^{-2}\,\mathrm{pc}$, and of course in light-years we have $l \leq (20)/(365)\,\mathrm{ly}$, which evaluates to $l \leq 5.5 \times 10^{-2}\,\mathrm{ly}$.

Hence the maximum size of the region emitting at 5100 Å is $5 \times 10^{16}\,\mathrm{cm}$, $2 \times 10^{-2}\,\mathrm{pc}$, or $6 \times 10^{-2}\,\mathrm{ly}$, where we have rounded to only 1 significant figure in each case.

Question 33

Dust grains can survive so long as their temperature is below that at which sublimation occurs. This requires a temperature of $\lesssim 2000\,\mathrm{K}$. Near-infrared emission can hence (cf. Figure 9) be emitted by dust grains, and the hottest and brightest dust grains surrounding an AGN will be those which are just far enough away from the central irradiating source to remain solid. This distance is known as the sublimation radius, and depends on the luminosity of the central source. Observations of Fairall 9 reported by Clavel, Wamsteker and Glass in 1989 showed a pronounced fading in the continuum emission. The near-IR continuum lagged behind the UV continuum by about 400 days. The sublimation radius corresponding to the luminosity of Fairall 9 is about 3×10^{18} cm, which corresponds to a light travel time of about 400 days. Thus it appears that the near-IR emission from Fairall 9 arises from dust grains heated by the shorter wavelength radiation from the central source. The delay between the UV and near-IR light curves can be naturally explained by the light travel time delay as light from the central source travels out to dust grains at the sublimation radius.

Question 34

(a) To an X-ray astronomer, the typical photon energy is $E_{ph} \sim 10^3$ eV, and using the formula $h\nu \sim kT$ this corresponds to a gas temperature $T \sim h\nu/k$.

Converting from electronvolts to ergs (using the conversion factors given in the Appendix), the typical photon energy, $h\nu$, is $1 \times 10^3 \times 1.602 \times 10^{-12}$ erg, i.e. $E_{ph} \sim 1.6 \times 10^{-9}$ erg, hence

$$T \sim \frac{h\nu}{k} \sim \frac{E_{ph}}{k} \sim \frac{1.6 \times 10^{-9}}{1.4 \times 10^{-16}} \, \text{K} \qquad (89)$$

where we have retained 2 significant figures for the intermediate steps of the calculation. Evaluating this we get $T \sim 10^7$ K.

Thus we see that the typical energy of an X-ray photon is characteristic of a thermal temperature $\sim 10^7$ K. Hence to an X-ray astronomer, a temperature of 10^4 K is 'cold', as a gas at this temperature will not radiate appreciable numbers of X-ray photons. Such 'cold' gas may, however, affect the detected X-ray emission by absorbing or scattering X-rays emitted elsewhere.

(b) To an IR astronomer, the typical photon wavelength is $\lambda \sim 10 \, \mu$m, i.e. $\lambda \sim 10 \times 10^{-4}$ cm, and the typical photon energy at this wavelength is obtained from the formula $E_{ph} = hc/\lambda$.

So the typical IR photon has energy $E_{ph} \sim (6.6 \times 10^{-27} \times 3.0 \times 10^{10})/(1 \times 10^{-3})$ erg, which evaluates to give $E_{ph} \sim 2.0 \times 10^{-13}$ erg. As always, we should check our work wherever possible, so we should make sure a ratio of 10^4 between the X-ray and IR photon energies is consistent with what is expected. One quick and easy way to do this is to look at the horizontal axes of Peterson's Fig. 4.1, where we see that there are about 4 decades in photon frequency (i.e. log ν increases from ~14 to ~18) between the IR and X-ray parts of the SED (where we can read the photon wavelength or frequency from the labelling on the top axis of the figure).

Substituting the value $E_{ph} \sim 2.0 \times 10^{-13}$ erg into Equation 89, we therefore obtain the temperature characteristic of an IR photon:

$$T \sim \frac{E_{ph}}{k} \sim \frac{2.0 \times 10^{-13}}{1.4 \times 10^{-16}} \, \text{K}$$

which evaluates to 1.4×10^3 K, or to 1 significant figure, $T \sim 10^3$ K. Hence to an IR astronomer, gas at 10^4 K is 'hot', as it exceeds the temperature required to radiate IR photons.

This question demonstrates the need to be careful when using terms like hot and cold, dense and tenuous: it is important to understand what is 'normal' in the context. Of course, strictly speaking X-ray astronomers should say 'cold compared to 10^7 K' while IR astronomers should say 'hot compared to 10^3 K', but they usually do not, for the same reason that weather forecasters do not say 'tomorrow will be hot compared to 0 °C'. In each case, the speaker assumes the listeners belong to a culture which understands what is 'normal'. One of our goals in this course is to introduce you to the cultural assumptions made when astronomers communicate with each other.

Question 35

(a) From Block 1, Equation 145, the average translational energy of the particles in a gas is given by

$$\langle E_{KE} \rangle = \tfrac{3}{2} kT$$

where k is Boltzmann's constant. If the thermal width of a spectral line is $5000 \, \text{km s}^{-1}$, this implies the particles in the gas have a typical speed of $\sim 5000 \, \text{km s}^{-1}$. Since

$$\langle E_{KE} \rangle \sim \tfrac{1}{2} m_p \langle v^2 \rangle$$

where we have assumed the particles have a typical mass similar to the mass of the proton, m_p, we have a way of estimating the temperature corresponding to a particular spectral line width. Equating the two expressions for $\langle E_{KE} \rangle$:

$$\tfrac{1}{2} m_p \langle v^2 \rangle \sim \tfrac{3}{2} kT$$

leading to

$$T \sim \frac{1}{3} \frac{m_p}{k} \langle v^2 \rangle$$

If we substitute in values for the constants (in cgs units) and use $v \sim 5000 \, \text{km s}^{-1}$, so that $\langle v^2 \rangle \sim 2.5 \times 10^{17} \, \text{cm}^2 \, \text{s}^{-2}$ (where we have converted to cgs units and squared), then our estimate of the temperature is

$$T \sim \frac{1}{3} \times \frac{1.7 \times 10^{-24}}{1.4 \times 10^{-16}} \times 2.5 \times 10^{17} \, \text{K} \quad \sim \quad 1 \times 10^9 \, \text{K}$$

(b) The estimate of a billion kelvin for a thermal width of $5000 \, \text{km s}^{-1}$ is a very high temperature. A gas at this temperature would be extremely highly ionized, so that the spectral lines found in the optical region of the spectrum would not be present. In particular hydrogen would be completely ionized at this temperature, so the Balmer series would not be emitted.

Question 36

(a) The broad-line region is filamentary and clumpy, and the individual clouds have a large spread in velocities, these bulk motions lead to the broad line widths.

(b) The 'ionizing UV' part of the spectrum consists of photons which have energy in excess of that required to ionize hydrogen. Since hydrogen is abundant throughout the Universe, and the cross-section for absorption is high for photons with energies just in excess of the ionization energy, ionizing UV photons are very likely to be absorbed in an ionization event where a hydrogen atom becomes a hydrogen ion. The Universe is thus, effectively, opaque to photons in this part of the electromagnetic spectrum, and we cannot directly observe this emission from AGN.

(c) The absorption and scattering of short-wavelength photons by the interstellar material will cause the flux from both lines to appear lower than the true values. The effect will be stronger for the shorter wavelength line, so a ratio like Lyα/Hβ, where the shorter wavelength line is in the numerator, will appear smaller than its true value.

Question 37

Peterson Fig. 5.3 gives the results of a photoionization calculation for $n_e = 10^{11}$ cm^{-3}. Reading off the axes, noting that $U = 10^{-2}$ corresponds to $\log U = -2$, we see that

$$\log I(\text{CIV})/I(\text{Ly}\alpha) = 0.25$$

while $\log I(\text{CIII]})/I(\text{Ly}\alpha) = -1.2$

In each case the left-hand side is the quantity $\log(x/y)$ where x is the intensity, I, of carbon line in question, and y is intensity of the Lyman α line.

Hence using the law of logarithms (Block 1, Equation 14):

$$\log(x/y) = \log x - \log y$$

to expand both expressions, and subtracting the two to eliminate $\log I(\text{Ly}\alpha)$

$$\log I(\text{CIV}) - \log I(\text{CIII]}) = 0.25 - (-1.2) = 1.45$$

We can re-express the left-hand side as a ratio

$$\log I(\text{CIV})/I(\text{CIII]}) = 1.45$$

and so
$$I(\text{CIV})/I(\text{CIII]}) = 10^{1.45} \approx 28$$

Thus, the information given on the graph suggests that for an ionization parameter of $U = 10^{-2}$ and $n_e = 10^{11}$ cm^{-3}, the intensity of the CIV line at 1550 Å is about 28 times the intensity of the CIII] line at 1909 Å.

Question 38

(a) At $U \approx 0$, there will be little C^{2+}; as the ionization parameter increases, the number of carbon atoms which are doubly ionized will increase, so the line emission from this species will also increase. At higher values of U, the average ionization level will increase, so that an increasing proportion of the carbon atoms will have lost more than two electrons. Eventually all the carbon will be in the form of CIV or higher ionization states.

(b) The stellar photospheric Balmer absorption lines first increase in strength with T_{eff} as an increasing proportion of hydrogen atoms have sufficient energy to populate the $n = 2$ lower level of the Balmer series. As T_{eff} increases further an increasing proportion of the H atoms are ionized, so in O stars the Balmer absorption is negligible because all the hydrogen is in the form of HII ($= H^+$).

Question 39

(a) PIZ stands for partially ionized zone.

(b) Ionizing photons are most effectively absorbed when they have energies only just exceeding the Lyman limit, for higher and higher energies the cross-section for absorption gets smaller and smaller. Consequently a high-energy ionizing photon will typically pass through a higher column density of hydrogen before being absorbed than will a photon with energy just exceeding the Lyman limit.

(c) An O star produces a thermal spectrum in which the Wien tail cutoff causes the number of photons to decrease rapidly with energy above the Lyman limit. Consequently most of the ionizing photons are absorbed within about the same hydrogen column density of the O star, producing a Strömgren sphere where the gas abruptly makes a transition from fully ionized to neutral. The PIZ in broad-line regions is photoionized by the non-thermal power-law spectrum of the central source, in which there is no abrupt fall in the number of photons above the Lyman limit. Hence there are ionizing photons corresponding to a wide range of typical column densities before absorption occurs. This leads to a much more gradual transition between fully ionized material close to the central source and almost completely neutral material far from the source. This extended transition zone is the PIZ.

Question 40

If the parameters determined are self-consistent, this would increase confidence that the method used is reasonably unbiased. With ionization equilibrium calculations such as that used to produce Peterson Fig. 5.3, the ionization structure is stratified with the parts of the cloud facing the central source being most highly ionized. If a simple photoionization model is tuned (by adjusting parameters such as n_e and U) to reproduce a number of observed emission line strengths, for example the CIV emission, and is then found to be simultaneously consistent with other lines which it *hasn't* been tuned to, we would be encouraged. This is an example of the 'scientific method': observations are used to determine a model, the model then generates predictions, and the predictions are tested.

Question 41

Your sketch should illustrate the outflow of clouds in an attenuating medium and the inflow of clouds which radiate predominantly from their inward face, as in Figure 105.

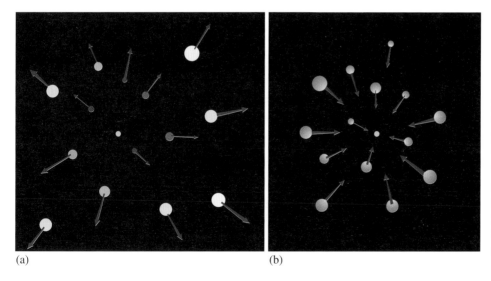

(a) (b)

Figure 105 Two mechanism which would cause blueward asymmetric line profiles: (a) outflowing clouds within an attenuating medium, so the nearest (approaching) ones appear brightest (b) inflowing clouds which are radiating predominantly from the edges facing the central illuminating source.

Question 42

In interacting binary stars the entire system is in orbit around the common centre of mass, thus the emitting region rotates through 360° during a binary orbit. The observations from all the different orientations are combined to produce a two-dimensional map in velocity space. In AGN we view the system from the same fixed orientation, and while individual clouds may be orbiting, there is no analogous way to reconstruct a two-dimensional picture in velocity space.

Question 43

The basic assumptions are points (1) to (4) given on Peterson page 84, which we paraphrase here:

(i) the continuum originates in a central source which may be regarded as a point, compared with the size of the BLR.

(ii) the broad-line clouds have a small filling factor, and photons travel direct from the central source to the broad-line cloud in which they cause a photoionization.

(iii) the emission line flux responds to the continuum flux. When the continuum flux increases, the emission line flux increases in response.

(iv) the time taken for the continuum light to travel from its source to the BLR is much longer than the time between the ionizing photon being absorbed and an emission line photon being produced in response.

(v) the time for continuum light to travel from its source to the BLR is much shorter than the time needed for the overall structure of the BLR to change, i.e. the broad-line clouds do not move appreciably in relation to the position of the central source, nor does their ionization structure change appreciably, during the time for a continuum photon to travel between the central source and the BLR.

Question 44

The lag time for various emission lines has been measured for several AGN. Typically the lag is a few days for high ionization parameter species, and about 20 days for Balmer series lines. This supports the conclusion that the BLR has a stratified ionization structure, with the most highly ionized species being closer to the central source. The overall size of the BLR in the AGN which have been observed is ~10 light-days.

Question 45

(a) The peak of the cross-correlation function is at a shift of −10 days.

(b) The shift of −10 days means that the emission line light curve needs to be shifted 10 days earlier in order to correlate with the continuum light curve. The emission line light curve therefore lags 10 days after the continuum light curve.

(c) This indicates that in this case, the emission line flux could be caused by reprocessing or reflection of the continuum flux after an interval of 10 days. This may represent the light travel time from the site of emission of the continuum to the site of emission of the emission line light.

Question 46

The purely algebraic expression is

$$f \approx \frac{N_c \pi l^2}{4\pi r^2}$$

and the factors of π cancel.

If we set r to 8 light-days, and measure l in cm, we must also express r in cm.

Since $c = 3.0 \times 10^{10}$ cm s^{-1}, 1 light-second is 3.0×10^{10} cm.

A light-day is $24 \times 60 \times 60 \times 1$ light-second, hence:

$$8 \text{ light-days} = 8 \times 24 \times 60 \times 60 \times 3.0 \times 10^{10} \text{ cm}$$

$$8 \text{ light-days} = 2.07 \times 10^{16} \text{ cm}$$

Therefore $r \approx 8$ light-days is the same as $r \approx 2 \times 10^{16}$ cm.

After cancelling π, the denominator is $4r^2$, so evaluating this we have:

$$4 \times (2 \times 10^{16})^2 \, \text{cm}^2 = 1.6 \times 10^{33} \, \text{cm}^2$$

Question 47

(a) The narrow-line region is much more massive than the broad-line region; the difference in masses is $\sim 10^9$, as is seen by comparing Peterson Equation 5.9 with Equation 6.19.

(b) The amount of line flux produced in each of these two regions is roughly the same.

(c) The broad-line region is the more efficient emitter of line flux per unit mass.

(d) The vastly different emission efficiencies arise because the emissivity of recombination lines is $\propto n_e{}^2$ and the broad-line region is much denser.

Question 48

The number of individual clouds multiplied by the volume of each cloud is equal to the total volume of the narrow-line region multiplied by the filling factor for the narrow-line region, i.e.

$$N_c l^3 = \epsilon r^3 \qquad\qquad (90)$$

We are told to take $l \gtrsim r_1$, with $r_1 \approx 10^{18} n_3^{-1}$ cm. We also known (from Example 8) that the size of the narrow-line region is given by

$$r = 5.79 \times 10^{19} \left(\frac{L_{41}(\text{H}\beta)}{\epsilon n_3^2} \right)^{1/3} \text{cm}$$

From Equation 90 and the limit on l we have

$$N_c \leq \epsilon \left(\frac{r}{r_1} \right)^3$$

and substituting in for r and r_1 this becomes

$$N_c \leq \epsilon (5.79 \times 10^{19})^3 \left(\frac{L_{41}(\text{H}\beta)}{\epsilon n_3^2} \right) \left(\frac{n_3}{10^{18}} \right)^3$$

where the units (cm^3/cm^3) have cancelled. This simplifies to

$$N_c \leq 2 \times 10^5 n_3 L_{41}(\text{H}\beta)$$

as required.

Question 49

(a) The Faber–Jackson relationship is an observed correlation between the luminosity, L, and the velocity dispersion, σ, of elliptical galaxies and of the bulges of spiral galaxies such that $L \propto \sigma^4$.

(b) Galaxies are bound by gravity, so the virial theorem applies:

$$\langle \sigma^2 \rangle \approx \frac{GM}{r}$$

where we have used the form derived in Example 1, noting that here the symbol σ has been used for the typical velocity. So

$$\sigma^2 \propto \frac{M}{r}$$

The central surface brightness of galaxies are all about the same. If we denote this fiducial central surface brightness as Σ_0, the luminosity is roughly given by

$$L \propto \Sigma_0 r_s^2$$

where r_s measures the size of the galaxies, i.e. L and r_s vary from galaxy to galaxy, but Σ_0 is roughly the same for all of them, so $L \propto r^2$.

Furthermore, the luminosity of the elliptical galaxies and the spiral bulges is generated by starlight. Assuming stars form with roughly the same properties in all such cases, then the ratio of the total mass, M, to the total luminosity, L, should be constant, so $M \propto L$.

Using the last two proportionalities we can eliminate both M and r from the expression we got from the virial theorem:

$$\sigma^2 \propto \frac{M}{r} \propto \frac{L}{r} \propto \frac{L}{L^{1/2}} \propto L^{1/2}$$

or squaring both sides:

$$\sigma^4 \propto L$$

as found by observation.

Question 50

Your figure should resemble Figure 106. The BL Lac objects are viewed along the direction of the approaching jet, which is assumed to be the axis of the obscuring torus. The broad-lined radio galaxies correspond to viewing angles which look down the 'throat' of the torus, and are therefore unobscured by the torus. Narrow-lined radio galaxies correspond to viewing angles for which the broad-line region is obscured by the torus.

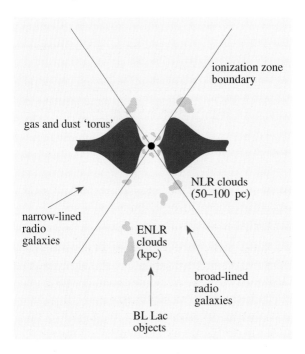

Figure 106 A copy of Peterson's conceptual scheme for AGN unification, with the viewing directions for BL Lac objects, broad-lined radio galaxies, and narrow-lined radio galaxies shown.

Question 51

We make two assumptions: (i) that Seyfert 2 galaxies are AGN in which the broad-line region is obscured by the torus, while in Seyfert 1 galaxies we see the broad-line region through the axial opening of the torus, and (ii) that all Seyferts are randomly oriented. Consequently, the relative numbers of Seyfert 1 galaxies and Seyfert 2 galaxies will tell us the fraction of the sky viewed from the centre of the AGN which is covered by the torus. This fraction multiplied by the 4π steradians in a full sphere is the solid angle required.

Question 52

Your revised sketch should look like Figure 107.

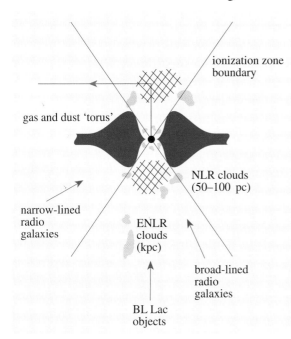

Figure 107 The cross-hatched region is where scattering takes place. In NGC 1068 some of the broad-line region photons are scattered into the line of sight, even though the torus obscures the BLR. The path of a scattered BLR photon is indicated by the blue arrow.

Question 53

(a) Up to 25% of the Seyfert 2 galaxies observed by Veilleux, Goodrich and Hill were found likely to harbour obscured broad-line regions.

(b) The widths of the Paschen and Brackett lines in these proposed obscured Seyfert 1 galaxies, ~2000 km s^{-1}, are comparable to the line widths in Seyfert 1 galaxies, but tend to be on average slightly narrower.

(c) The predicted Hβ fluxes found for these objects are similar to those directly observed for Seyfert 1 galaxies.

(d) The broad-line region luminosity inferred from these infrared observations is in general about 10 times that which would be inferred from the optical spectropolarimetry which reveals the spectrum of the scattered light.

(e) Yes, these observations are encouraging for the obscuring torus scenario for the unification of Seyferts outlined in Peterson Section 7.2. Other models which have been considered include: (i) a geometrically thin but strongly warped disc which replaces the torus as the obscuring body; (ii) a dusty wind which produces the highest extinction in the plane perpendicular to the symmetry axis. The authors of this paper conclude that possibility (i) 'has difficulties accounting for many of the properties of Seyfert galaxies', while the 'results are consistent with' possibility (ii).

Question 54

The only components of AGN emission which might reasonably be expected to emit isotropically are the extended radio emission and the extended narrow-line emission. The problem with using the extended radio emission as an indicator of the intrinsic AGN luminosity is that it is powered by the central engine *as it was* millions of years earlier. The problem with using the extended narrow-line emission as an indicator of the intrinsic AGN luminosity is that it is often partially obscured by dust in the host galaxy.

The core radio emission is strongly affected by relativistic beaming. The broad-line region and the hard X-ray emitting region often lie behind an obscuring torus. The far-IR emission is relatively unaffected by this obscuration, but the far-IR emission by the torus itself is dependent upon the orientation at which the torus is viewed.

Question 55

Veilleux, Sanders and Kim (1997, ApJ, 484, 92) report near-IR spectroscopy of 25 ULIGs. Being ULIGs, they have very high IR luminosities, which could be due to AGN activity, however none of the objects chosen show any indication of a broad-line region (BLR) in their optical spectra. This could be either because they do not harbour BLRs, or because the BLRs are obscured. Broad-line emission (Paα) was detected in two objects for the first time, confirmed in two other objects, and may have been detected in three other objects, but these require confirmation.

The IR spectra also show evidence for [SiVI] emission in three or four objects: five times ionized Si is an indicator of AGN activity because something like the power-law ionizing continuum of an AGN is required to produce such a high degree of photoionization.

Combining the evidence from [SiVI] emission and the broad Paα emission, 7 (or perhaps 9) of the 10 optical Seyfert 2 type galaxies show evidence for hidden AGN activity in the spectra at 2 μm, suggesting that the obscuring dust screen becomes optically thin at these wavelengths.

After correcting the measured emission line luminosities for extinction, the ULIGs with hidden AGNs have emission line luminosities which are the same fraction of bolometric emission as are the emission lines in optical quasars. This suggests these objects are buried quasars.

The LINERs in the sample may have buried AGN with dust which remains optically thick at 2 μm. The HII galaxies emit narrow Paα, and do not harbour buried AGN.

20–30% of ULIGs appear to be AGN. The fraction of AGN amongst ULIGs increases with increasing IR luminosity.

Question 56

(a) The Big Bang occurred when the size of the Universe was zero. Hence the highest value for the current age of the Universe is suggested by the curve which crosses size = 0 at the longest time before the current epoch. This is the straight line curve corresponding to $q_0 = 0$.

(b) If the Universe is currently accelerating in its expansion, this would suggest a curve with a gradient which increases with time. Such a curve would reach size = 0 at a longer time before the current epoch than any shown, i.e. if the Universe is accelerating it would be older than the age suggested by q_0.

Question 57

RD300 has redshift $z = 5.50$. The conversion between redshift and lookback time is dependent on the (unknown) value of the deceleration parameter q_0, as shown in Figure 87. If we take the two extreme values shown for q_0, namely $q_0 = 0$ and $q_0 = 1$, and read off values for lookback time for $z = 5.50$ from we find the values given in Table 6.

This means that the light from the quasar has been travelling for between 0.84 and 0.94 times the current age of the Universe. The light was emitted when the Universe was between 0.06 and 0.16 times its current age (!)

Table 6 Lookback times estimated from Figure 87.

q_0	lookback time for $z = 5.50$
0	0.84
1	0.94

Question 58

(a) At redshift $z = 2$ the QSO luminosity function is a monotonically decreasing function of luminosity, i.e. there are fewer and fewer QSOs per unit volume at higher and higher luminosities. The shape of the function is a 'broken' power law: at both the highest luminosities and the lowest luminosities the function is a power law. The power-law index at high luminosities is steeper than that at low luminosities. At intermediate luminosities the function gradually changes slope from one power law to the other.

(b) The basic shape of the QSO luminosity function at redshift $z = 0.5$ is similar to that at redshift $z = 2$. The density of QSOs is less at redshift $z = 0.5$ than at redshift $z = 2$ for all values of luminosity. The main difference in the shape of the luminosity function is that the change in slope from the steep high-luminosity power law to the shallow low-luminosity power law occurs at a lower value of luminosity for redshift $z = 0.5$ than it does for redshift $z = 2$.

Question 59

(a) In the pure density evolution scenario (i) almost all galaxies harbour AGN, but these AGN spend much of their time in a dormant state, (ii) the fraction of galaxies harbouring an active AGN changes between the $z = 2$ epoch and the present, $z = 0.5$, epoch, and (iii) the relative numbers of bright and faint AGN is fixed.

(b) In the pure luminosity evolution scenario the number of galaxies which harbour AGN is a small, unchanging subsample of the whole population of galaxies, and the change in the luminosity function is attributed to the luminosities of the individual sources changing in time.

(c) The pure density evolution scenario is not consistent with the observation that very bright AGN were a higher proportion of the entire population at redshift $z = 2$ compared with redshift $z = 0.5$.

Question 60

From the various values given in Peterson Chapters 5 and 6, Table 7 (overleaf) may be constructed. The line widths are clearly much larger in the BLR than in the NLR, by definition. The two regions have similar temperatures, but the inferred electron density is far higher in the BLR than in the NLR. The BLR is a factor of around 10^4 smaller in radius (hence around 10^{12} smaller in volume) than the NLR, and has an overall mass which is a factor of around 10^9 smaller. The total number of clouds in the BLR is also much larger than in the NLR, but the individual BLR clouds are a factor of around 10^{14} less massive and 10^8 smaller in radius (so 10^{24} smaller in volume) than the NLR clouds. The filling factor of the BLR is also considerably smaller than the NLR.

Table 7 Estimates of the properties of the BLR and NLR in a typical AGN (completed version of Table 5).

Property	Broad-line region	Narrow-line region
line widths, Δv	~5000 km s^{-1}	~350–400 km s^{-1}
cloud temperature, T	10 000 K	~16 000 K
cloud electron density, n_e	10^8–10^{11} cm^{-3}	~2000 cm^{-3}
overall size of region, r	a few $\times 10^{16}$ cm	> a few $\times 10^{20}$ cm
total mass of region	$\geq 10^{-3} M_\odot$	~$10^6 M_\odot$
total number of clouds, N_c	~10^{10}	$\leq 10^5$
filling factor, ϵ	a few $\times 10^{-7}$	$\leq 10^{-2}$
size of a typical cloud, l	> a few $\times 10^{10}$ cm	$\geq 10^{18}$ cm
covering factor, f	0.1	–

Question 61

(a) It is assumed that in Seyfert galaxies which are seen close to 'face-on', both the NLR and BLR are visible. Consequently, these galaxies will display both narrow and broad emission lines and are classified as Seyfert 1 galaxies. In Seyfert galaxies which are seen close to 'edge-on' the central regions of the AGN (i.e. the BLR) are obscured by an optically thick dusty torus. Hence, these galaxies display only narrow emission lines and are classified as Seyfert 2 galaxies.

(b) The ratio of the number of Seyfert 1 galaxies to the number of Seyfert 2 galaxies is about 1 : 3. This implies that in roughly 3/4 of the Seyfert galaxies, the BLR is obscured. Consequently, the obscuring torus must hide about 3/4 of the sky as seen from the centre.

Question 62

(a) The relativistic form of the equations describing the aberration of light show that electromagnetic radiation emitted isotropically by a jet of material, travelling at speeds which are a significant fraction of the speed of light, will be *beamed* into a narrow cone directed along the direction of travel of the jet. The opening angle of the cone is proportional to $1/\gamma$ where γ is the Lorentz factor, $[1 - (v^2/c^2)]^{-1/2}$. This beaming effect enhances the emission of radiation along the direction of the jet by a factor of order γ^2. As a result of the relativistic Doppler shift, the emission is boosted by a further factor of $\gamma^{1+\alpha}$, where α is the power-law index of the synchrotron radiation. Overall therefore, synchrotron radiation is preferentially beamed along the direction of travel of the jet and boosted in intensity by a factor of $\gamma^{3+\alpha}$. The interpretation of blazars is that they are AGN which are viewed such that one of the jets from the central engine of the AGN is directed close to our line of sight. We therefore see an increased amount of radiation due to this relativistic boosting.

(b) In some radio galaxies, high spatial resolution observations of their central, compact cores reveal that structural components appear to move with speeds which exceed the speed of light. The explanation of this apparent superluminal motion is that material is emitted at high speeds (but less than c) in a direction close to our line of sight. The rapidly moving material effectively 'catches up' the light it emitted earlier. The geometry of the situation then results in an apparently faster-than-light motion being observed. The transverse velocity measured by an observer, relative to the speed of light is:

$$\beta_{\mathrm{T}} = \frac{\beta \sin\theta}{1 - \beta \cos\theta}$$

where β is the actual speed of the material, v, divided by the speed of light, and θ is the angle between the direction of motion and the line of sight.

Question 63

There are no right answers to this question, but the example below shows one appropriate response.

Both AGN and interacting binaries are powered by accretion onto a compact object. In AGN this is a supermassive black hole with a mass of order $10^9 \mathrm{M}_\odot$, whilst in interacting binaries it is either a white dwarf, neutron star or black hole, each of which has a mass of order $1\mathrm{M}_\odot$. In both AGN and interacting binaries, the compact object is surrounded by an accretion disc which emits radiation as a result of viscous dissipation. The spectrum of radiation from the accretion disc in each case is modelled as a sum of blackbody spectra of different temperatures corresponding to different radii in the disc. The typical temperature of the accretion disc depends on the mass accretion rate multiplied by the 'compactness' of the central object $(T^4 \propto \dot{M} \times M/R^3)$. If mass is accreted at the Eddington rate ($\dot{M}_{\mathrm{E}} \propto M$), then the temperature dependence is $T^4 \propto M^2/R^3$. From this (remembering that for a black hole $R = 2GM/c^2$) it can be shown that accretion discs around solar-mass neutron stars emit predominantly in the X-ray whilst accretion discs around supermassive black holes emit predominantly in the ultraviolet. Accretion discs form because, in general, the accreting material will possess angular momentum. If accretion occurred by direct radial infall on to a black hole, then material passing beyond the event horizon would not emit any radiation, as all the gravitational potential energy of the accreted material would be transformed into kinetic energy and then swallowed. In interacting binaries containing white dwarfs and neutron stars a solid surface is present onto which the accreted material is deposited. Energetic radiation may also therefore be emitted from the white dwarfs or neutron stars in these systems.

Question 64

There are no right answers to this question, but the example below shows one appropriate response.

The principal non-thermal emission mechanism of importance to AGN is *synchrotron radiation*. This arises when energetic electrons move through a region containing a magnetic field. As a result of the magnetic Lorentz force, the electrons travel in helical paths around the magnetic field lines, emitting electromagnetic radiation. For a single electron, the spectral energy distribution of the emitted radiation reaches a peak at a frequency which is proportional to $B_\perp^2 \gamma^2$ where γ is the Lorentz factor of the electron (which is in turn proportional to the electron's total relativistic energy via $E_{\mathrm{TOT}} = \gamma m_e c^2$). For an ensemble of electrons, with a power-law energy distribution of the form $N(E)\mathrm{d}E = N_0 E^{-s}\mathrm{d}E$, the resulting spectrum of synchrotron radiation will also have a power-law form, namely $F_v \propto v^{-\alpha}$ where $\alpha = (s-1)/2$. In AGN, the synchrotron radiation power-law index is typically $\alpha \sim 0.7$ (implying an electron energy distribution power-law index $s \sim 2.4$).

The synchrotron spectrum can be modified by two effects. First, the low-energy tail of the spectrum of synchrotron radiation may undergo absorption by the very electrons which were responsible for the emission in the first place. This *synchrotron self-absorption* results in a turnover of the low-energy part of the spectrum, such that it typically follows a different power law, $F_v \propto v^{5/2}$. Second, the radiation may be upscattered to higher frequencies by *inverse Compton scattering*. In this process, relatively low-energy photons scatter off the high-energy electrons which produced the original radiation, and gain energy at the expense of the electrons which lose energy. The modified radiation produced in this way is therefore referred to as *synchrotron self-Compton* emission.

Thermal emission mechanisms of importance to AGN include both *thermal bremsstrahlung* and *blackbody* radiation. Thermal bremsstrahlung (literally 'braking radiation') is also known as free-free radiation since it involves emission from electrons which are unbound both before and after the radiation is emitted. It occurs when electrons with a thermal energy distribution (i.e. a Maxwellian speed distribution) are accelerated by the Coulomb force as they pass close to positive ions.

Finally, blackbody radiation is emitted by atoms in thermal equilibrium. The overall spectrum of this radiation is described by the *Planck function*:

$$B_v(T) = \frac{2hv^3}{c^2} \frac{1}{\exp\left(\dfrac{hv}{kT}\right) - 1}$$

At low frequencies the spectral shape is referred to as the *Rayleigh–Jeans tail* and follows a simpler form:

$$B_v(T) = 2kTv^2/c^2 \quad (\text{i.e. } F_v \propto v^2)$$

whilst at high frequencies the spectral shape is known as the *Wien tail* and has an approximate form:

$$B_v(T) = \frac{2hv^3}{c^2} \exp\left(-\frac{hv}{kT}\right)$$

Question 65

Forbidden emission lines arise from forbidden atomic transitions, whilst permitted emission lines arise from permitted atomic transitions. Permitted transitions (i.e. those which obey quantum mechanical selection rules) are, in general, much more likely to occur than forbidden transitions (i.e. those which violate selection rules). So, if an atom in an excited state has a permitted transition to a lower energy level available to it, it is not likely to make a forbidden transition. If, on the other hand, no permitted transitions are available, an atom will typically remain in an excited state for a long period of time, since the forbidden transitions have an extremely low probability of occurrence. During this time, an atom is prone to suffer a collision with another atom, ion or free electron and so undergo collisional de-excitation, without the emission of a photon. The probability of a collision is clearly higher if the density of the gas is higher. Consequently, if forbidden lines are observed, it indicates that the region in which they arise must have a low density, so that collisions are sufficiently infrequent.

COMMENTS ON ACTIVITIES

Completed spreadsheets for all the activities have been installed on your hard disk along with the S381 MM guide. The relevant spreadsheet can be found as *BX_AcY.sdc* where *X* is the block number and *Y* is the activity number, via a link from the multimedia guide.

Activity 4

For an input electron power-law index of 2.4 (i.e. $N(E) = N_0 E^{-2.4}$), the slope of the synchrotron spectrum should be −0.7.

Activity 10

The expression for luminosity that you need is

$$L_2 = L_1 \times 10^{\left(\frac{M_1 - M_2}{2.5}\right)}$$

Activity 14

The completed spreadsheet for this activity is found by clicking on the spreadsheet tab on the S381 MM guide.

Activity 25

The expression for β that you need is

$$\beta = \sqrt{1 - \frac{1}{\gamma^2}}$$

If you followed the advice about where to type various entries, the formula you need to type into cell B5 (corresponding to $\theta = 0°$ and $\gamma = 1.25$, $\beta = 0.60$) is:

```
=(B$2*sin($A5*pi()/180))/(1-(B$2*cos($A5*pi()/180)))
```

The notation B$2 ensures that row 2 remains fixed, but the columns vary as the formula is dragged to other cells (varying β), and similarly the notation $A5 ensures that column A remains fixed but the rows vary as the formula is dragged to other cells (varying θ). The notation pi() is the spreadsheet's function for π and multiplying the angles by pi()/180 converts them into radians. This formula may then be dragged to other cells in the spreadsheet corresponding to different values of θ and β.

Activity 40

The completed spreadsheet for this activity is found by clicking on the Spreadsheet tab on the S381 MM guide.

ACKNOWLEDGEMENTS

We gratefully acknowledge Dr Katherine Blundell and her collaborators Dr Steve Rawlings and Dr Chris Willott for providing the material used in Section 8.3. We are also extremely grateful to Dr Atsunori Yonehara who provided the basis of our discussion of gravitational lensing. Professor Harriet Dinerstein gave very prompt and helpful input concerning the material covered in Activity 33, and Professor Bill

Keel was a source of encouragement and several useful figures, as well as the author of the most entertaining website encountered in the research. We thank Dr Martin Hardcastle for various very helpful comments on a draft of this block, and Mr Chris Brockwell and Mr Craig Powell for checking the questions and answers.

Grateful acknowledgement is made to the following sources for permission to reproduce material in this book:

Cover © 2000 Mark A. Garlick

Figures 1, 37, 38 Courtesy of Bill Keel, University of Alabama; *Figure 2* Adam Block/ AURA/NOAO/NSF; *Figure 3* Charles Steidel (California Institute of Technology, Pasadena, CA) and NASA; *Figure 4* Reprinted by permission from *Nature*. Maarten Schmidt, Vol. 197:1040 (1963), Macmillan Magazines Limited; *Figure 5* John Bahcall (Institute for Advanced Study, Princeton), Mike Disney (University of Wales) and NASA; *Figure 6* Courtesy of Royal Astronomical Society; *Figure 7* Courtesy of Jun-Hui Zhao and W. M. Goss/AOC/NRAO; *Figure 8* Galactic Center Research, Max Planck Institute; *Figure 13* Courtesy of ESRF, France; *Figure 14* Courtesy of ESRF/ Artechnique; *Figure 21* AOC/NRAO; *Figure 22(a)* www.jb.man.ac.uk/atlas; *Figure 22(b)* Chris Carilli/Rick Perley/NRAO; *Figures 23(a) and 103(a)* Isituto di Radioastronomia del CNR, Italy; *Figures 23(b) and 103(b)* © Nuffield Radio Astronomy Laboratories, Jodrell Bank, Cheshire; *Figure 27* Donald Schneider and Xiaohui Fan, SDSS Collaboration; *Figure 28(a)* Courtesy of Axel Mellinger, University of Potsdam, Germany; *Figure 28(b)* Courtesy of Ned Wright; *Figure 29* R. Williams (ST ScI), NASA; *Figure 30* Chiang, J., Reynolds, C. S. *et al.* (2000) *The Astrophysical Journal*, Vol. 528, American Astronomical Society for the University of Chicago; *Figure 34* Courtesy of Montpellier University Collections; *Figure 39* Schmid, H. M. *et al.* (2001) *Astronomy and Astrophysics*, Vol. 372, © ESO; *Figure 40* Cooke, A. J. *et al.* (2000) *The Astrophysical Journal*, Supplement 129, American Astronomical Society for the University of Chicago; *Figure 41* Wei Zheng, *et al.* (1997) *The Astrophysical Journal*, Vol. 475, American Astronomical Society for the University of Chicago; *Figure 42* Small, T. A. *et al.* (1997) *The Astronomical Journal*, Vol. 114, No. 6, American Astronomical Society for the University of Chicago; *Figure 43* SDSS Collaboration; *Figure 44* Luis, C. Ho, *et al.* (2000) *The Astrophysical Journal*, Vol. 541, American Astronomical Society for the University of Chicago; *Figure 54* Bloom, S. D. *et al.* (1997) 'Observations of a correlated gamma-ray....', *The Astrophysical Journal*, Vol. 490, American Astronomical Society for the University of Chicago; *Figure 56* Longair, M. S. (1981) 'High energy astrophysics: an informal introduction ...', Kluwer Academic Publishers, B. V.; *Figure 57(a)* Tanaka, Y. Reprinted with permission from *Nature*, Vol. 375, p. 659, Copyright 1995, Macmillan Magazines Limited; *Figure 57(b)* Sako, M. *et al.* (2001) 'Letter to the editor: complex resonance absorption structure ...', *Astronomy and Astrophysics*, Vol. 365, Springer-Verlag, GMBH & Co. KG.; *Figure 60(a)* J. Rhoads (StSci) *et al.* WIYN, AURA, NOAO, NSF;*Figure 60(b)* © NASA; *Figure 62* Atsunori Yonehara, (2001) 'Evidence for a source size of less than 2000 ...', *The Astrophysical Journal*, Vol. 548, American Astronomical Society for the University of Chicago; *Figure 64(a)* NASA, Donald Walter (South Carolina State University), Paul Scowen and Brian Moore (Arizona State University); *Figure 74* The Anglo-Australian Observatory/David Malin; *Figure 82(a)* Kaper, L. *et al. The Astrophysical Journal*, Vol. 475, pp. L37–40, 1997, American Astronomical Society for the University of Chicago; *Figure 82(b)* Courtesy of European Southern Observatory; *Figure 88* Courtesy of NOAO/AURA/NSF.

APPENDIX

A1 SI units and cgs units

The main units used in science are SI (standing for Système International [d'Unités]).

SI base units

Physical quantity	Name of unit	Symbol of unit
length	metre	m
mass	kilogram	kg
time	second	s
electric current	ampere	A
temperature	kelvin	K
luminous intensity	candela	cd
amount of substance	mole	mol

Standard SI multiples and submultiples

Multiple	Prefix	Symbol for prefix	Sub-multiple	Prefix	Symbol for prefix
10^{12}	tera	T	10^{-3}	milli	m
10^{9}	giga	G	10^{-6}	micro	μ
10^{6}	mega	M	10^{-9}	nano	n
10^{3}	kilo	k	10^{-12}	pico	p
10^{0}	–	–	10^{-15}	femto	f

Common SI unit conversions and derived units

Quantity	Unit	Conversion		
speed	$m\,s^{-1}$			
acceleration	$m\,s^{-2}$			
angular speed	$rad\,s^{-1}$			
angular acceleration	$rad\,s^{-2}$			
linear momentum	$kg\,m\,s^{-1}$			
angular momentum	$kg\,m^2\,s^{-1}$			
force	newton (N)	$1\,N$	$=$	$1\,kg\,m\,s^{-2}$
energy	joule (J)	$1\,J$	$=$	$1\,N\,m = 1\,kg\,m^2\,s^{-2}$
power	watt (W)	$1\,W$	$=$	$1\,J\,s^{-1} = 1\,kg\,m^2\,s^{-3}$
pressure	pascal (Pa)	$1\,Pa$	$=$	$1\,N\,m^{-2} = 1\,kg\,m^{-1}\,s^{-2}$
frequency	hertz (Hz)	$1\,Hz$	$=$	$1\,s^{-1}$
charge	coulomb (C)	$1\,C$	$=$	$1\,A\,s$
potential difference	volt (V)	$1\,V$	$=$	$1\,J\,C^{-1} = 1\,kg\,m^2\,s^{-3}\,A^{-1}$
electric field	$N\,C^{-1}$	$1\,N\,C^{-1}$	$=$	$1\,V\,m^{-1} = 1\,kg\,m\,s^{-3}\,A^{-1}$
magnetic field	tesla (T)	$1\,T$	$=$	$1\,N\,s\,m^{-1}\,C^{-1} = 1\,kg\,s^{-2}\,A^{-1}$

In astrophysics, you will frequently see some quantities expressed in the cgs system (standing for centimetre, gram, second). The difference here is that the base units for length and mass are the centimetre and gram, rather than the metre and kilogram, where $1\,\mathrm{cm} = 10^{-2}\,\mathrm{m}$ and $1\,\mathrm{g} = 10^{-3}\,\mathrm{kg}$.

Use of the cgs system in turn gives rise to different derived units, so you will often see speeds quoted in $\mathrm{cm\,s^{-1}}$ for instance. Three particular derived units that you should be aware of are the cgs units for energy, force and magnetic field, namely the erg, the dyne and the gauss respectively.

The conversions are

energy	$1\text{ joule} = 10^7\text{ erg}$	or	$1\text{ erg} = 10^{-7}\text{ joule} = 1\,\mathrm{g\,cm^2\,s^{-2}}$
force	$1\text{ newton} = 10^5\text{ dyne}$	or	$1\text{ dyne} = 10^{-5}\text{ newton} = 1\,\mathrm{g\,cm\,s^{-2}}$
magnetic field	$1\text{ tesla} = 10^4\text{ gauss}$	or	$1\text{ gauss} = 10^{-4}\text{ tesla}$

The basic unit of electric charge is also defined somewhat differently in the cgs system. In fact, *two* different definitions are sometimes seen, the simplest of which is the 'emu' system where

$$1\text{ coulomb} = 0.1\text{ emu} \quad\text{or}\quad 1\text{ emu} = 10\text{ coulomb}$$

A2 Useful constants and conversions

Name of constant	Symbol	cgs/emu value	SI value
Fundamental constants			
gravitational constant	G	$6.673 \times 10^{-8}\,\mathrm{dyne\,cm^2\,g^{-2}}$	$6.673 \times 10^{-11}\,\mathrm{N\,m^2\,kg^{-2}}$
Boltzmann constant	k	$1.381 \times 10^{-16}\,\mathrm{erg\,K^{-1}}$	$1.381 \times 10^{-23}\,\mathrm{J\,K^{-1}}$
speed of light in vacuum	c	$2.998 \times 10^{10}\,\mathrm{cm\,s^{-1}}$	$2.998 \times 10^{8}\,\mathrm{m\,s^{-1}}$
Planck constant	h	$6.626 \times 10^{-27}\,\mathrm{erg\,s}$	$6.626 \times 10^{-34}\,\mathrm{J\,s}$
	$\hbar = h/2\pi$	$1.055 \times 10^{-27}\,\mathrm{erg\,s}$	$1.055 \times 10^{-34}\,\mathrm{J\,s}$
fine structure constant	$\alpha = e^2/4\pi\varepsilon_0\hbar c$	$1/137.0$	$1/137.0$
Stefan–Boltzman constant	σ	$5.671 \times 10^{-5}\,\mathrm{erg\,cm^{-2}\,K^{-4}\,s^{-1}}$	$5.671 \times 10^{-8}\,\mathrm{J\,m^{-2}\,K^{-4}\,s^{-1}}$
Thomson cross-section	σ_e	$6.652 \times 10^{-25}\,\mathrm{cm^2}$	$6.652 \times 10^{-29}\,\mathrm{m^2}$
permittivity of free space	ε_0	$8.854 \times 10^{-23}\,\mathrm{cm^{-2}\,s^2}$	$8.854 \times 10^{-12}\,\mathrm{C^2\,N^{-1}\,m^{-2}}$
permeability of free space	μ_0	$4\pi\,\mathrm{dyne\,emu^{-2}\,s^2}$	$4\pi \times 10^{-7}\,\mathrm{T\,m\,A^{-1}}$
Particle constants			
charge of proton	e	$1.602 \times 10^{-20}\,\mathrm{emu}$	$1.602 \times 10^{-19}\,\mathrm{C}$
charge of electron	$-e$	$-1.602 \times 10^{-20}\,\mathrm{emu}$	$-1.602 \times 10^{-19}\,\mathrm{C}$
electron rest mass	m_e	$9.109 \times 10^{-28}\,\mathrm{g}$	$9.109 \times 10^{-31}\,\mathrm{kg}$
		$0.511\,\mathrm{MeV}/c^2$	$0.511\,\mathrm{MeV}/c^2$
proton rest mass	m_p	$1.673 \times 10^{-24}\,\mathrm{g}$	$1.673 \times 10^{-27}\,\mathrm{kg}$
		$938.3\,\mathrm{MeV}/c^2$	$938.3\,\mathrm{MeV}/c^2$
neutron rest mass	m_n	$1.675 \times 10^{-24}\,\mathrm{kg}$	$1.675 \times 10^{-27}\,\mathrm{kg}$
		$939.6\,\mathrm{MeV}/c^2$	$939.6\,\mathrm{MeV}/c^2$
atomic mass unit	u or amu	$1.661 \times 10^{-24}\,\mathrm{g}$	$1.661 \times 10^{-27}\,\mathrm{kg}$
Astronomical constants			
mass of the Sun	$M_\odot$	$1.99 \times 10^{33}\,\mathrm{g}$	$1.99 \times 10^{30}\,\mathrm{kg}$
radius of the Sun	$R_\odot$	$6.96 \times 10^{10}\,\mathrm{cm}$	$6.96 \times 10^{8}\,\mathrm{m}$
luminosity of the Sun	$L_\odot$	$3.83 \times 10^{33}\,\mathrm{erg\,s^{-1}}$	$3.83 \times 10^{26}\,\mathrm{J\,s^{-1}}$

angular measure

$1° = 60$ arcmin $= 3600$ arcsec

$1° = 0.01745$ radian

1 radian $= 57.30°$

temperature

absolute zero: $0\,\mathrm{K} = -273.15\,°\mathrm{C}$

$0\,°\mathrm{C} = 273.15\,\mathrm{K}$

energy

$1\,\mathrm{eV} = 1.602 \times 10^{-19}\,\mathrm{J} = 1.602 \times 10^{-12}\,\mathrm{erg}$

$1\,\mathrm{erg} = 10^{-7}\,\mathrm{J} = 6.242 \times 10^{11}\,\mathrm{eV}$

$1\,\mathrm{J} = 10^{7}\,\mathrm{erg} = 6.242 \times 10^{18}\,\mathrm{eV}$

spectral flux density

$1\,\text{jansky (Jy)} = 10^{-26}\,\mathrm{W\,m^{-2}\,Hz^{-1}} = 10^{-23}\,\mathrm{erg\,s^{-1}\,cm^{-2}\,Hz^{-1}}$

$1\,\mathrm{W\,m^{-2}\,Hz^{-1}} = 10^{26}\,\mathrm{Jy} = 10^{3}\,\mathrm{erg\,s^{-1}\,cm^{-2}\,Hz^{-1}}$

$1\,\mathrm{erg\,s^{-1}\,cm^{-2}\,Hz^{-1}} = 10^{-3}\,\mathrm{W\,m^{-2}\,Hz^{-1}} = 10^{23}\,\mathrm{Jy}$

mass-energy equivalence

$1\,\mathrm{kg} = 8.99 \times 10^{16}\,\mathrm{J}/c^2 \qquad (c \text{ in } \mathrm{m\,s^{-1}})$

$1\,\mathrm{kg} = 5.61 \times 10^{35}\,\mathrm{eV}/c^2 \quad (c \text{ in } \mathrm{m\,s^{-1}})$

$1\,\mathrm{g} = 8.99 \times 10^{16}\,\mathrm{erg}/c^2 \quad (c \text{ in } \mathrm{cm\,s^{-1}})$

$1\,\mathrm{g} = 5.61 \times 10^{28}\,\mathrm{eV}/c^2 \qquad (c \text{ in } \mathrm{cm\,s^{-1}})$

wavelength

$1\,\text{nanometre (nm)} = 10\,\text{Å} = 10^{-9}\,\mathrm{m} = 10^{-7}\,\mathrm{cm}$

$1\,\text{ångstrom (Å)} = 0.1\,\mathrm{nm} = 10^{-10}\,\mathrm{m} = 10^{-8}\,\mathrm{cm}$

distance

$1\,\text{astronomical unit (AU)} = 1.496 \times 10^{11}\,\mathrm{m} = 1.496 \times 10^{13}\,\mathrm{cm}$

$1\,\text{light-year (ly)} = 9.461 \times 10^{15}\,\mathrm{m} = 9.461 \times 10^{17}\,\mathrm{cm} = 0.307\,\mathrm{pc}$

$1\,\text{parsec (pc)} = 3.086 \times 10^{16}\,\mathrm{m} = 3.086 \times 10^{18}\,\mathrm{cm} = 3.26\,\mathrm{ly}$

A3 Mathematical signs and symbols

$\equiv$	identical to
$=$	equals
$\approx$	approximately equals
$\sim$	is of order of (i.e. is less than 10 times bigger or smaller than)
$\neq$	is not equal to
$>$	is greater than
$\gg$	is much greater than
$\geq$	is greater than or equal to (i.e. is no less than)
$\gtrsim$	is greater than or of order of
$<$	is less than
$\ll$	is much less than
$\leq$	is less than or equal to (i.e. is no more than)
$\lesssim$	is less than or of order of
$\propto$	is proportional to
∞	infinity
$\sqrt{x}$	the positive square root of x
$\sqrt[n]{x}$	the nth root of x which is equal to $x^{1/n}$
$\pm$	plus and minus the following number
$\mp$	minus and plus, taken in the same order as a preceding $\pm$
Δx	the change in x
$f(x)$	a function f depending on the variable x
$|x|$	the absolute value of a number (i.e. ignoring any $-$ sign)
$|a|$	the magnitude or length of a vector
$\sum\limits_{i=1}^{N} m_i$	the sum of $m_1 + m_2 + m_3 + \cdots + m_N$
$\langle x \rangle$	the average value of x
$dy/dt,\ y',\ \dot{y}$	the derivative of y with respect to t; or the gradient of y versus t
$d^2y/dt^2,\ y'',\ \ddot{y}$	the second derivative of y with respect to t
$\displaystyle\int_{t_A}^{t_B} x(t)\,dt$	the definite integral of the t-dependent function $x(t)$ with respect to t, evaluated over the interval from $t = t_A$ to $t = t_B$

A4 The Greek alphabet

name	upper case	lower case	name	upper case	lower case
alpha	A	α	nu	N	ν
beta	B	β	xi	Ξ	ξ
gamma	Γ	γ	omicron	O	o
delta	Δ	δ	pi	Π	π
epsilon	E	ε	rho	P	ρ
zeta	Z	ζ	sigma	Σ	σ
eta	H	η	tau	T	τ
theta	Θ	θ, ϑ	upsilon	Y	υ
iota	I	ι	phi	Φ	ϕ, φ
kappa	K	κ	chi	X	χ
lambda	Λ	λ	psi	Ψ	ψ
mu	M	μ	omega	Ω	ω

A5 Taxonomy of AGN

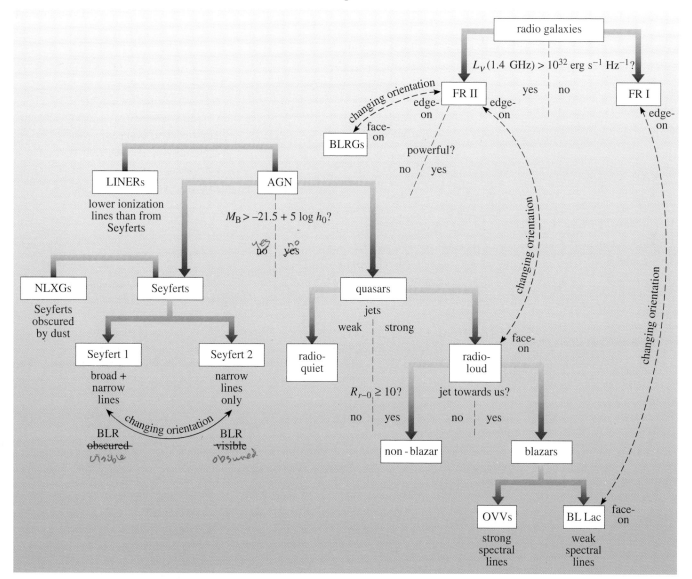

Figure 108 A block diagram illustrating the relationships between the various subclasses of AGN, largely based upon the information in Section 3 of this Study Guide and Peterson. The possible unification between FR II galaxies and BLRGs or quasars and FR I galaxies and BL Lac objects has been added for completeness, and is based on recent reseach findings.

INDEX

Glossary terms and their page references are printed in **bold**.